Theory and Applications of the Analytic Network Process:
Decision Making with Benefits, Opportunities, Costs, and Risks

Thomas L. Saaty

Library of Congress Cataloging-in-Publication Data
Saaty, Thomas L.

Theory and Applications of the Analytic Network Process: Decision Making with Benefits, Opportunities, Costs, and Risks

CIP 95-069523
ISBN 1-888603-06-2

1. Priorities 2. Decision Making 3. Analytic Hierarchy Process (AHP) 4. Analytic Network Process (ANP) 5. Decision Making with Dependence and Feedback 6. Feedback and Dependence in Decision Making 7. Economic Priorities 8. Social Priorities 9. Complex Decision Making

Thomas L. Saaty
University of Pittsburgh
322 Mervis Hall
Pittsburgh, PA 15260
Phone: 412-648-1539

RWS Publications
4922 Ellsworth Avenue
Pittsburgh, PA 15213 USA
Phone: 412-414-5984
FAX: 412-681-4510

THOMAS L. SAATY

University of Pittsburgh

322 Mervis Hall
University of Pittsburgh
Pittsburgh, PA 15260
E-mail: saaty@katz.pitt.edu

Dedication

To Rozann

For her patient and persevering support to develop the SuperDecisions software used to create many of the examples in the book

CONTENTS

Preface

The ideas in this book are guaranteed to expand the reader's consciousness and ability to understand and deal with the complexities of the world more rationally and more effectively. These ideas are also helpful for a group of people or nations to get together to deal with their differences and decide collectively, when necessary. If they do not wish to get together, a third party can do it for them before and after consulting with them to determine the best mutual outcome from their own standpoint after making the necessary tradeoffs. They involve cycling and feedback of judgment priorities and allow for sensitivity and change, something we cannot do directly with logic alone.

The great French philosopher and mathematician René Descartes, in reflecting on how he knew he existed, wrote in Latin "Cogito ergo sum", "I think therefore I am." Today we live in a highly complex world, far more complex than the one in which Descartes lived. We have more and more varied choices to make than at any time in the past. Information is more widely and freely available than at any time in history. Modern innovations, like personal computers and the Internet, are constantly changing the ways in which people conduct their daily activities. The process of making sense out of the vast complexity we face is, to say the least, very challenging, and at the same time the decisions we make now have implications for the future of mankind. Today, Descartes might look at the world and say, "I *choose* therefore I am". Our scientific tradition has focused in the past on a materialistic view of the universe in which matter and energy played the fundamental role. Quantum theoretic thinking has demonstrated that there is a third basic element that is not visible to the senses but underlies all information and understanding, and that is consciousness and awareness. Awareness is so fundamental and so basic that it confers on us a power of independence and responsibility. What we think and do are at least as important to us as what gravity does to moving objects and what light and sound, as forms of energy, carry as information and how they do it through periodic vibration. Some have thought of a communication field. The psychologist Karl Jung advocated the idea of a collective subconscious. Teilhard de Chardin in his book the *Phenomenon of Man* introduced the idea of a worldwide communication network of human thought, the *noosphere*, and Rupert Sheldrake of Cambridge University in his book *A New Science of Life*, wrote about a morphogenetic field in which after considerable repetition knowledge automatically spreads from one person to another unknown person separated by great distance. There is a great mystery in science about crystal growth in that once a crystal is created it immediately becomes easier to duplicate it elsewhere. There are numerous people occupied with the determination of how much truth there is to these ideas. For example the Global Consciousness Project, also called the EGG Project, has been collecting data from a global network of random event generators since August, 1998.

Our ability to choose by reflecting on the complexities of a decision and how that decision may affect the future is largely what separates us from other forms of life. The choices we make depend mostly on what purpose we want to achieve. Our purpose arises out of our vision of what we think is ultimately of greatest importance to us. We then take actions that we believe will allow us to carry out our purpose and fulfill our vision. There are cases, however, when one's freedom of choice is constrained. Many decisions involve groups of people who must reconcile their different criteria and goals. In the end, decision-making is closely related to conflict resolution. Thus, the benefits we derive from the decisions we make are largely determined by how well we can deal with differences in opinion and how well we can foresee risks and opportunities and plan for the future.

The basic building blocks of all knowledge are *elements* (things and people) and *collections* of elements. We also observe appropriately: *form*, *disposition, feelings* and *ideas* of these elements, *influences* within and among them, *meaning* assigned to them according to *purpose*(s) and a *system* to lay out and *synthesize* the influences according to the meaning. It is all done by us in order to understand and when necessary to *act* on the outcome, which is another kind of influence that is part of the system. In addition there is a *variety* of entities (people, animals, plants) that create meaning according to their *interactions* and purposes. There are an unlimited number of ways to approach a situation to extract meaning from it. The diversity of creatures in the world do it in different ways and under different moods and conditions. Animals and plants do it their way. There are synergies and unanticipated happenings that we may never be aware of to include in our models. There are numerous intangibles that have great impact that we must first measure before we can include them as variables. What is most significant is that intangibles can only be measured through expert judgment and only relative to the goals of concern in a particular situation. In a way similar to the fact that there are undecidable propositions and we cannot use logic to answer every question with a yes or a no, it is also true that we cannot give an absolute meaning to every event that is the outcome of diverse influences. Thus it is a forlorn hope to have a fixed template that models the complexity we face hoping to extract an absolute order from it.

To take the most effective action, we need to know several things: what is going on in the environment, who are the people who will be affected, and what are their concerns, how to include the many perspectives we all have on a given problem and so on. The knowledge we acquire must be reliable in some sense. It is best obtained by using the scientific method and through appropriate perspective developed from experience about what *might* work best under the circumstances we face at the time of a decision.

In the end, the meaning of anything and its value can only be determined by a conscious and aware mind. Some things can mean nothing to us if they do not connect in some way to an experience or explanation we have in our collective mind. So how does the mind put it all together?

Multicriteria decision making (MCDM) is a field that chooses the best of a discrete set of alternatives. Unlike the usual methods of optimization that assume the availability of measurements, measurements in MCDM are assumed to be derived or interpreted subjectively as indicators of preference and of the strength of preference. One person's preference is different than another person's and thus the outcome depends on who is making the decisions and what his/her preferences and goals are.

The Analytic Hierarchy Process (AHP) and its generalization to dependence and feedback, the Analytic Network Process (ANP), are methods of relative measurement of intangibles. They can help bring together a diverse group of people with different perspectives to make the complex decisions required in our time. They offer a structured framework for discussion and debate, a way to include the important intangibles of every major decision together with the tangibles, and a way to resolve conflicts over turf and achieve buy-in to implement the decision at the end of the day.

Our progress generally depends on the interaction of our minds with our technology to create tools that enable us to survive better in a difficult and often harsh environment. Our tools give us power but also limit us because of our dependence on them and because they become obsolete. Yet we have no other way. We need these tools to understand ourselves, and the world around us, and this understanding helps us create new tools, an essential process that goes on forever. It is not our minds alone that give us understanding, but our minds applied to the world through myriads of experiments with these tools that help us understand better what we want to know. Technology, an extension of our minds, frees us from the frustrations of living within our mental box in a physical world that does not move by ideas alone, but by tools we shape from it to order it to our liking. The modern way of decision-making is one of these tools. It has both mental and physical components. It needs the mind to make it a sound approach and the computer to lay things out explicitly and to keep track of the many judgments we make. When decisions are implemented, all sorts of mental (managerial) and physical tools are needed to make them happen according to plan.

In a book *The Wisdom of Crowds: Why the Many Are Smarter Than the Few and How Collective Wisdom Shapes Business, Economies, Societies and Nation, Doubleday, Little, Brown,* described in The Economist, May 29, 2004, the author, James Surowiecki puts forward a paradox: often, the multitude knows better than the wise individual. By examining many cases he concludes that the amalgamated views of a crowd reach a more accurate conclusion than the single expert does. "Under the right circumstances, groups are remarkably intelligent, and are often smarter than the smartest people in them." The two ultimate tests of the wisdom of crowds are the market and democracy. His faith in crowds leads him to argue for decentralized decision-making in companies. "Any major decision should be taken by as large a group of managers as is logistically possible," he argues – admitting that this is a suggestion "so radical as to seem ludicrous". "With most things, the average is mediocrity." "With collective intelligence, it's excellence. You could say it's as if we've been programmed to be collectively smart." A group works better when its members learn on their own independently rather than following the crowd. Thomas Jefferson said, "State a moral case to a ploughman and a professor. The former will decide it as well and often better than the latter because he has not been led astray by artificial rules." A crowd of plough-persons is thus wiser than a plurality of professors, writes The Economist.

People and animals, and even plants, have intensities of response to nearly everything. We are not logic machines; logic was invented for us. We have feelings of varying intensities developed through experience and judgment. It is reasonable that these intensities have different magnitudes. The question then is how to derive numerical values to represent them. How can we incorporate feelings and judgments in an accountable, rational way, to make use of it in deciding the next step to take in facing a complex problem? That is our purpose in developing in this book. In dealing with such a question we need to consider the difference between explicit, precise and unambiguous knowledge and tacit, or unspoken, knowledge.

People often wonder about how one can rely on judgments instead of on an instrument of measurement. Here is one query and our reply to it. "I read about measurement and discussed with my friend about tangibles. Everything that can be measured must have a tool for standardizing the measurement. For example length can be measured with the standard of a meter. However, with intangibles, how can an expert make a standard for a scale? It would be different than those of other experts in a group making a decision together." When you have measurement, you can normalize it and use it, or you can interpret it and use the priorities you assign to its importance to you. In the end it is not the measurement that counts but what importance one assigns to it. If one wants to assign the same importance as what the measurements are, one can do that. Measurement is not something absolute but is an indicator like any other information that we use to judge importance. When you have different experts, they can have different standards. It then becomes a matter of politics and persuasion to hammer out a group standard.

The new paradigm of our times is that everything is interconnected to everything else and there is a flow of influence among them. The connections can be physical, political, mental, spiritual, and so on. The Analytic Network Process (ANP) is now used to capture different aspects of tacit knowledge by comparing intensities of preference and deriving meaningful numbers, and not by guessing at their values on some scale between one and one hundred, for example. Tacit knowledge might well be aimed at discovering 'truth', but it is not necessarily in a form that can be stated in propositional or formal terms. The ANP serves to bridge this gap and reconcile different kinds of magnitudes on different properties, attributes or criteria within a formal mathematical system, and synthesizes them to arrive at an answer that parallels what people actually do as a result of reacting to all the influences that impact their consciousness (and their subconscious from which they develop feelings for whatever reasons). Briefly and realistically, the ANP is concerned with measuring tangibles and intangibles. It is a descriptive theory that combines these measures to match what people actually do or guides them to do better than they were previously able to do using only qualitative thinking and hunches. Proof that the ANP matches what thoughtful people do is validated through the many examples and exercises that we have been diligent in documenting. There is no way to prevent someone from putting in poor judgments, which do not in fact faithfully reflect their feelings or the experience they are attempting to represent, and when this occurs the ANP does not give back good results. Thus it helps to have a group critique what an individual does to remind that individual about facts that may have been forgotten or point out judgments that may be wrong. The ANP makes it possible for people to debate and combine their judgments. Its assumptions are not some esoteric inventions that make it convenient to work out some arithmetic schemes that technical people cleverly dream up under the cover of an academic umbrella. In that sense, using the ANP raises the level of human consciousness from muddling through to explicit and organized thinking, sufficiently unambiguous to lead one to understand the influences and the choices, changes and improvements that one needs to make. It opens the door for taking anyone's suggestion and including it in the considerations and giving it a high or a low priority in the end.

Unlike the usual yes-no, or 0-1 logic, the AHP is a multi-valued logic. The AHP scale admits different intensities and captures priorities that indicate a range of possibilities for our preferences rather than the zero (not preferred) or one (preferred) of traditional logic. In it a single number is used to represent a preference judgment between two elements. The use of a single number has been validated with many examples and shown to work very well in practice by checking results obtained with judgments against existing measurements.

We now have literally dozens of examples which show that people can, for example, determine the relative market share of companies that compete in some particular area. They do not know or use numerical data about the companies. They structure a network of clusters and factors and make links among them with regard to market share influences. What they then do is to make pairwise comparison judgments of elements and of clusters of elements. To do this successfully they need to be very familiar with the area of competition. The reader may need to see it happen to believe it. It has been done numerous times in class in about an hour without the participants having anticipated the assignment from the instructor at all. The results can be validated instantaneously with the data available about public companies on the Internet.

The ANP has been applied to a large variety of decisions: marketing, medical, political, social, and forecasting and prediction and many others. Its accuracy is impressive in predicting economic trends, winners in sports and other events for which the outcome later became known. Detailed case studies of applications are included in the ANP SuperDecisions software manual and in the *Encyclicon*, a dictionary of ANP examples. One may optimistically anticipate that international organizations such as the United Nations, the World Bank and the International Court at The Hague, leading governments in the world, and all major national and international organizations would find the organized Benefits, Opportunities, Costs and Risks framework evaluated in terms of strategic criteria of the ANP useful to develop their policies on paper. This approach provides a good opportunity for improving understanding. It also facilitates group discussion and agreement and making tradeoffs to resolve conflicts.

I am grateful to my friend Professor Jian Chen of Tsinghua University, Beijing, for giving me permission to use material from several articles of mine that appeared in 2004 and 2005 in several issues of the Journal of Systems Science and Systems Engineering (JSSSE) of which he is the chief editor. My great appreciation goes to my caring and diligent Ph.D. student, Alia Stanciu, for her careful and methodical reading of the manuscript, editing and improving the presentation, and to Eric Kiefer, for helping with the formatting and layout and for his great patience with me. Also, my thanks go to Nathan Salla, for his very attractive design of the cover of the book. Special thanks to William J. Adams for his intelligent design of the SuperDecisions software.

Chapter 1
Decision Making – The Analytic Hierarchy and Network Processes (AHP/ANP)

1-1. Introduction

Decision-making involves criteria and alternatives to choose from. The criteria usually have different importance and the alternatives in turn differ in our preference for them on each criterion. To make such tradeoffs and choices we need a way to measure. Measuring needs a good understanding of methods of measurement and different scales of measurement [46, 50, 56, 58, 59].

Many people think that measurement needs a physical scale with a zero and a unit to apply to objects or phenomena. That is not true. Surprisingly enough, we can also derive accurate and reliable relative scales that do not have a zero or a unit by using our understanding and judgments that are, after all, the most fundamental determinants of why we want to measure something. In reality we do that all the time and we do it subconsciously without thinking about it. Physical scales help our understanding and use of the things that we know how to measure. After we obtain readings from a physical scale, they still need to be interpreted according to what they mean and how adequate or inadequate they are to satisfy some need we have. But the number of things we don't know how to measure is infinitely larger than the things we know how to measure, and it is highly unlikely that we will ever find ways to measure everything on a physical scale with a unit. For example, how would one measure love and hate? Scales of measurement are inventions of a technological mind. Our minds and ways of understanding we have had with us and will always have. The brain is an electrical device of neurons whose electrical firing signals and their synthesis must perform measurement with great accuracy to give us all the meaning and understanding needed to enable us to survive and reach out to control a complex world. Can we rely on our judgments to be accurate guides? The answer depends on how well we know the phenomena to which we apply measurement and how good our judgments are to represent our understanding. In our own personal affairs we are the best judges of what may be good for us. In situations involving many people, we need the inputs from all the participants. In general we think that there are people who are more expert than others in some areas and their judgments should have precedence over the judgments of those who know less, as in fact it is often the case in practice.

Judgments expressed in the form of comparisons are fundamental in our biological makeup. They are intrinsic in the operations of our brains and that of animals and one might even say of plants since, for example, they control how much sunlight to admit. We all make decisions every moment, consciously or unconsciously, today and tomorrow, now and forever, it seems. Decision-making is a fundamental process that is integral in everything we do. How do we do it? The Harvard psychologist Arthur Blumenthal tells us in his book *The Process of Cognition,* Prentice-Hall, Inc., Englewood Cliffs, New Jersey, 1977, that there are two types of judgment: "Comparative judgment, which is the identification of some relation between two stimuli both present to the observer, and absolute judgment, which involves the relation between a single stimulus and some information held in short term memory about some former comparison stimuli or about some previously experienced measurement scale with which the observer rates the single stimulus."

When we think about it, both these processes involve making comparisons. Comparisons imply that all things we know are understood in relative terms to other things. It does not seem possible to know an absolute in itself independently of something else that influences it or that it influences. The question then is how do we make comparisons in a scientific way and derive from these comparisons scales of relative measurement? When we have many scales with respect to a diversity of criteria and subcriteria, how do we synthesize these scales to obtain an overall relative scale? Can we validate this process so that we can trust its reliability? What can we say about other ways people have proposed to deal with judgment and measurement, how do they relate to this fundamental idea of comparisons, and can they be relied on for validity? These are all questions we need to consider in making a decision. It is useful to remember that there are many people in the world who only know their feelings and may never have gone to school or learned to count. They may know nothing about numbers and never heard of them but can still make good decisions, how do they do it? It is unlikely that by guessing at numbers and assigning them directly to the alternatives to indicate order under a criterion will yield meaningful priorities because the numbers are arbitrary. Even if they are taken from a scale for a particular criterion, how would we combine them across the criteria as they would likely be from different scales? Our answer to this conundrum is to derive a relative scale for the criteria with respect to the goal and to derive relative scales for the alternatives with respect to each of the criteria and use a weighting and adding process that will make these scales alike. The scale we derive under each criterion is the same priority scale that measures the preference we have for the alternatives with respect to each criterion, and the importance we attribute to the criteria in terms of the goal. As we shall see below, the judgments made use of absolute numbers and the priorities derived from them are also absolute numbers that represent relative dominance. Among the many applications made by companies and governments, now perhaps numbering in the thousands, the Analytic Hierarchy Process was used by IBM as part of its quality improvement strategy to design its AS/400 computer and win the prestigious Malcolm Baldrige National Quality Award [5].

1-2. Deriving a Scale of Priorities from Pairwise Comparisons

Suppose we wish to derive a scale of relative importance according to size (volume) of three apples A, B, C shown in Figure 1-1. Assume that their volumes or sizes are known respectively as S_1, S_2 and S_3. For each position in the matrix below the volume of the apple at the left is compared with that of the apple at the top and the ratio is entered. A matrix of judgments $A = (a_{ij})$ is constructed with respect to a particular property the elements have in common. It is reciprocal, that is, $a_{ji} = 1/a_{ij}$, and $a_{ii} = 1$. For the matrix in Figure 1-1, it is necessary to make only three judgments with the remainder being automatically determined. There are $n(n-1)/2$ judgments required for a matrix of order *n*. Sometimes one (particularly an expert who knows well what the judgments should be) may wish to make a minimum set of judgments and construct a consistent matrix defined as one whose entries satisfy $a_{ij}a_{jk} = a_{ik}$, i,j,k=1,…,n (or $a_{jk} = a_{ik}/a_{ij}$ and all judgments can be obtained from one row). To do this, one can enter *n*-1 judgments in a row or in a column, or in a spanning set with at least one judgment in every row and column, and construct the rest of the entries in the matrix using the consistency condition. Redundancy in the number of judgments generally improves the validity of the final answer because the judgments of the few elements one chooses to compare may be more biased.

Size Comparison	Apple A	Apple B	Apple C
Apple A	S_1/S_1	S_1/S_2	S_1/S_3
Apple B	S_2/S_1	S_2/S_2	S_2/S_3
Apple C	S_3/S_1	S_3/S_2	S_3/S_3

Figure 1-1: Reciprocal structure of pairwise comparison matrix for apples

Assume that we know the volumes of the apples so that the values we enter in Figure 1-2a are consistent. Apple A is twice as big in volume as apple B, and apple B is three times as big as apple C, so we enter a 2 in the (1,2) position and its reciprocal value ½ in the (2,1) position, and so on. Ones are entered on the diagonal by default as every entity equals itself on any criterion. Note that in the (2, 3) position we can enter the value 3 because we know the judgments are consistent as they are based on actual measurements. We can deduce the value this way: from the first row A = 2B and A=6C, thus B = 3C.

Pairwise Comparison

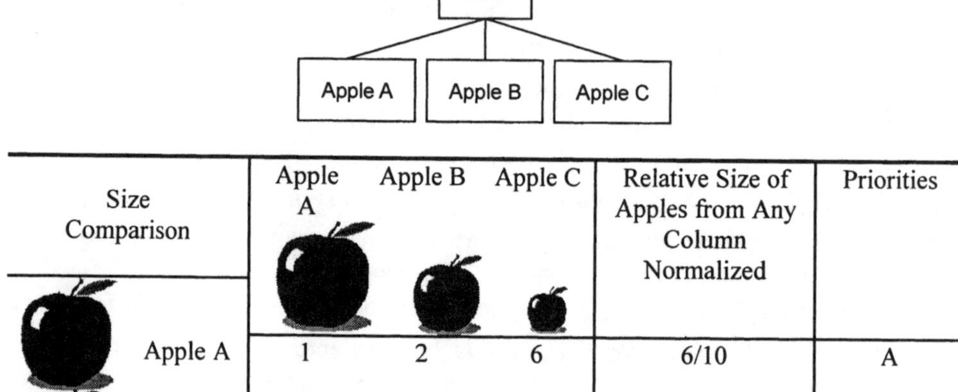

Size Comparison	Apple A	Apple B	Apple C	Relative Size of Apples from Any Column Normalized	Priorities
Apple A	1	2	6	6/10	A
Apple B	1/2	1	3	3/10	B
Apple C	1/6	1/3	1	1/10	C

Figure 1-2a Pairwise comparison matrix for apples using judgments

If we did not have actual measurements, we could not be certain that the judgments in the first row are accurate, and we would not mind estimating the value in the (2, 3) position directly by comparing apple B with apple C. We are then very likely to be inconsistent. How inconsistent can we be before we think it is intolerable? Later we give an actual measure of inconsistency and argue that a consistency of about 10% is considered acceptable.

We obtain from the consistent pairwise comparison matrix above a vector of priorities showing the relative sizes of the apples. Note that we do not have to go to all this trouble to derive the relative volumes of the apples. We could simply have normalized the actual measurements by dividing each measurement value by the sum of all the measurement values. The reason behind our approach is to lay the foundation for what to do when we have no measures for the property in question. When judgments are consistent as they are here, this vector of priorities can be obtained in two ways: by dividing the elements in any column by the sum of its entries (normalizing it), or by summing the entries in each row to obtain the overall dominance in size of that alternative relative to the others and then normalizing the resulting column of values. Incidentally, calculating dominance plays an important role in computing the priorities when judgments are inconsistent for then an alternative may dominate another by different magnitudes by transiting to it through intermediate alternatives. Thus the story is very different if the judgments are inconsistent, and we need to allow inconsistent judgments for good reasons. In sports, team A beats team B, team B beats team C, but team C beats team A. How would we admit such an occurrence in our attempt to explain the real world if we do not allow inconsistency? Most theories have taken a stand against such an occurrence with an axiom that assumes transitivity and prohibits intransitivity, although one does not have to be intransitive to be inconsistent in the values obtained. Others have wished it away by saying that it should not happen in human thinking. But it does, and we offer a theory that copes with intransitivity. In Figure 1-2b we compare three known politicians using our perception of their political astuteness:

1-3. The Fundamental Scale of the AHP for Making Comparisons with Judgments

If we were to use judgments instead of ratios, we would estimate the ratios as numbers using the Fundamental Scale of the AHP, shown in Table 1-1 and derived analytically later in the chapter, and enter these judgments in the matrix. A judgment is made on a pair of elements with respect to a property they have in common. The smaller element is considered to be the unit and one estimates how many times more important, preferable or likely, more generally “dominant”, the other is by using a number from the Fundamental Scale. Dominance is often interpreted as importance when comparing the criteria and as preference when comparing the alternatives with respect to the criteria. It can also be interpreted as likelihood as in the likelihood of a person getting elected as president, or other terms that fit the situation.

Pairwise Comparisons using Judgments and the Derived Priorities

Politician comparisons	B. Clinton 	M. Thatcher 	G. Bush 	Normalized	Total
 B. Clinton	1	3	7	0.6220	1
 M. Thatcher	1/3	1	5	0.2673	0.4297
 G. Bush	1/7	1/5	1	0.1107	0.1780

Figure 1-2b: Comparison of Three Politicians

The set of objects being pairwise compared must be homogeneous. That is, the dominance of the largest object must be no more than 9 times the smallest one (this is the widest span we use for many good reasons discussed elsewhere in the AHP literature). Things that differ by more than this range can be clustered into homogeneous groups and dealt with by using this scale. If measurements from an existing scale are used, they can simply be normalized without regard to homogeneity. When the elements being compared are very close, they should be compared with other more contrasting elements, and the larger of the two should be favored a little in the judgments over the smaller. We have found this approach to be effective to bring out the actual priorities of the two close elements. Otherwise we have proposed the use of a scale between 1 and 2 using decimals and similar judgments to the Fundamental Scale below. We note that human judgment is relatively insensitive to such small decimal changes.

Table 1-2 shows how an audience of about 30 people, using consensus to arrive at each judgment, provided judgments to estimate the dominance of the consumption of drinks in the United States (which drink is consumed more in the US and how much more than another drink?). The derived vector of relative consumption and the actual vector, obtained by normalizing the consumption given in official statistical data sources, are at the bottom of the table.

If the objects are not homogeneous, they may be divided into groups that are homogeneous. If necessary additional objects can be added merely to fill out the intervening clusters to move from the smallest object to the largest one. Figure 1-3 shows how this process works in comparing a cherry tomato with a water-melon, which appears to be two orders of magnitude bigger in size, by introducing intermediate objects in stages.

Table 1-1: The Fundamental Scale of absolute numbers

Intensity of Importance	*Definition*	*Explanation*
1	*Equal Importance*	*Two activities contribute equally to the objective*
2	*Weak or slight*	
3	*Moderate importance*	*Experience and judgment slightly favor one activity over another*
4	*Moderate plus*	
5	*Strong importance*	*Experience and judgment strongly favor one activity over another*
6	*Strong plus*	
7	*Very strong or demonstrated importance*	*An activity is favored very strongly over another; its dominance demonstrated in practice*
8	*Very, very strong*	
9	*Extreme importance*	*The evidence favoring one activity over another is of the highest possible order of affirmation*
Reciprocals of above	*If activity i has one of the above nonzero numbers assigned to it when compared with activity j, then j has the reciprocal value when compared with i*	*A reasonable assumption*
Rationals	*Ratios arising from the scale*	*If consistency were to be forced by obtaining n numerical values to span the matrix*

Table 1-2: Relative consumption of drinks

Which Drink is Consumed More in the U.S.?

An Example of Estimation Using Judgments

Drink Consumption in the U.S.	Coffee	Wine	Tea	Beer	Sodas	Milk	Water
Coffee	1	9	5	2	1	1	1/2
Wine	1/9	1	1/3	1/9	1/9	1/9	1/9
Tea	1/5	2	1	1/3	1/4	1/3	1/9
Beer	1/2	9	3	1	1/2	1	1/3
Sodas	1	9	4	2	1	2	1/2
Milk	1	9	3	1	1/2	1	1/3
Water	2	9	9	3	2	3	1

The derived scale based on the judgments in the matrix is:

Coffee	Wine	Tea	Beer	Sodas	Milk	Water
.177	.019	.042	.116	.190	.129	.327

with a consistency ratio of .022.

The actual consumption (from statistical sources) is:

.180	.010	.040	.120	.180	.140	.330

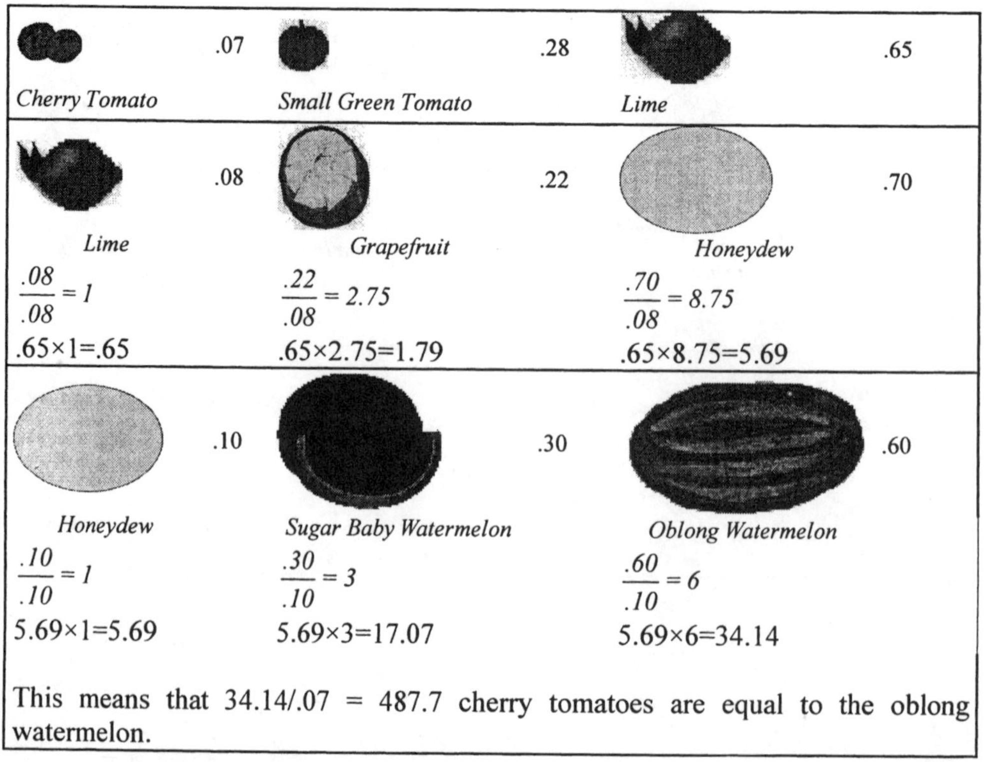

Cherry Tomato .07	*Small Green Tomato* .28	*Lime* .65
Lime .08 $\frac{.08}{.08} = 1$ $.65 \times 1 = .65$	*Grapefruit* .22 $\frac{.22}{.08} = 2.75$ $.65 \times 2.75 = 1.79$	*Honeydew* .70 $\frac{.70}{.08} = 8.75$ $.65 \times 8.75 = 5.69$
Honeydew .10 $\frac{.10}{.10} = 1$ $5.69 \times 1 = 5.69$	*Sugar Baby Watermelon* .30 $\frac{.30}{.10} = 3$ $5.69 \times 3 = 17.07$	*Oblong Watermelon* .60 $\frac{.60}{.10} = 6$ $5.69 \times 6 = 34.14$

This means that 34.14/.07 = 487.7 cherry tomatoes are equal to the oblong watermelon.

Figure 1- 3: Clustering to compare non-homogeneous objects

1-4. Scales of Measurement

Mathematically, a scale is a triple: a set of numbers, a set of objects, and a mapping of the objects to the numbers. There are two ways to perform measurement: one is by using an instrument and making the correspondence directly, and the other is by using judgment. When using judgments one can either assign numbers to the objects by guessing their value on some scale of measurement when there is one, or derive a scale by considering a subset of objects in some fashion such as comparing them in pairs, thus making the correspondence indirect. In addition there are two kinds of origin: one is an absolute origin, as in absolute temperature (0 Kelvin), where nothing falls below that reading, and the other where the origin is a dividing point of positive and negative values with no bound on either side such as with a thermometer. Underlying both these ways are the following kinds (there can be more) of general scales:

Nominal Scale: Invariant under one to one correspondence where a number is assigned to each object; for example, handing out numbers for order of service to people in a queue.

Ordinal Scale: Invariant under monotone transformations, where things are ordered by number but the magnitudes of the numbers only serve to designate order, increasing or decreasing; for example, assigning two numbers 1 and 2, to two people to indicate that one is taller than the other, without including any information about their actual heights. The smaller number may be assigned to the taller person and vice versa.

Interval Scale: Invariant under a positive linear transformation; for example, the linear transformation F = (9/5) C + 32 for converting a Celsius to a Fahrenheit temperature reading. Note that one cannot add two readings x_1 and x_2 on an interval scale because then $y_1+y_2 = (a\,x_1+b) + (a\,x_2 + b) = a\,(x_1 + x_2) \ +2b$ which is of the form $ax+2b$ and not of the form $ax+b$. However, one can take an average of such readings because dividing by 2 yields the correct form.

Ratio Scale: Invariant under a similarity transformation, $y = ax$, $a > 0$. An example is converting weight measured in pounds to kilograms by using the similarity transformation $K = 2.2\ P$. The ratio of the weights of the two objects is the same regardless of whether the measurements are done in pounds or in kilograms. Zero is not the measurement of anything; it applies to objects that do not have the property and in addition one cannot divide by zero to preserve ratios in a meaningful way. Note that one can add two readings from a ratio scale, but not multiply them because $a^2 x_1 x_2$ does not have the form ax. The ratio of two readings from a ratio scale such as 6 kg/ 3 kg = 2 is a number that belongs to an absolute scale that says that the 6 kg object is twice heavier than the 3 kg object. The ratio 2 cannot be changed by some formula to another number. Thus we introduce the next scale.

Absolute Scale: Invariant under the identity transformation $x = x$; for example, numbers used in counting the number of people in a room.

There are also other less well-known scales like a logarithmic and a log-normal scale.

The fundamental scale of the AHP is a scale of absolute numbers used to answer the basic question in all pairwise comparisons: **how many times more dominant is one element than the other with respect to a certain criterion or attribute?** The derived scale, obtained by solving a system of homogeneous linear equations whose coefficients are absolute numbers, is also an absolute scale of relative numbers. Such a relative scale does not have a unit nor does it have an absolute zero. The derived scale is like probabilities in not having a unit or an absolute zero.

In a judgment matrix A, instead of assigning two numbers w_i and w_j (that generally we do not know), as one does with tangibles, and forming the ratio w_i / w_j, we assign a single number drawn from the fundamental scale of absolute numbers shown in Table 1 to represent the ratio $(w_i / w_j)/1$. It is a nearest integer approximation to the ratio w_i / w_j. The ratio of two numbers from a ratio scale (invariant under multiplication by a positive constant) is an absolute number (invariant under the identity transformation) and is dimensionless. In other words it is not measured on a scale with a unit starting from zero. The numbers of an absolute scale are defined in terms of similarity or equivalence. The (absolute) number of a class is the class of all those classes that are similar to it; that is they can be put into one-to-one correspondence with it. But that is not our complete story about absolute numbers transformed to relative form – relative absolute numbers. We now continue our account.

The derived scale will reveal what w_i and w_j are. This is a central fact about the relative measurement approach. It needs a fundamental scale to express numerically the relative dominance relationship by using the smaller or lesser element as the unit of each comparison. Some people who do not understand this and regard the AHP as controversial, forget that most people in the world don't think in terms of numbers but of how they feel about intensities of dominance. They think that the AHP would have a greater theoretical strength if the judgments were made in terms of "ratios of preference differences". I think that the layman would find this proposal laughable as I do for its paucity of understanding, taking the difference of non-existing numbers that one is trying to find in the first place. He needs first to see a utility doctor who would help him create an interval scale utility function so he can take values from it to form differences and then form their ratios to get one judgment!

A useful observation has emerged from recent research in psychology that relates to the use of the fundamental scale of the absolute numbers 1-9 to represent judgments in the AHP/ANP. In his book *The Number Sense, How the Mind Creates Mathematics*, the mathematician and cognitive neuropsychologist Stanislas Dehaene (Oxford University Press 1997, p.73) writes "Introspection suggests that we can mentally represent the meaning of numbers 1 through 9 with actual acuity. Indeed, these symbols seem equivalent to us. They all seem equally easy to work with, and we feel that we can add or compare any two digits in a small and fixed amount of time like a computer. In summary, the invention of numerical symbols should have freed us from the fuzziness of the quantitative representation of numbers."

1-5. From Consistency to Inconsistency

Consistency is essential in human thinking because it enables us to order the world according to dominance. It is a necessary condition for thinking about the world in a scientific way, but it is not sufficient because a mentally disturbed person can think in a perfectly consistent way about a world that does not exist. We need actual knowledge about the world to validate our thinking. But if we were always consistent we would not be able to change our minds. New knowledge often requires that we see things in a new light that can contradict what we thought was correct before. Thus we live with the contradiction that we must be consistent to capture valid knowledge about the world but at the same time be ready to change our minds and be inconsistent if new information requires that we think differently than we thought before. It is clear that large inconsistency unsettles our thinking and thus we need to change our minds in small steps to integrate new information in the old total scheme. This means that inconsistency must be large enough to allow for change in our consistent understanding, but small enough to make it possible to adapt our old beliefs to new information. *This means that inconsistency must be precisely one order of magnitude less important than consistency, or simply 10% of the total concern with consistent measurement. If it were larger it would disrupt consistent measurement and if it were smaller it would make insignificant contribution to change in measurement.*

The paired comparisons process using actual measurements for the elements being compared leads to the following consistent reciprocal matrix:

$$\begin{array}{c} \\ \\ A_1 \\ A_2 \\ \vdots \\ A_n \end{array} \begin{array}{c} \begin{array}{cccc} A_1 & A_2 & \cdots & A_n \\ w_1 & w_2 & \cdots & w_n \end{array} \\ \left[\begin{array}{cccc} w_1/w_1 & w_1/w_2 & \cdots & w_1/w_n \\ w_2/w_1 & w_2/w_2 & \cdots & w_2/w_n \\ \vdots & \vdots & \cdots & \vdots \\ w_n/w_1 & w_n/w_2 & \cdots & w_n/w_n \end{array}\right] \end{array}$$

We note that we can recover the vector $w=(w_1,\dots,w_n)$ by solving the system of equations defined by:

$$Aw = \begin{bmatrix} w_1/w_1 & w_1/w_2 & \cdots & w_1/w_n \\ w_2/w_1 & w_2/w_2 & \cdots & w_2/w_n \\ \vdots & \vdots & \cdots & \vdots \\ w_n/w_1 & w_n/w_2 & \cdots & w_n/w_n \end{bmatrix} \cdot \begin{bmatrix} w_1 \\ w_2 \\ \vdots \\ w_n \end{bmatrix} = n \begin{bmatrix} w_1 \\ w_2 \\ \vdots \\ w_n \end{bmatrix} = nw$$

Solving this homogeneous system of linear equations $Aw = nw$ to find w is a trivial eigenvalue problem, because the existence of a solution depends on whether or not n is an eigenvalue of the characteristic equation of A. But A has rank one and thus all its eigenvalues but one are equal to zero. The sum of the eigenvalues of a matrix is equal to its trace, the sum of its diagonal elements, which in this case is equal to n. Thus n is the largest or the principal eigenvalue of A and w is its corresponding principal eigenvector that is positive and unique to within multiplication by a constant, and thus belongs to a ratio scale. We now know what must be done to recover the weights w_i, whether they are known in advance or not.

We said earlier that an n by n matrix $A=(a_{ij})$ is consistent if $a_{ij}a_{jk} = a_{ik}$, $i,j,k=1,\dots,n$ holds among its entries. We have for a consistent matrix $A^k = n^{k-1}A$, a constant times the original matrix. In normalized form, both A and A^k have the same principal eigenvector. That is not so for an inconsistent matrix. A consistent matrix always has the form $A = (\frac{w_i}{w_j})$. Of course, real-world pairwise comparison matrices are very unlikely to be consistent.

In the inconsistent case, the normalized sum of the rows of each power of the matrix contributes to the final priority vector. Using Cesaro summability and the well-known theorem of Perron, we are led to derive the priorities in the form of the principal right eigenvector. Now we give an elegant mathematical discussion, based on the concept of invariance, to show why we still need for an inconsistent matrix the principal right eigenvector for our priority vector. It is clear that no matter what method we use to derive the weights w_i, we need to get them back as proportional to the expression $\sum_{j=1}^{n} a_{ij} w_j \quad i = 1,...,n$, that is, we must solve $\sum_{j=1}^{n} a_{ij} w_j = cw_i \quad i = 1,...,n$. Otherwise $\sum_{j=1}^{n} a_{ij} w_j \quad i = 1,...,n$ would yield another set of different weights and they in turn can be used to form new expressions $\sum_{j=1}^{n} a_{ij} w_j \quad i = 1,...,n$, and so on ad infinitum. Unless we solve the principal eigenvalue problem, our quest for priorities becomes meaningless.

We learn from the consistent case that what we get on the right side of $\sum_{j=1}^{n} a_{ij} w_j = cw_i \quad i = 1,...,n$ is proportional to the sum on the left that involves the same ratio scale used to weight the judgments that we are looking for. Thus we have the proportionality constant c. A better way to see this is to use the derived vector of priorities to weight each row of the matrix and take the sum. This yields a new vector of priorities (relative dominance of each element) represented in the comparisons. This vector can again be used to weight the rows and obtain still another vector of priorities. In the limit (if one exists), the limit vector itself can be used to weight the rows and get the limit vector back perhaps proportionately. Our general problem possibly with inconsistent judgments takes the form:

$$Aw = \begin{bmatrix} 1 & a_{12} & \cdots & a_{1n} \\ 1/a_{12} & 1 & \cdots & a_{2n} \\ \vdots & \vdots & \vdots & \vdots \\ 1/a_{1n} & 1/a_{2n} & \cdots & 1 \end{bmatrix} \begin{bmatrix} w_1 \\ w_2 \\ \vdots \\ w_n \end{bmatrix} = cw$$

This homogeneous system of linear equations $Aw = cw$ has a solution w if c is the principal eigenvalue of A. That this is the case can be shown using an argument that involves both left and right eigenvectors of A. Two vectors $x = (x_1,...,x_n)$, $y = (y_1,...,y_n)$ are orthogonal if their scalar product $x_1y_1 + ... + x_ny_n$ is equal to zero. It is known that any left eigenvector of a matrix corresponding to an eigenvalue is orthogonal to any right eigenvector corresponding to a different eigenvalue. This property is known as biorthogonality [25].

Theorem For a given positive matrix A, the only positive vector w and only positive constant c that satisfy $Aw = cw$, is a vector w that is a positive multiple of the principal eigenvector of A, and the only such c is the principal eigenvalue of A.

Proof. We know that the right principal eigenvector and the principal eigenvalue satisfy our requirements. We also know that the algebraic multiplicity of the principal eigenvalue is one, and that there is a positive left eigenvector of A (call it z) corresponding to the principal eigenvalue. Suppose there is a positive vector y and a (necessarily positive) scalar d such that $Ay = dy$. If d and c are not equal, then, by biorthogonality, y is orthogonal to z, which is impossible since both vectors are positive. If c and d are equal, then y and w are dependent since c has algebraic multiplicity one, and y is a positive multiple of w. This completes the proof.

1-6. An Example of an AHP Decision

The simple decision is to choose the best city in which to live. We shall show how to make this decision using both methods of the AHP that conform to what Blumenthal said. We do it first with relative (comparative) measurement and second with absolute measurement. With the relative measurement method the criteria are pairwise compared with respect to the goal, the alternatives are pairwise compared with respect to each criterion and the results are synthesized or combined using a weighting and adding process to give an overall ranking of the alternatives. With the absolute measurement method standards are established for each criterion and the cities are rated one-by-one against the standards rather than being compared with each other.

Making the Decision with a Relative Measurement Model

The relative measurement model by Mary Reiter for picking the best city in which to live is shown below in Figure 1-4.

For each cell in the comparison matrix there is associated a row criterion (listed on the left), call it X, and a column criterion (on the top), call it Y. One answers this question for the cell: How much more important is X than Y in choosing a best city in which to live? The judgments, shown in Table 1-2, are entered using the Fundamental Scale of the AHP. Fractional values between the integers such as 4.32 can also be used when they are known from measurement.

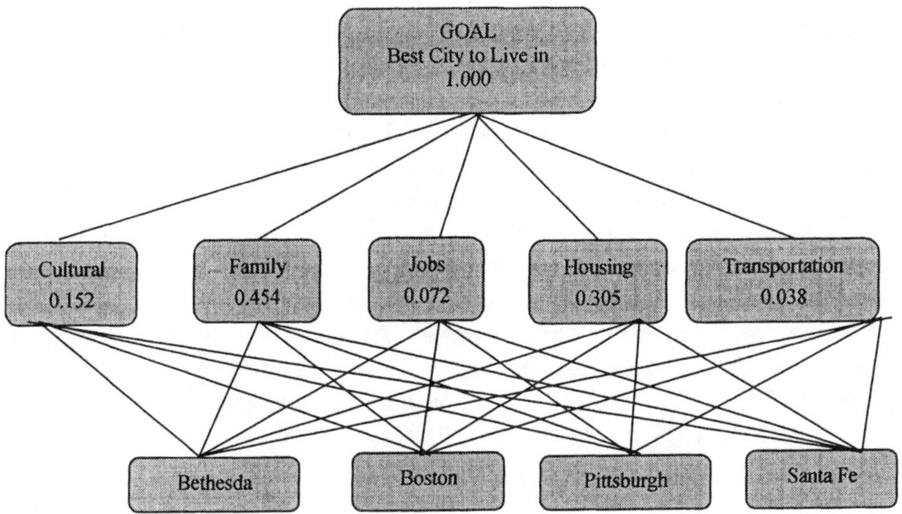

Figure 1-4: Relative model for choosing best city to live in

THE NUMBER OF JUDGMENTS AND CONSISTENCY

In this decision there are 10 judgments to be entered. As we shall see later, inconsistency for a judgment matrix can be computed as a function of its maximum eigenvalue λ_{max} and the order n of the matrix. The time gained, from making fewer judgments than 10 along a spanning tree for example can be offset by not having sufficient redundancy in the judgments to fine tune and improve the overall outcome. There can be no inconsistency when the minimum number of judgments is used.

Next the alternatives are pairwise compared with respect to each of the criteria. The judgments and the derived priorities for the alternatives are shown in Table 1-4. The priority vectors are the principal eigenvectors of the pairwise comparison matrices. They are in the distributive form, that is, they have been normalized by dividing each element of the principal eigenvector by the sum of all its elements so that after normalization they sum to 1. The priority vectors can be transformed to their idealized form by selecting the largest element in the vector and dividing all the elements by it so that it takes on the value 1, with the others proportionately less. The element (or elements) with a priority of 1 become the ideal(s). Later we explain why we use these two forms of synthesis.

SYNTHESIS

The outcome of the distributive form of normalized values is shown in Table 1-5 and that for the ideal form is shown in Table 1-6. Table 1-5 gives the priority vectors for the cities from Table 1-4 and the columns in Table 1-6 are these same vectors in idealized form with respect to each criterion. Using either form the totals vector is obtained by multiplying the priority of each criterion times the priority of each alternative with respect to it and summing. The overall priority vector is obtained from the totals vector by normalizing: dividing each element in the totals vector by the sum of its elements. The final outcome with either form of synthesis is that Pittsburgh is the highest ranked city for this individual. Though the final priorities are somewhat different the order is the same: Pittsburgh, Boston, Bethesda and Santa Fe. The ratios of the final priorities are meaningful. Pittsburgh is almost twice as preferred as Bethesda.

Table 1-3: Criteria weights with respect to the goal

GOAL	Culture	Family	Housing	Jobs	Transportation	Priorities
Culture	1	1/5	3	1/2	5	0.152
Family	5	1	7	1	7	0.433
Housing	1/3	1/7	1	1/4	3	0.072
Job	2	1	4	1	7	0.305
Transportation	1/5	1/7	1/3	1/7	1	0.038

Inconsistency 0.05

Table 1-4: Alternatives' weights with respect to criteria

Culture	**Bethesda**	**Boston**	**Pittsburgh**	**Santa Fe**	**Priorities**
Bethesda	1	1/2	1	1/2	0.163
Boston	2	1	2.5	1	0.345
Pittsburgh	1	1/2.5	1	1/2.5	0.146
Santa Fe	2	1	2.5	1	0.345

Inconsistency .002

Family	Bethesda	Boston	Pittsburgh	Santa Fe	Priorities
Bethesda	1	2	1/3	4	0.210
Boston	1	1	1/8	2	0.098
Pittsburgh	3	8	1	9	0.635
Santa Fe	1/4	1/2	1/9	1	0.057

Inconsistency .012

Housing	Bethesda	Boston	Pittsburgh	Santa Fe	Priorities
Bethesda	1	5	1/2	2.5	0.262
Boston	1/5	1	1/9	1/4	0.047
Pittsburgh	2	9	1	7	0.571
Santa Fe	1/2.5	4	1/7	1	0.120

Inconsistency .012

Jobs	Bethesda	Boston	Pittsburgh	Santa Fe	Priorities
Bethesda	1	1/2	3	4	0.279
Boston	2	1	6	8	0.559
Pittsburgh	1/3	1/6	1	1	0.087
Santa Fe	1/4	1/8	1	1	0.075

Inconsistency .004

Transportation	Bethesda	Boston	Pittsburgh	Santa Fe	Priorities
Bethesda	1	1.5	1/2	4	0.249
Boston	1/1.5	1	1/3.5	2.5	0.157
Pittsburgh	2	3.5	1	9	0.533
Santa Fe	1/4	½.5	1/9	1	0.061

Inconsistency .001

When synthesizing in the distributive form the totals vector and the overall priorities vector are the same. When synthesizing in the ideal form as shown in Table 1-5 they are not. Ideal synthesis gives slightly different results from distributive synthesis in this case.

Table 1-5: Synthesis using the distributive mode to obtain the overall priorities for the alternatives

Synthesis	Cultural *0.152*	Family *0.433*	Housing *0.072*	Jobs *0.305*	Transport *0.038*	Totals Multiply and Add	Overall Priorities Normalize Totals
Bethesda	0.163	0.210	0.262	0.279	0.249	0.229	0.229
Boston	0.345	0.098	0.047	0.559	0.157	0.275	0.275
Pittsburgh	0.146	0.635	0.571	0.087	0.533	0.385	0.385
Santa Fe	0.345	0.057	0.120	0.075	0.061	0.111	0.111

Table 1-6: Synthesis using the ideal mode to obtain the overall priorities for the alternatives

Alternatives	Cultural .152	Family .433	Housing .072	Jobs .305	Transport .038	Totals Multiply and Add	Overall Priorities Normalize Totals
Bethesda	0.474	0.330	0.459	0.500	0.467	0.418	0.224
Boston	1.000	0.155	0.082	1.000	0.295	0.541	0.290
Pittsburgh	0.424	1.000	1.000	0.155	1.000	0.655	0.351
Santa Fe	1.000	0.089	0.209	0.135	0.115	0.251	0.135

IDEAL SYNTHESIS PREVENTS RANK REVERSAL

An important distinction to make between measurement in physics and measurement in decision-making is that in the first we usually seek measurements that approximate to the weight and length of things, whereas in human action we seek to order actions according to priorities. In mathematics a distinction is made between *metric topology* that deals with the measurement of length, mass and time and *order topology* that deals with the ordering of priorities through the concept of *dominance* rather than closeness used in metric methods. We have seen that the principal eigenvector of a matrix is necessary to capture dominance priorities. When we have a matrix of judgments we derive its priorities in the form of its principal eigenvector. When we deal with a hierarchy the principle of hierarchic composition involves weighting and adding as a special case of the more general principle of network composition in which priorities are also derived as the principal eigenvector of a stochastic matrix which involves weighting and adding in the process of raising a matrix to powers. Some scholars whose specialization is in the physical sciences are perhaps unaware of the methods of order topology and have used various arguments to justify why they would use a metric approach to derive priorities and also to obtain the overall synthesis. It may be worthwhile to discuss this at some length in the following paragraph [56, 77].

Ideal synthesis should be used when one wishes to prevent reversals in rank of the original set of alternatives from occurring when a new dominated alternative is added. With the distributive form rank reversal can occur to account for the presence of many other alternatives in cases where adding many things of the same kind or of nearly the same kind can depreciate the value of any of them. It has been established that 92% of the time, there is no rank reversal in the distributive mode when a new dominated alternative is added [72]. We note that uniqueness or manyness are not criteria that can be included when the alternatives are assumed to be independent of one another, for then to rank an alternative one would have to see how many other alternatives there are thus creating dependence among them.

Both the distributive and ideal modes are necessary for use in the AHP. We have shown that idealization is essential and is independent of what method one may use. There are people who have made it an obsession to find ways to avoid rank reversal in every decision and wish to alter the synthesis of the AHP away from normalization or idealization. They are likely to obtain outcomes that are not compatible with what the real outcome of a decision should be, because in decision-making we also want uniqueness of the answer we get.

Here is a failed attempt by some people to do things their metric way to preserve rank other than by the ideal form. The multiplicative approach to the AHP uses the familiar methods of taking the geometric mean to obtain the priorities of the alternatives for each criterion without normalization, and then raising them to the powers of the criteria and again taking the geometric mean to perform synthesis in a distorted way to always preserve rank. It is essentially a consequence of attempting to minimize the logarithmic least squares expression [73]:

$$\sum_{i=1}^{n}\sum_{j=1}^{n}(\log a_{ij} - \log\frac{w_i}{w_j})^2$$

It does not work when the same measurement is used for the alternatives with respect to several criteria as one can easily verify and that should be sufficient to throw it out. Second and more seriously, the multiplicative method has an untenable mathematical problem. Assume that an alternative has a priority 0.2 with respect to each of two criteria whose respective priorities are 0.3 and 0.5. It is logical to assume that this alternative should have a higher priority with respect to the more important criterion, the one with the value of 0.5, after the weighting is performed. But $0.2^{0.5} < 0.2^{0.3}$ and alas it does not, it has a smaller priority. One would think that the procedure of ranking in this way would have been abandoned at first knowledge of this observation.

We conclude that in order to preserve rank indiscriminately from any other alternative, one can use the rating approach of the AHP described below in which alternatives are evaluated one at a time using the ideal mode. In addition, by deriving priorities from paired comparisons, rank is always preserved if one idealizes only the first time, and then compares each alternative with the ideal, allowing the value to exceed one. On the other hand, idealizing repeatedly only preserves rank from irrelevant alternatives.

Remark: On occasion someone has suggested the use of Pareto optimality instead of weighting the priorities of the alternatives by the priorities of the criteria and adding to find the best alternative. It is known that a concave function for the synthesis, if one could be found, would serve the purpose of finding the best alternative when it is known what it should be. But if the best alternative is already known for some property that it has which makes it the best, then one has a single not a multiple criteria decision. Naturally a multiple criteria problem may not yield the expected outcome. This is a special case of when the weights of the criteria depend on those of the alternatives. We will see in Chapter 2 that the final overall choice is automatically made in the process of finding the priorities of the criteria as they depend on the alternatives. Pareto optimality plays no role to determine the best outcome in that general case.

Making the Decision with an Absolute or Ratings Model

Using the absolute or ratings method of the AHP, categories (intensities) or standards are established for the criteria and cities are rated one at a time by selecting the appropriate category under each criterion rather than compared against other cities. The standards are prioritized for each criterion by making pairwise comparisons. For example, the standards for the criterion Job Opportunities are: Excellent, Above Average, Average, Below Average and Poor. Judgments are entered for such questions as: “How much more preferable is Excellent than Above Average for this criterion?” Each city is then rated by selecting the appropriate category for it for each criterion. The city’s score is then computed by weighting the priority of the selected category by the priority of the criterion and summing for all the criteria. The prioritized categories are essentially absolute scales, abstract yardsticks, which have been derived and are unique to each criterion. Judgment is still required to select the appropriate category under a criterion for a city, but the cities are no longer compared against each other. In absolute measurement, the cities are scored independently of each other. In relative measurement, there is dependence, as a city’s performance depends on what other cities there are in the comparison group. Figure 1-5 and Tables 1-7, 1-8 and 1-9 represent what one does in the ratings or absolute measurement approach of the AHP. Table 1-7 illustrates the pairwise comparisons of the intensities under one criterion. The process must be repeated to compare the intensities for each of the other criteria. We caution that such intensities and their priorities are only appropriate for our given problem and should not be used with the same priorities for all criteria nor carelessly in other problems.

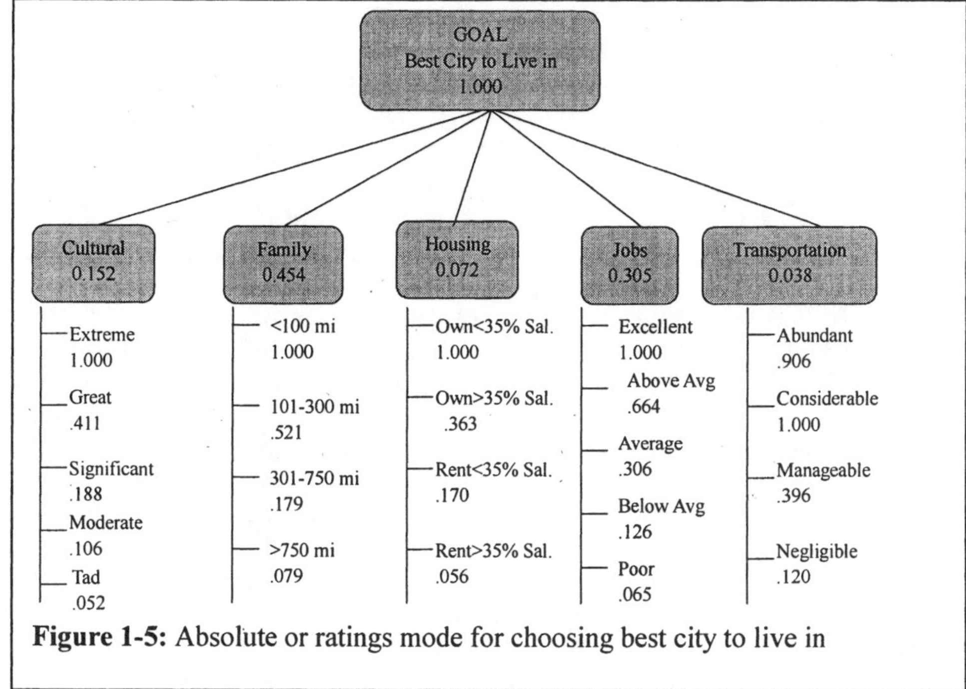

Figure 1-5: Absolute or ratings mode for choosing best city to live in

Table 1-7: Deriving priorities for the cultural criterion categories

	Extreme	Great	Significant	Moderate	Tad	Derived Priorities	Idealized Priorities
Extreme	1	5	6	8	9	.569	1.000
Great	1/5	1	4	5	7	.234	.411
Significant	1/6	1/4	1	3	5	.107	.188
Moderate	1/8	1/5	1/3	1	4	.060	.106
Tad	1/9	1/7	1/5	1/4	1	.030	.052

Inconsistency = .112

Table 1-8: Verbal ratings of cities under each criterion

Alternatives	Cultural *.195*	Family *.394*	Housing *.056*	Jobs *.325*	Transport *.030*	Total Score	Priorities (Normal.)
Pittsburgh	Signific.	<100 mi	Own>35%	Average	Manageable	.562	.294
Boston	Extreme	301-750 mi	Rent>35%	Above Avg	Abundant	.512	.267
Bethesda	Great	101-300 mi	Rent<35	Excellent	Considerable	.650	.339
Santa Fe	Signific.	>750 mi	Own>35%	Average	Negligible	.191	.100

Table 1-9: Priorities of ratings of cities under each criterion

Alternatives	Cultural *.195*	Family *.394*	Housing *.056*	Jobs *.325*	Transport *.030*	Total Score	Priorities (Normalized)
Pittsburgh	0.188	1.000	0.363	0.306	0.396	.562	.294
Boston	1.000	0.179	0.056	0.664	0.906	.512	.267
Bethesda	0.411	0.521	0.170	1.000	1.000	.650	.339
Santa Fe	0.188	0.079	0.363	0.306	0.120	.191	.100

When the intensities are intangible, like excellent, very good and so on down to poor, there may be alternatives that fall above or below that range because what is excellent for one group of alternatives may not be applicable to alternatives that are much better or much worse than the given alternatives. In that case we need to expand the intensities by putting them into categories. We may use the same names for them but we may have order of magnitude categories in which we compare the elements in each category or even use the same scale but then combine that category with an adjacent category using the top or bottom rated intensity as a pivot as in the cherry tomato-watermelon example. To determine which category an alternative should be rated on, we first start with any alternative and rate it. From then on before rating a new alternative we need to compare it with the previous alternative if it is better or worse and in doing that we need to reason through and insert hypothetical alternatives to place it correctly just as we did in the cherry tomato-watermelon example. In real life, alternatives that naturally occur in a certain activity tend to be alike or homogeneous. Even when they are not alike they generally differ by one or two categories of intensity on each criterion. When they differ by more, they are unlikely to be considered as serious contenders and are assigned a zero value. The concern is usually from the top rated alternatives downwards for the intensities of each criterion.

Let us elaborate further. For rating banks one at a time for example, one needs intensities like high medium and low, or very high, high, medium low and very low. In theory there should be different intensities for each criterion. In practice one cheats sometimes and uses the same intensities. One pairwise compares the intensities. If the range of alternatives is so varied then this division needs to be extended into categories of intensities under a criterion. Let us explain. In the example of the cherry tomato-watermelon it is not enough to put the watermelon as high and assign it the intensity one and give the cherry tomato the value very low. One uses a different order of magnitude high medium, low, for the upper range and then uses the low of the upper range as the high of a second range on intensities of a slightly smaller range and so on to create different ranges of intensities and their final idealized values (that is "high" in the top range gets the value one and the other values are divided by that value to get their proportionate value less than one.) Then the banks are each assigned an intensity value under that criterion. So we have used the same idea of pivot on the intensities. One can do this once and use the same set of intensities for all the criteria for example. If one wants to do it perfectly as the theory says, one generates different sets of levels of intensities and their priorities for each criterion. For example one set of intensities ranging from high to low would not be sufficient to rate the watermelon with its very large value and the cherry tomato with its very small value that is 487 times smaller than the watermelon. One range of intensities is useful for only rating alternatives that differ by about one order of magnitude in priority for that criterion. If the banks are very different under some criterion one may need to do what has been described above.

What I have suggested is scientifically the most accurate way to do ratings. Other ways people use is to assign numbers from one to a hundred to an alternative for each criterion. But that is just a guess that in my view can be very wrong for a problem that is done with the delicacy of someone who knows about rating.

1-7. Sanctioning China? An Application with Benefits, Costs and Risks

This example was developed in February 1995 when media were voicing strong opinion about whether the US government should sanction China about intellectual property rights. I and my coauthor Professor Jen Shang sent our analysis to Mr. Mickey Kantor, the then chief US negotiator, before his trip to Beijing. Mr. Kantor acknowledged reading our article in a very positive way by calling me. We are not taking credit that the US did not sanction China. But we are quite happy that the outcome of the decision was along the lines of our recommendation. The model we used, shown in Figure 1-6, is a three part Benefits, Costs and Risks model. Note that in this example we formed the (marginal) ratio of the benefits which are positive, to the costs and risks both of which are opposite because we must respond to the question, which alternative is more costly (risky) for a give criterion.

In later examples, instead of forming ratios of absolute numbers, we use subtraction and negative priorities [64] after carefully rating one at a time the highest ranked alternative under each of the benefits (B), opportunities (O), the costs (C) and the risks (R) or as a collective we refer to them as (BOCR). The highest ranked alternative is often different under each. In this manner instead of obtaining marginal (per unit) results by forming the ratio we obtain the totals. It is clear from this analysis that the US should not have taken any action that would be averse to cultivating a successful working relation between the two great countries for the foreseeable future.

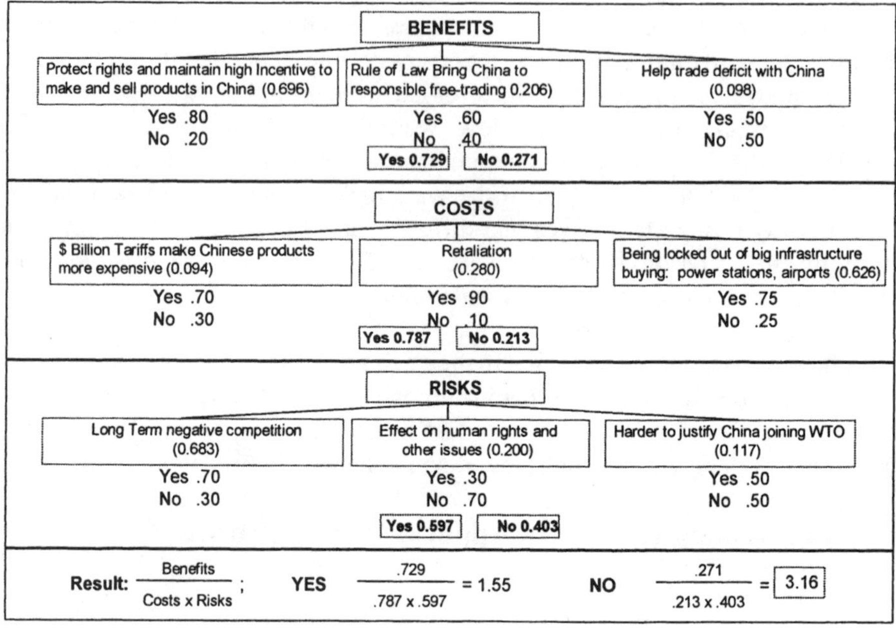

Figure 1-6: China trade sanction model

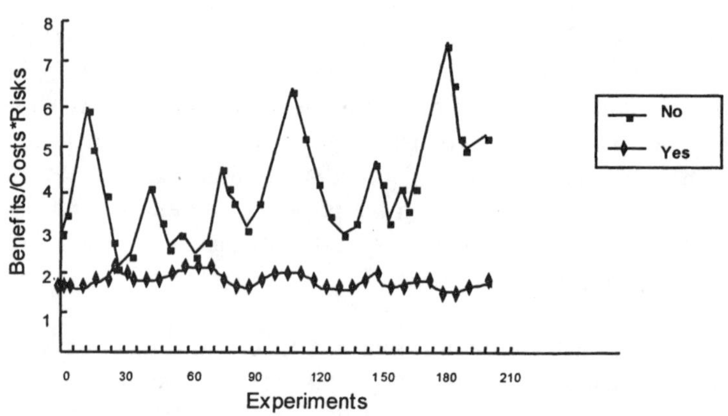

Figure 1-7: Sensitivity analysis of the outcome of the China decision

1-8. Stimulus-Response and the Fundamental Scale

We shall see in Chapter 2 that a hierarchy is a special case of a network whose priorities and interactions are represented in a supermatrix W. As a result, hierarchic synthesis of priorities is a special case of network synthesis of priorities. The limit priorities of W, limit as $k \to \infty$ of W^k, yield its network synthesis. Equivalently, because W is column stochastic as its columns sum to one, its network synthesis can be obtained by solving the principal eigenvalue problem $Ww = w$ with $\lambda_{max} = 1$. Invariance of the eigenvector makes additive hierarchic synthesis necessary to obtain priorities for a hierarchy.

To be able to perceive and sense objects in the environment our brains miniaturize them within our system of neurons so that we have a proportional relationship between what we perceive and what is out there. Without proportionality we cannot coordinate our thinking with our actions with the accuracy needed to control the environment. Proportionality with respect to a single stimulus requires that our response to a proportionately amplified or attenuated stimulus we receive from a source should be proportional to what our response would be to the original value of that stimulus. If $w(s)$ is our response to a stimulus of magnitude s, then the foregoing gives rise to the functional equation $w(as) = b\, w(s)$. This equation can *also* be obtained as the necessary condition for solving the Fredholm equation of the second kind:

$$\int_a^b K(s,t)\, w(t)\, dt = \lambda_{\max}\, w(s)$$

obtained as the continuous generalization of the discrete formulation $Aw = \lambda_{\max} w$ for deriving priorities where instead of the positive reciprocal matrix A in the principal eigenvalue problem, we have a positive kernel, $K(s,t) > 0$, with $K(s,t)\, K(t,s) = 1$ that is also consistent i.e. $K(s,t)\, K(t,u) = K(s,u)$, for all s, t, and u. The solution of this functional equation in the real domain is given by

$$w(s) = Ce^{\log b \frac{\log s}{\log a}} P\left(\frac{\log s}{\log a}\right)$$

where P is a periodic function of period 1 and $P(0) = 1$. One of the simplest such examples with $u = \log s / \log a$ is $P(u) = \cos(u/2\pi)$ for which $P(0) = 1$.

The logarithmic law of response to stimuli can be obtained as a first order approximation to this solution through series expansions of the exponential and of the cosine functions as:

$$v(u) = C_1 e^{-\beta u} P(u) \approx C_2 \log s + C_3$$

$\log ab \equiv -\beta, \beta > 0$. The expression on the right is known as the Weber-Fechner law of logarithmic response $M = a \log s + b, a \neq 0$ to a stimulus of magnitude s. This law was empirically established and tested in 1860 by Gustav Theodor Fechner who used a law formulated by Ernest Heinrich Weber regarding discrimination between two nearby values of a stimulus. We have now shown that Fechner's version can be derived by starting with a functional equation for stimulus response.

The integer-valued scale of response used in making paired comparison judgments can be derived from the logarithmic response function as follows. The larger the stimulus, the larger a change in it is needed for that change to be detectable. The ratio of successive just noticeable differences (the well-known "jnd" in psychology) is equal to the ratio of their corresponding successive stimuli values. Proportionality is maintained. Thus, starting with a stimulus s_0 successive magnitudes of the new stimuli take the form:

$$s_1 = s_0 + \Delta s_0 = s_0 + \frac{\Delta s_0}{s_0} s_0 = s_0(1+r)$$

$$s_2 = s_1 + \Delta s_1 = s_1(1+r) = s_0(1+r)^2 \equiv s_0 \alpha^2$$

$$\vdots$$

$$s_n = s_{n-1}\alpha = s_0 \alpha^n (n = 0,1,2,...)$$

We consider the responses to these stimuli to be measured on a ratio scale (b=0). A typical response has the form $M_i = a \log \alpha^i$, i =1,…, n, or one after another they have the form:

$$M_1 = a \log \alpha, M_2 = 2a \log \alpha, ..., M_n = na \log \alpha$$

We take the ratios M_i / M_1, i = 1,...,*n*, of these responses in which the first is the smallest and serves as the unit of comparison, thus obtaining the *integer* values 1, 2, ..., *n* of the fundamental scale of the AHP. It appears that numbers are intrinsic to our ability to make comparisons, and that they were not an invention by our primitive ancestors. We must be grateful to them for the discovery of the symbolism. In a less mathematical vein, we note that we are able to distinguish ordinally between high, medium and low at one level and for each of them in a second level below that also distinguish between high, medium and low giving us nine different categories. We assign the value one to (low, low) which is the smallest and the value nine to (high, high) which is the highest, thus covering the spectrum of possibilities between two levels, and giving the value nine for the top of the paired comparisons scale as compared with the lowest value on the scale. Because of increase in inconsistency when we compare more than about 7 elements, we don't need to keep in mind more than 7 ± 2 elements. This was first conjectured by the psychologist George Miller in the 1950's and explained in the AHP in the 1970's [55]. Finally, we note that the scale just derived is attached to the importance we assign to judgments. If we have an exact measurement such as 2.375 and want to use it as it is for our judgment without attaching significance to it, we can use its entire value without approximation.

A person may not be schooled in the use of numbers, and there are many in our world who do not, but still have feelings, judgments and understanding that enable him or her to make accurate comparisons (equal, moderate, strong, very strong and extreme and compromises between these intensities). Such judgments can be applied successfully to compare stimuli that are not too disparate but homogeneous in magnitude. By homogeneous we mean that they fall within specified bounds. Table 1-1, the Fundamental Scale for paired comparisons, summarizes the foregoing discussion.

The idea of using time dependent judgments is examined in detail in Chapter 7 and in reference [55].

1-9. When is a Positive Reciprocal Matrix Consistent?

Let $A = [a_{ij}]$ be an *n*-by-*n* positive reciprocal matrix, so all $a_{ii} = 1$ and $a_{ij} = 1/a_{ji}$ for all $i,j = 1,\dots,n$. Let $w = [w_i]$ be the Perron vector of A, let $D = \text{diag}(w_1, \dots, w_n)$ be the *n*-by-*n* diagonal matrix whose main diagonal entries are the entries of w, and set $E \equiv D^{-1}AD = [a_{ij}\, w_j / w_i] = [\varepsilon_{ij}]$. Then E is similar to A and is a positive reciprocal matrix since $\varepsilon_{ji} = a_{ji} w_i / w_j = (a_{ij}\, w_j / w_i)^{-1} = 1/\varepsilon_{ij}$. Moreover, all the row sums of E are equal to the principal eigenvalue of A :

$$\sum_{j=1}^{n} \varepsilon_{ij} = \sum_j a_{ij} w_j / w_i = [Aw]_i / w_i$$
$$= \lambda_{\max} w_i / w_i = \lambda_{\max}$$

The computation

$$n\lambda_{\max} = \sum_{i=1}^{n}\left(\sum_{j=1}^{n} \varepsilon_{ij}\right) = \sum_{i=1}^{n} \varepsilon_{ii} + \sum_{\substack{i,j=1 \\ i \neq j}}^{n} (\varepsilon_{ij} + \varepsilon_{ji})$$
$$= n + \sum_{\substack{i,j=1 \\ i \neq j}}^{n} (\varepsilon_{ij} + \varepsilon_{ij}^{-1}) \geq n + 2(n^2 - n)/2 = n^2 \tag{1}$$

reveals that $\lambda_{\max} \geq n$. Moreover, since $x + 1/x \geq 2$ for all x > 0, with equality if and only if $x = 1$, we see that $\lambda_{\max} = n$ if and only if all $\varepsilon_{ij} = 1$, which is equivalent to having all $a_{ij} = w_i / w_j$.

The foregoing arguments show that a positive reciprocal matrix A has $\lambda_{\max} \geq n$, with equality if and only if A is consistent. As our measure of deviation of A from consistency, we choose the *consistency index*

$$\mu \equiv \frac{\lambda_{\max} - n}{n-1}.$$

We have seen that $\mu \geq 0$ and $\mu = 0$ if and only if A is consistent. These two desirable properties explain the term "n" in the numerator of μ ; what about the term "n-1" in the denominator? Since trace $A = n$ is the sum of all the eigenvalues of A, if we denote the eigenvalues of A that are different from $\lambda_{\max}$ by $\lambda_2, \ldots, \lambda_{n-1}$, we see that

$$n = \lambda_{\max} + \sum_{i=2}^{n} \lambda_i ,$$

so

$$n - \lambda_{\max} = \sum_{i=2}^{n} \lambda_i \quad \text{and} \quad \mu = -\frac{1}{n-1} \sum_{i=2}^{n} \lambda_i$$

is the negative average of the non-principal eigenvalues of A.

It is an easy, but instructive, computation to show that $\lambda_{max} = 2$ for every 2-by-2 positive reciprocal matrix:

$$\begin{bmatrix} 1 & \alpha \\ \alpha^{-1} & 1 \end{bmatrix} \begin{bmatrix} 1+\alpha \\ (1+\alpha)\alpha^{-1} \end{bmatrix} = 2 \begin{bmatrix} 1+\alpha \\ (1+\alpha)\alpha^{-1} \end{bmatrix}$$

Thus, every 2-by-2 positive reciprocal matrix is consistent.

Not every 3-by-3 positive reciprocal matrix is consistent, but in this case we are fortunate to have again explicit formulas for the principal eigenvalue and eigenvector. For

$$A = \begin{bmatrix} 1 & a & b \\ 1/a & 1 & c \\ 1/b & 1/c & 1 \end{bmatrix},$$

we have $\lambda_{max} = 1 + d + d^{-1}$, $d = (ac/b)^{1/3}$ and

$$\begin{aligned} w_1 &= bd/(1 + bd + \frac{c}{d}) \\ w_2 &= c/d(1 + bd + \frac{c}{d}), \\ w_3 &= 1/(1 + bd + \frac{c}{d}) \end{aligned} \qquad (2)$$

Note that $\lambda_{max} = 3$ when d = 1 or c = b/a, which is true if and only if A is consistent.

In order to get some feel for what the consistency index might be telling us about a positive n-by-n reciprocal matrix A, consider the following simulation: choose the entries of A above the main diagonal at random from the 17 values $\{1/9, 1/8,\ldots,1/2, 1, 2,\ldots,8, 9\}$. Then fill in the entries of A below the diagonal by taking reciprocals. Put ones down the main diagonal and compute the consistency index. Do this 50,000 times and take the average, which we call the *random index*. Table 4 shows the values obtained from one set of such simulations, for matrices of size 1, 2,…, 10.

Since it would be pointless to try to discern any priority ranking from a set of random comparison judgments, we should probably be uncomfortable about proceeding unless the consistency index of a pairwise comparison matrix is very much smaller than the corresponding random index value in Table 1-10. The *consistency ratio* (C.R.) of a pairwise comparison matrix is the ratio of its consistency index μ to the corresponding random index value in Table 1-10.

Table 1-10: Random index

N	1	2	3	4	5	6	7	8	9	10
Random Index	0	0	.52	.89	1.11	1.25	1.35	1.40	1.45	1.49

If the C.R. is larger than desired, we do three things: 1) Find the most inconsistent judgment in the matrix, 2) Determine the range of values to which that judgment can be changed corresponding to which the inconsistency would be improved, 3) Ask the decision maker to consider, if he can, changing his judgment to a plausible value in that range. If he is unwilling, we try with the second most inconsistent judgment and so on. If no judgment is changed the decision is postponed until better understanding of the criteria is obtained. Three methods are plausible for changing the judgments to improve inconsistency. All require theoretical investigation of convergence and efficiency. The first uses an explicit formula for the partial derivatives of the principal eigenvalue with respect to the matrix entries.

For a given positive reciprocal matrix $A = [a_{ij}]$ and a given pair of distinct indices $k > l$, define $A(t) = [a_{ij}(t)]$ by $a_{kl}(t) \equiv a_{kl} + t$, $a_{lk}(t) \equiv (a_{lk} + t)^{-1}$, and $a_{ij}(t) \equiv a_{ij}$ for all $i \neq k, j \neq l$, so $A(0) = A$. Let $\lambda_{\max}(t)$ denote the Perron eigenvalue of $A(t)$ for all t in a neighborhood of $t = 0$ that is small enough to ensure that all entries of the reciprocal matrix $A(t)$ are positive there. Finally, let $v = [v_i]$ be the unique positive eigenvector of the positive matrix A^T that is normalized so that $v^T w = 1$. Then a classical perturbation formula (see [25], theorem 6.3.12) tells us that

$$\left.\frac{d\lambda_{\max}(t)}{dt}\right|_{t=0} = \frac{v^T A'(0) w}{v^T w} = v^T A'(0) w = v_k w_l - \frac{1}{a_{kl}^2} v_l w_k .$$

We conclude that

$$\frac{\partial \lambda_{\max}}{\partial a_{ij}} = v_i w_j - a_{ji}{}^2 v_j w_i \qquad \text{for all } i,j = 1,\ldots,n.$$

Because we are operating within the set of positive reciprocal matrices we have:

$$\frac{\partial \lambda_{max}}{\partial a_{ji}} = - \frac{\partial \lambda_{max}}{\partial a_{ij}} \quad \text{for all } i \text{ and } j.$$

Thus, to identify an entry of A whose adjustment within the class of reciprocal matrices would result in the largest rate of change in λ_{max} we should examine the n(n-1)/2 values $\{v_i w_j - a_{ji}^2 v_j w_i\}, i > j$ and select (any) one of largest absolute value. It is significant to note here that if one compares more than about seven elements in a homogeneous group, the rise in inconsistency is generally so small that it is then difficult to determine which judgment should be changed [65].

Table 1-10a gives the first order differences of the numbers in the second row of Table 1-10, and extends them to matrices of size 1, 2,…,15 just to show that one should not compare more than about 7 elements.

Table 1-10a: Random Index

Order	1	2	3	4	5	6	7	8	9	10	11	12	13	14	15
R.I.	0	0	0.52	0.89	1.11	1.25	1.35	1.40	1.45	1.49	1.52	1.54	1.56	1.58	1.59
First Order Differences		0	0.52	0.37	0.22	0.14	0.10	0.05	0.05	0.04	0.03	0.02	0.02	0.02	0.01

Figure 1-8 below is a plot of the first two rows of Table 1-10a. It shows the asymptotic nature of random inconsistency.

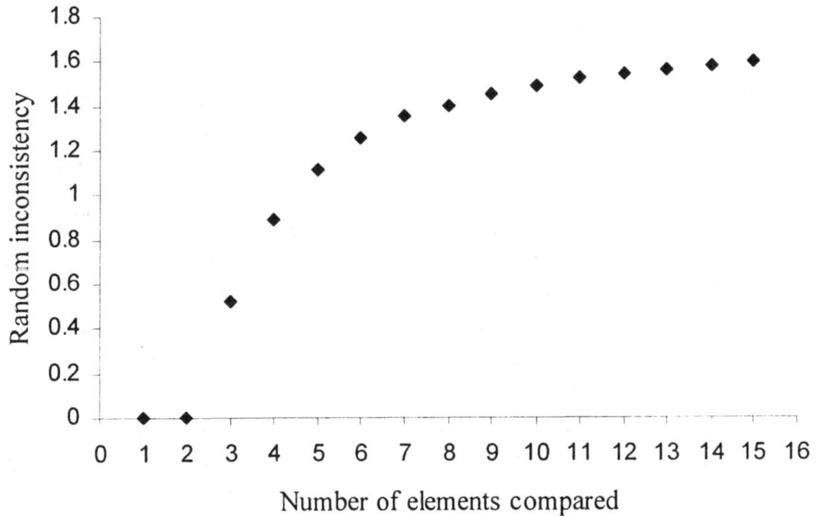

Figure 1-8: Plot of Random Inconsistency

Since it would be pointless to try to discern any priority ranking from a set of random comparison judgments, we should probably be uncomfortable about proceeding unless the consistency index of a pairwise comparison matrix is very much smaller than the corresponding random index value in Table 1-9a. The consistency ratio (C.R.) of a pairwise comparison matrix is the ratio of its consistency index μ to the corresponding random index value in Table 1-9a. The notion of order of magnitude is essential in any mathematical consideration of changes in measurement. When one has a numerical value say between 1 and 10 for some measurement and one wishes to determine whether change in this value is significant or not, one reasons as follows: A change of a whole integer value is critical because it changes the magnitude and identity of the original number significantly. If the change or perturbation in value is of the order of a percent or less, it would be so small (by two orders of magnitude) and would be considered negligible. However if this perturbation is a decimal (one order of magnitude smaller) we are likely to pay attention to modify the original value by this decimal without losing the significance and identity of the original number as we first understood it to be. Thus in synthesizing near consistent judgment values, changes that are too large can cause dramatic change in our understanding, and values that are too small cause no change in our understanding. We are left with only values of one order of magnitude smaller that we can deal with incrementally to change our understanding. It follows that our allowable consistency ratio should be not more than about .10. The requirement of 10% cannot be made smaller such as 1% or .1% without trivializing the impact of inconsistency. But inconsistency itself is important because without it, new knowledge that changes preference cannot be admitted. Assuming that all knowledge should be consistent contradicts experience that requires continued revision of understanding.

If the *C.R.* is larger than desired, we do three things: 1) Find the most inconsistent judgment in the matrix (for example, that judgment for which $\varepsilon_{ij} = a_{ij}\, w_j / w_i$ is largest), 2) Determine the range of values to which that judgment can be changed corresponding to which the inconsistency would be improved, 3) Ask the judge to consider, if he can, change his judgment to a plausible value in that range. If he is unwilling, we try with the second most inconsistent judgment and so on. If no judgment is changed the decision is postponed until better understanding of the stimuli is obtained. Judges who understand the theory are always willing to revise their judgments often not the full value, but partially, and then examine the second most inconsistent judgment and so on. It can happen that a judge's knowledge does not permit one to improve his or her consistency and more information is required to improve the consistency of judgments.

1-10. How to Combine Several Tangibles on the same Scale and on Different Scales into Single Overall criteria

Important Remark about Combining Tangibles: Note that if we have the same measurement on two criteria C_1 and C_2 such as dollars, and two alternatives A and B to obtain the relative values by normalizing the alternatives yields the necessary final relative values only if the criteria are assigned relative weights equal to the measurement under them to the total measurement under all the criteria that use dollars. Here the weights of the criteria depend on the weights of the alternatives. This idea is illustrated in Table 1-11 with a simple example.

Table 1-11: Absolute and Normalized Composition with Dollar Measurement on Two Criteria

	Absolute Sums				Relative Sums		
	C_1	C_2	Sum	Normalized	C_1 3/10	C_2 7/10	Weighted Sum
A	2	3	5	0.5	2/3	3/7	0.5
B	1	4	5	0.5	1/3	4/7	0.5
Total	3	7	10	1	1	1	1

One must do this for all criteria measured on the same tangible scale, combining them into a single overall criterion for that tangible. In the end the set of tangibles on the same scale are measured by a criterion that is then compared with the other criteria, combines tangible ones and intangible ones. Thus dollars would all be combined under a single overall economic criterion, yards under a single overall length measurement criterion and so on. These are then compared pairwise with respect to a higher criterion or goal.

1-11. Nonlinearity and Multilinear Forms in the AHP

Hierarchic composition produces sums of products of priorities. These define a special kind of mathematical function known as a multilinear form. It is useful for us to examine briefly how these forms that arise here naturally, may tell us something useful about the real world. This subject is wide open for investigation.

A **monomial** is a single term that is a product of one coefficient and several variables each with an exponent indicating a power (often restricted to be a non-negative integer) of that variable. Examples are $-3x^5, a^2x^3y^2, -a$. A **polynomial** is the sum or difference of monomials as $-5x^3y^7z^2+2xy^4+7$ from which we can define a polynomial in one variable as $2x^4-x^2+x+1$. A polynomial is a rational integral algebraic expression with nonnegative powers of the variables. The coefficients of a polynomial can be real or complex. A **multinomial** is another term for polynomial, although one would prefer the former to apply to several variables and the latter to a single variable. A **form** is a polynomial in several variables in which the sum of the powers of the variables in each term is equal to that in any other term. A form is binary, ternary etc. depending on whether it has two, three etc. variables. It is linear, quadratic etc the sum of the degrees of the variables that is the same in each term. For example $7xz-3y^2+2yz$ is a ternary quadratic form. A **multilinear** form is a form in which the variables are divided into sets so that in each term a variable from every set appears to the first power. It has the general form

$$\sum_{i,j,\dots,l=1}^{n} a_{ij\dots l}x_i y_j \dots z_l$$

with m sets of variables with n variables in each set, $x_1, x_2, \dots, x_n; y_1, y_2, \dots, y_n; z_1, z_2, \dots, z_n$ and because it is linear in the variables of each set, it is called a multilinear form. When m=1, the form $\sum_{i=1}^{n} a_i x_i$ is known as a linear form. When m=2, the form

$$\sum_{i,j=1}^{n} a_{ij}x_i y_i$$

is known as a bilinear form. Any form can be obtained from a multilinear form by identifying certain of the variables. Conversely, transforming any form to a multilinear form is carried out by polarization. For example $x_1^2+2x_1x_2+x_2^2$ can be written as a multilinear form $x_1y_1+x_1y_2+x_2y_1+x_2y_2$ with y_1 identified with x_1 and y_2 identified with x_2. A multilinear form is a particular case of a multilinear mapping or operator (not defined here) as a result of which one can think of it as symmetric, skew symmetric, alternating, symmetrized and skew symmetrized forms. Let us now turn to hierarchies using more uniform notation.

Hierarchic composition yields multilinear forms which are of course nonlinear and have the form

$$\sum_{i_1,\cdots,i_p} x_1^{i_1} x_2^{i_2} \cdots x_p^{i_p}$$

The richer the structure of a hierarchy in breadth and depth the more complex are the derived multilinear forms from it. There seems to be a good opportunity to investigate the relationship obtained by composition to covariant tensors and their algebraic properties. More concretely we have the following covariant tensor for the priority of the *i*th element in the *h*th level of the hierarchy.

$$w_i^h = \sum_{i_2,\cdots,i_{h-1}=1}^{N_{h-1},\cdots,N_1} w_{i_1 i_2}^{h-1} \cdots w_{i_{h-2} i_{h-1}}^{2} w_{i_{h-1}}^{1} \qquad i_1 \equiv i$$

The composite vector for the entire *h*th level is represented by the vector with covariant tensorial components. Similarly, the left eigenvector approach to a hierarchy gives rise to a vector with contravariant tensor components. Tensors are generalizations of scalars (which have no indices), vectors (which have a single index), and matrices or arrays (which have two indices) to an arbitrary number of indices. They are widely known and used in physics and engineering.

Another interpretation follows the lines of polynomial approximation. We see above that polynomials in one and in several variables are intimately linked to multilinear forms. The **Weierstrass approximation theorem** says that every continuous function defined on an interval $[a,b]$ can be uniformly approximated as closely as desired by a polynomial function. It assures us that one can get arbitrarily close to any continuous function as the polynomial order is increased. Because polynomials are the simplest functions, and computers can directly evaluate polynomials, this theorem has both practical and theoretical relevance. The **Stone-Weierstrass theorem** generalizes the Weierstrass approximation theorem in two directions: instead of the compact interval $[a, b]$, an arbitrary compact Hausdorff X is considered, and instead of the algebra of polynomial functions, approximation with elements from other subalgebras is investigated. Thus we see that the multilinear forms generated in the AHP represent or converge closely to a continuous function in many variables, differentiable or non-differentiable, assumed to underlie our understanding of a complex decision. In the ANP, raising the matrix to infinite powers generates a multilinear form that is an infinite series of numerical terms that converges to some limit. Performing sensitivity analysis generates a large number of limit points presumed to lie on a function to which the multilinear form as a function of its variables converges. As a result, the ANP, discussed in Chapter 2, is more likely to provide accurate answers about real world decisions than the AHP with its truncated relations.

1-12. The Analytic Hierarchy Process and Resource Allocation

Intangible resources such as quality, care, attention, and intelligence are often needed to develop a plan, design a system or solve a problem [84]. Thus far, resource allocation models have not dealt with intangibles directly, but rather by assigning them worth in terms of such phenomena as time and money. Although there is no direct scale of measurement for an intangible, it can be measured in relative terms together with tangibles. A ratio scale of priorities can thus be derived for both. These priorities serve as coefficients in an optimization framework to derive relative amounts of resources to be allocated. For intangible resources, because there is no unit of measurement, no absolute amount of a resource can be specified. However, in the presence of tangibles, it becomes possible to compute their absolute equivalents because of the proportionality inherent in their priorities. The coefficients of a mathematical linear programming (LP) model can be represented with priorities obtained with relative (i.e., pairwise comparisons) measurement. The result is that when measurement scales exist, the solution to the relative linear programming (RLP) model (with coefficients normalized to unity to make them correspond to priorities obtained with relative measurement) and the solution to the absolute linear programming (LP) model (the "usual" model with measurements on physical scales) are the same to within a multiplicative constant. It is then possible to construct LP models using solely relative measurement to optimize the allocation of intangible resources, as follows (see Chapter 8):

	Traditional LP	$\Leftrightarrow$	Relative LP
Decision Variables:	$\bar{x} = (\bar{x}_1, \cdots, \bar{x}_n)^T$		$\bar{w} = (w_1, \cdots, w_n)^T$

Objective Function: $$\sum_j c_j x_j \rightarrow {}_R c_j = \frac{c_j}{\sum_k |c_k|} \rightarrow \sum_j {}_R c_j w_j$$

$$\text{Constraints: } \sum_j a_{ij}x_j \le b_i \rightarrow \left\{ \begin{array}{l} {}_Ra_{ij} = \dfrac{a_{ij}}{\sum_k |a_{ik}|} \\ {}_Rb_i = \dfrac{\frac{b_i}{\sum_k |a_{ik}|}}{\sum_h \frac{|b_h|}{\sum_k |a_{hk}|}} \\ w_j = \dfrac{x_j}{\sum_h \frac{|b_h|}{\sum_k |a_{hk}|}} \end{array} \right\} \rightarrow \sum_j {}_Ra_{ij}w_j \le {}_Rb_i$$

$$\text{Primal:} \quad \begin{array}{r} Max \sum_j c_j x_j \\ s.t.: \sum_j a_{ij}x_j \le b_i \\ x_j \ge 0 \end{array} \quad \Leftrightarrow \quad \begin{array}{r} Max \sum_j {}_Rc_j w_j \\ s.t.: \sum_j {}_Ra_{ij}w_j \le {}_Rb_i \\ w_j \ge 0 \end{array}$$

$$\text{Dual:} \quad \begin{array}{r} Min \sum_i b_i y_i \\ s.t.: \sum_i a_{ij}y_i \ge c_j \\ y_i \ge 0 \end{array} \quad \Leftrightarrow \quad \begin{array}{r} Min \sum_i {}_Rb_i v_i \\ s.t.: \sum_i {}_Ra_{ij}v_i \ge {}_Rc_j \\ v_j \ge 0 \end{array}$$

It is significant to note that all coefficients in the relative formulation are unit free, although their relative magnitudes are preserved. Thus, the underlying magnitudes they represent can be compared in pairs.

There are three places where intangibles can arise in an LP model: the objective function and in estimating the left side and the right side of the coefficients of the constraints. The most common is in the objective function wherein the coefficients can be estimated as priorities, with the rest of the model formulated in the usual way. This presents no practical complications since the solution is the same if the objective function coefficients are given in relative terms, which is tantamount to dividing by a constant. For general treatment and examples, see [80].

1-13. Group Decision Making

Here we consider two issues relating to group decision-making. The first is how to aggregate individual judgments, and the second is how to construct a group choice from individual choices. The reciprocal property plays an important role in combining the judgments of several individuals to obtain a judgment for a group. Judgments must be combined so that the reciprocal of the synthesized judgments must be equal to the syntheses of the reciprocals of these judgments. It has been proved that the geometric mean is the unique way to do that. If the individuals are experts, they my not wish to combine their judgments but only their final outcome from a hierarchy. In that case one takes the geometric mean of the final outcomes. If the individuals have different priorities of importance, their judgments (final outcomes) are raised to the power of their priorities and then the geometric mean is formed.

How to Aggregate Individual Judgments

Let the function $f(x_1,...,x_n)$ for synthesizing the judgments given by n judges, satisfy the [54]

Separability condition (S): $f(x_1,...,x_n) = g(x_1)...g(x_n)$, for all $x_1,...,x_n$ in an interval P of positive numbers, where g is a function mapping P onto a proper interval J and is a continuous, associative and cancellative operation. [(S) means that the influences of the individual judgments can be separated as above.]

Unanimity condition (U): $f(x,...,x) = x$ for all x in P. [(U) means that if all individuals give the same judgment x, that judgment should also be the synthesized judgment.]

Homogeneity condition (H): $f(ux_1,...,ux_n) = uf(x_1,...,x_n)$ where $u>0$ and x_k, ux_k (*k=1,2,...,n*) are all in P. [For ratio judgments (H) means that if all individuals judge a ratio u times as large as another ratio, then the synthesized judgment should also be u times as large.]

Power condition (P_p): $f(x_1^p,...,x_n^p) = f^p(x_1,...,x_n)$. [($P_2$) for example means that if the *k*th individual judges the length of a side of a square to be x_k, the synthesized judgment on the area of that square will be given by the square of the synthesized judgment on the length of its side.]

Special case ($R=P_{-1}$):

$$f(\frac{1}{x_1},...,\frac{1}{x_n}) = 1/f(x_1,...,x_n)$$

.

[(R) is of particular importance in ratio judgments. It means that the synthesized value of the reciprocal of the individual judgments should be the reciprocal of the synthesized value of the original judgments.]

Aczel and Saaty [54] proved the following theorem:

Theorem The general separable (S) synthesizing functions satisfying the unanimity (U) and homogeneity (H) conditions are the geometric mean and the root-mean-power. If moreover the reciprocal property (R) is assumed even for a single n-tuple $(x_1,...,x_n)$ of the judgments of n individuals, where not all x_k are equal, then only the geometric mean satisfies all the above conditions.

In any rational consensus, those who know more should, accordingly, influence the consensus more strongly than those who are less knowledgeable. Some people are clearly wiser and more sensible in such matters than others, others may be more powerful and their opinions should be given appropriately greater weight. For such unequal importance of voters not all *g*'s in (S) are the same function. In place of (S), the weighted separability property (WS) is now: $f(x_1,...,x_n) = g_1(x_1)...g_n(x_n)$ [(WS) implies that not all judging individuals have the same weight when the judgments are synthesized and the different influences are reflected in the different functions $(g_1,..., g_n)$.]

In this situation, Aczel and Alsina [54] proved the following theorem:

Theorem The general weighted-separable (WS) synthesizing functions with the unanimity (U) and homogeneity (H) properties are the weighted geometric mean $f(x_1, x_2,..., x_n) = \quad = x_1^{q_1} x_2^{q_2} ... x_n^{q_n}$ and the weighted root-mean- powers $f(x_1, x_2,..., x_n) = \sqrt[\gamma]{q_1 x_1^\gamma + q_2 x_2^\gamma ... + q_n x_n^\gamma}$, where $q_1 + ... + q_n = 1$, $q_k > 0, k = 1,...,n$, $\gamma > 0$, but otherwise $q_1,...,q_n,\gamma$ are arbitrary constants.

If *f* also has the reciprocal property (R) and for a single set of entries $(x_1,...,x_n)$ of judgments of *n* individuals, where not all x_k are equal, then *only the weighted geometric mean* applies. We give the following theorem that is an explicit statement of the synthesis problem that follows from the previous results, and applies to the second and third cases of the deterministic approach:

Theorem If $x_1^{(i)}, \ldots, x_n^{(i)}$ i=1, ..., m are rankings of n alternatives by m independent judges and if a_i is the importance of judge i developed from a hierarchy for evaluating the judges, and hence $\sum_{i=1}^{m} a_i = 1$,then $\left(\prod_{i=1}^{m} x_1^{a_i}\right), \ldots, \left(\prod_{i=1}^{m} x_n^{a_i}\right)$ are the combined ranks of the alternatives for the m judges.

The power or priority of judge i is simply a replication of the judgment of that judge (as if there are as many other judges as indicated by his/her power a_i), which implies multiplying his/her ratio by itself a_i times, and the result follows.

The first requires knowledge of the functions which the particular alternative performs and how well it compares with a standard or benchmark. The second requires comparison with the other alternatives to determine its importance.

On the Construction of Group Choice from Individual Choices

Given a group of individuals, a set of alternatives (with cardinality greater than 2), and individual ordinal preferences for the alternatives, Arrow proved with his Impossibility Theorem that it is impossible to derive a rational group choice (construct a social choice function that aggregates individual preferences) from ordinal preferences of the individuals that satisfy the following four conditions, i.e., at least one of them is violated:

Decisiveness: the aggregation procedure must generally produce a group order.

Unanimity: if all individuals prefer alternative A to alternative B, then the aggregation procedure must produce a group order indicating that the group prefers A to B.

Independence of irrelevant alternatives: given two sets of alternatives which both include A and B, if all individuals prefer A to B in both sets, then the aggregation procedure must produce a group order indicating that the group, given any of the two sets of alternatives, prefers A to B.

No dictator: no single individual preferences determine the group order.

Using the ratio scale approach of the AHP, it can be shown that because now the individual preferences are cardinal rather than ordinal, it is *possible* to derive a rational group choice satisfying the above four conditions. It is possible because: a) Individual priority scales can always be derived from a set of pairwise cardinal preference judgments as long as they form at least a minimal spanning tree in the completely connected graph of the elements being compared; and b) The cardinal preference judgments associated with group choice belong to an absolute scale that represents the relative intensity of the group preferences [76].

1-14. Axioms of the AHP

The AHP includes four axioms. Informally, they are concerned with the reciprocal relation, comparison of homogeneous elements, hierarchic and systems dependence, and expectations about the validity of the rank and value of the outcome and their dependence on the structure used and its extension. The formalism for introducing the axioms would take us far a field in this presentation although we recommend examining them very highly to the reader by reference to my book on Fundamentals of the AHP [54, 56].

1-15. How to Structure a Hierarchy–Relationship to Automatic Control

What kinds of hierarchies are there and how should they be structured to meet certain needs? What is the main purpose of arranging goals, attributes, issues, and stakeholders in a hierarchy? Most problems arise because we do not know the internal dynamics of a system in sufficient detail to identify cause-effect relationships. If we were able to do so, the problem could be reduced to one of social engineering, as we would know at what points in the system intervention is necessary to bring about the desired objective. The crucial contribution of the AHP is that it enables us to make practical decisions based on a "pre-causal" understanding - namely, on our feelings and judgments about the relative impact of one variable on another [54].

Briefly, when constructing hierarchies one must include enough relevant detail to represent the problem as thoroughly as possible, but not so much as to include the whole universe in a small decision. One needs to: consider the environment surrounding the problem, identify the issues or attributes that onc feels influence and contribute to the solution, identify the participants associated with the problem. Arranging the goals, attributes, issues, and stakeholders in a hierarchy serves three purposes: it provides an overall view of the complex relationships inherent in the situation; it captures the spread of influence from the more important and general criteria to the less important ones; and it permits the decision maker to assess whether he or she is comparing issues of the same order of magnitude in weight or impact on the solution.

TWO GENERAL STRUCTURES OF HIERARCHIES

1) Generic Hierarchy for Forward Planning
The levels of the hierarchy successively descend from the goal down to:
~ Time Horizons
~ Uncontrollable Environmental Constraints
~ Risk Scenarios
~ Controllable Systemic Constraints
~ Overall Objectives of the Systems
~ Stakeholders
~ Stakeholder Objectives (Separate for each)
~ Stakeholder Policies (Separate for each)
~ Exploratory Scenarios (Outcomes)
~ Composite or Logical Scenario (Out- come)
Most prediction problems are of this kind. Contingency Planning policies must be devised to deal with unexpected occurrences and exploratory scenarios are included to allow for such a possibility. The exploratory scenarios are what each stakeholder would pursue if alone with no other stakeholders around.

2) The Backward Planning Hierarchy
The levels of this hierarchy successively descend from the goal of choosing a best outcome to:
~ Anticipatory Scenarios
~ Problems and Opportunities
~ Actors and Coalitions
~ Actor Objectives
~ Actor Policies
~ Particular Control Policies of a particular actor to Influence the Outcome

Most decision problems are of this kind. Planning involves testing the impact of the high priority policies in the bottom level. These policies are added to the policies of that particular actor in the forward process that results in a second forward process hierarchy. The iterations are repeated to close the gap between the dominant contrast scenarios (or composite scenario) of the forward process and the anticipatory scenarios of the backward process. See my book on planning [62].

In a hierarchy or network alternatives can be evaluated not simply in terms of the usual criteria but also separately in terms of control criteria that would expedite and ensure their implementation. That way an alternative that looks best under "state" criteria may not look as good under control criteria and may not come out best even if it is the most desired.

1-16. Judgments, Feelings and Measurement

Because decision-making involves judgments, preferences, feelings, and risk taking, it appears that it belongs in part to meta rational thinking. In rational thinking one uses logic based on explicit assumptions to derive one's conclusions. In decision making one elicits information about comparisons and preferences that belong to the domain of feelings and emotions.

A question that puzzles all of us brought up in the use of models is that usually a model is based on data from measurement that anyone can validate on their own. In the AHP we rely on the judgment of people. Where does this judgment originate, and how can we trust the subjective understanding of people to tell us something "objective" about the real world? We must assume that any understanding registers somewhere in our nervous system and we carry it with us. In the end we are the ones who provide the criteria and ways of understanding. At bottom all knowledge is subjectively derived. In this regard psychologists make the distinction between our cognitive and our affective (feeling) abilities. The changes in state of an organism due to the dynamic stresses in the psychological situation experienced are directly apprehended as sensations or perceptions belonging to our cognitive ability. The state itself is apprehended as feeling (affect), a global effect arising from a pattern of visceral impulses that is not easily localizable.

While "thinking" is generally thought to be carried out in the neo-cortex of the brain, feelings and partly emotions are associated with the autonomic (sympathetic and parasympathetic) nervous system that in part is known to operate independently of the thought processes of the brain. There is very little conscious control over many activities of the autonomic nervous system. It is as if there are two persons in each of us. One that looks out at the environment to give us information for survival of hazards, and another that looks inside to keep our system running. The sympathetic division, located in the spinal cord from its first thoracic to its third lumbar segments prepares the body in times of stress by dilating the blood vessels in the heart, muscles, and other vital organs, speeding the heart and blood flow (by stimulating production of adrenaline that liberates sugar from the liver) and constricting it in the skin. The parasympathetic division has two parts one originating in the midbrain, pons and medulla and consists of four cranial nerves mostly opposing sympathetic action as needed, and the other division comes from cells in the second, third and fourth segments of the sacral part of the spinal cord both stimulating parts of the body and inhibiting others like constricting the bronchi in the lungs.

Most animals have small brains but have effective autonomic systems to run their bodies, perhaps better in some ways than we have. Our brain looks out to the environment to provide data for adjustment and survival. Philosophically, decision making must be subject to the laws of science but its assumptions cannot be stated explicitly because of the use of feelings and intuition to express preference. Science has not yet learned enough about where emotions and feelings fit rationally into our system of logical thinking.

It has been pointed out to this author that there is a classification of types or levels of consciousness that originated in India which shows that truth belongs to different domains of existence of which logical thinking is only a part and not necessarily the ultimate means of discovering ideas and meaning. They are: 1) physical (matter and energy in the form of solids, liquids and gasses), 2) etheric (electromagnetic, subatomic particles), 3) emotional (feeling, emotion, desire, imagination, personal power), 4) mental (intellectual, understanding, beliefs, thoughts, knowledge, and cognitive processes), 5) causal (personal individuality, the enlivening source of life and consciousness), 6) physical to causal (the personality as a unit is made of several bodies: the mental/intellectual, the emotional, the etheric and the physical), 7) the different bodies combined, 8) manasic (consciousness of a bigger reality beyond the physical world), 9) social or religious buddhic/christic, (wider consciousness beyond individuality and integration with others with love and harmony), 10) atmic (identification not with individuals, not with groups, but with all pervading life-equanimity and peacefulness towards all.) Atmic consciousness is characterized by omnipotence and an extreme power of will that makes nearly all possible is that of pure equanimity with undifferentiated awareness - identification, not with individuality, not with groups of beings, but with all pervading life itself. It is the transcendence of both pain and bliss, extremely intense peace, 11) monadic (the generator of consciousness for all the previous levels, the power station from which will, love and intelligence are derived), and 12) logoic (the universal God consciousness encompassing all the beings living on the multiple levels mentioned above of which we are the atoms.) Decision-making, even as we try to explain it with logic, belongs to the tenth or atmic level of consciousness.

1-17. Conclusions

A reliable decision theory, as any scientific theory, should have the potential to describe and account for how people make decisions and how to generalize on that to help organize human thinking in a workable and harmonious way with what our instincts and feelings tell us. Thus we need to be aware of how to present our theories and validate them so they can provide a basis for further developments. How do we know that we have valid answers about the real world when we make a decision based on preferences? Do they survive well enough to capture what happens in the real world? How long should it take to find that out?

The Analytic Hierarchy Process (AHP) and its generalization to dependence and feedback, the Analytic Network Process (ANP), are our conscious analytical digitalization or discretization of thoughts in the brain of continuous natural processes that go on in our intuitive learning systems that are both mental thinking processes as well as long standing feelings, reflexes, preferences and judgments whose origins are tied to our autonomic system consisting of sympathetic and parasympathetic nervous systems. It is as if we are a form of intelligent life that uses the brain to obtain information about the global environment, but is otherwise self-sufficient to exist in the local environment. The AHP/ANP helps us in unfolding the complexity that is within us. The ANP will show greater depth and more widely usable applications of these ideas.

REMARKS

Remark 1(Priorities): One should not expect the concept of priority to apply to every measurement problem involving areas and volumes and other structured concerns of a quantitative nature in mathematics. The AHP/ANP consists of two parts: a structure and mathematical operations of measurement and synthesis within the structure. The structures used are not arbitrary, but take on the particular form of a hierarchy or network. There are much more general structures than these, such as general manifolds, which so far have not been used to formulate continuous decision problems outside the neural firing framework. The mathematical operations of the AHP/ANP as applied to criteria and other factors do not include all mathematical objects and how they are dealt with in mathematics. Thus even though the method of synthesis in the AHP/ANP is very general, it cannot be assumed to produce faithfully the right numerical outcome for every measurement derived through mathematics. It is intended to deal with the measurement of judgments and perceptions and not with every abstract numerical consideration simple examples of which are trigonometric and other kinds of functions of mathematical analysis. It works best when it is possible to associate the idea of importance with a measurement or a concept but not with a wholesale structure and its refinements that produce special outcomes in intricate mathematical ways.

Remark 2(Distributive and Ideal modes): We have the opportunity to explain why the distributive mode is often used even when the criteria are compared with respect to the goal rather than simply with respect to the alternatives. In the example given in section 1-10 for combining two tangibles measured on the same scale we found that it was necessary to keep the alternatives in the normalized (distributive) form to obtain the correct final outcome. One may think that the distributive mode should be used only when the weights of the criteria are derived by comparing them directly in terms of the alternatives. But that is not true. Even when we compare criteria with respect to a goal, we need to think of them in terms of their frequency of occurrence and importance in terms of alternatives. In that case they also depend on the alternatives to learn about their importance. It is only when the criteria are not intrinsic to the alternatives being considered but are indirectly related that we can treat them as if they are independent of the alternatives. For example medical diagnosis of anemia relates to the amount of iron in the blood. It is indirectly related to the foods one eats. In such cases the importance of the criteria may be assumed to be independent of the alternatives, in which case the ideal mode is used for the alternatives with respect to the criteria. It is clear that in many examples the importance of a criterion can depend on how many alternatives there are that embody that criterion. Here again we see that the importance of criteria can depend indirectly on the alternatives, in this case even less intrinsically because the number of alternatives is not a property of any one of them. Here again use of the distributive mode is often necessary as the election example in section 5-11 demonstrates.

Chapter 2
Fundamentals of the Analytic Network Process Dependence and Feedback in Decision-Making with a Single Network

2-1. Introduction

The Analytic Network Process (ANP) is a multicriteria theory of measurement used to derive relative priority scales of absolute numbers from individual judgments (or from actual measurements normalized to a relative form) that also belong to a fundamental scale of absolute numbers. These judgments represent the relative influence, of one of two elements over the other in a pairwise comparison process on a third element in the system, with respect to an underlying control criterion. Through its supermatrix, whose entries are themselves matrices of column priorities, the ANP synthesizes the outcome of dependence and feedback within and between clusters of elements. The Analytic Hierarchy Process (AHP) with its independence assumptions on upper levels from lower levels and the independence of the elements in a level is a special case of the ANP. The ANP is an essential tool for articulating our understanding of a decision problem. One had to overcome the limitation of linear hierarchic structures and their mathematical consequences. This part on the ANP summarizes and illustrates the basic concepts of the ANP and shows how informed intuitive judgments can lead to real life answers that are matched by actual measurements in the real world (for example, relative dollar values) as illustrated in market share examples that rely on judgments and not on numerical data [45, 56].

The ANP provides a general framework to deal with decisions without making assumptions about the independence of higher-level elements from lower level elements and about the independence of the elements within a level as in a hierarchy. In fact the ANP uses a network without the need to specify levels. As in the AHP, dominance or the relative importance of influence is a central concept. In the ANP, one provides a judgment from the fundamental scale of the AHP by answering two kinds of question with regard to strength of dominance: 1) Given a criterion, which of two elements is more dominant with respect to that criterion, 2) Which of two elements influences a third element more with respect to a criterion? In order that all such influences be considered with respect to the same criterion so they would be meaningful to synthesize, it is essential that the same criterion be used to make all the comparisons. Such a criterion is called a control criterion. A control criterion is an important way to focus thinking to answer the question of dominance, thus first decomposing a complex problem with a variety of influences and then pulling it back together by using the weights of these influences. Synthesis has the requirement that scales can be added and multiplied to deal with dependence and feedback using judgments about importance and preference along with likelihood as in presidential elections. Real data and statistics representing probabilities and likelihood can also be used in relative form instead of making pairwise comparisons in the ANP as they are in the AHP.

With regard to understanding the ANP, we would like to encourage the reader by telling him or her that there are numerous elaborately worked out examples of the ANP (numbered in the hundreds) mostly developed by managers, executives, industrial engineers, mature students, and others in the US and abroad (among which are Brazil, Chile, the Czech Republic, Germany, India, Indonesia, Italy, Korea, Poland, Russia, Spain, Taiwan and Turkey) who have studied and mastered its underlying concepts. About 100 of these applications have been summarized in a book called the *Encyclicon* by Saaty and Ozdemir [66] indicating the use of cycles in contrast with my other book the *Hierarchon* of which I am co-editor, which has more than five hundred examples of hierarchic applications. In the next paper following this one, examples of fully worked out decisions with benefits, opportunities, costs and risks will be illustrated.

The idea of influence is central in decision-making. It is a general term applicable in the physical world (e.g. gravitational pull), in biology (giving birth or dying), in psychology (loving and hating), in politics (persuading, negotiating and opposing), and in every conceivable domain of the world in which we live and the society in which we participate. Influence is a force that produces change, to make order or to create chaos. In process thinking, change is known to be the most fundamental process in nature. As time changes so do all things subject to the influences that exist from instant to instant. Anything that exists influences the behavior of other things or influences the state of the environment nearby and sometimes far away from where it is. When we make a decision we need to look at all the potential influences and not simply the influences from top to bottom or bottom to top as in a hierarchy. Influences spread as in a network or even more generally as in a manifold. Conscious existence is a function of time and is generally recognized in different acts of consciousness, although we try to think about it as a continuous historical event. It is more meaningful for us to understand decisions mathematically in the discrete form of the spread of influence rather than as continuous processes, although the necessary continuous mathematics is in a way easier to develop as generalization of the discrete case.

Most decisions are analyzed in terms of what is important to a person or a group and what is seen as preferred in making a choice. But when we allow feedback, what is likely to turn out as a result of all the influences is what one really would like to know. The resulting priorities enable one to take the necessary actions and make the investments in resources. One would also like to ensure, through sensitivity analysis, not only that the most preferred outcome will take place but also that it remain stable to perturbing forces that may occur after it is implemented. Thus the ANP is a useful tool for prediction and for representing a variety of competitors with their explicitly known and implicitly assumed interactions and the relative strengths with which they wield their influence in making a decision. It is also useful in conflict resolution where there can be many opposing influences.

The difference between a hierarchy and a network is illustrated in Figure 2-1. A hierarchy has a goal or a source node or cluster. It also has a sink node or cluster known in probability theory as an absorbing state that represents the alternatives of the decision. It is a linear top down structure with no feedback from lower to higher levels. However, it does have a loop at the bottom level to indicate that each alternative in that level only depends on itself and thus the elements are considered to be independent from each other. That is the case for any cluster or collection of elements that influences another group (by convention an arrow is directed towards it as in a hierarchy) but is not influenced by any other group; such a cluster is known as a source. A cluster of elements also has a loop if its elements were to depend on each other resulting in dependence known as inner dependence. Unlike a hierarchy, a network spreads out in all directions and its clusters of elements are not arranged in a particular order. In addition, a network allows influence to be transmitted from a cluster to another one (outer dependence) and back either directly from the second cluster or by transiting through intermediate clusters along a path which sometimes can return to the original cluster forming a cycle. The alternatives' cluster of a network may or may not have feedback to other clusters. Figure 2-2 characterizes the clusters of a system and their connections in greater detail. A system may be generated from a hierarchy by increasing its connections gradually, so that pairs of components are connected as desired and some components have an inner dependence loop.

In Figure 2-2 no arrow feeds into a source component, no arrow leaves a sink component, and arrows feed into and leave a transient component. A recurrent component falls on a cycle. Loops as in C_2, C_4 and C_5 feed back into the component itself. Each priority vector is derived and introduced in the appropriate position as a column vector in a supermatrix of impacts (with respect to one control criterion) displayed as shown below.

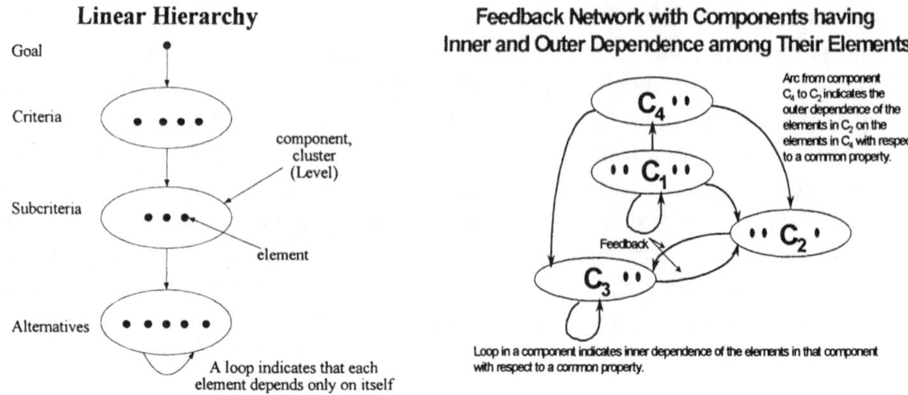

Figure 2-1: How a Hierarchy Compares to a Network

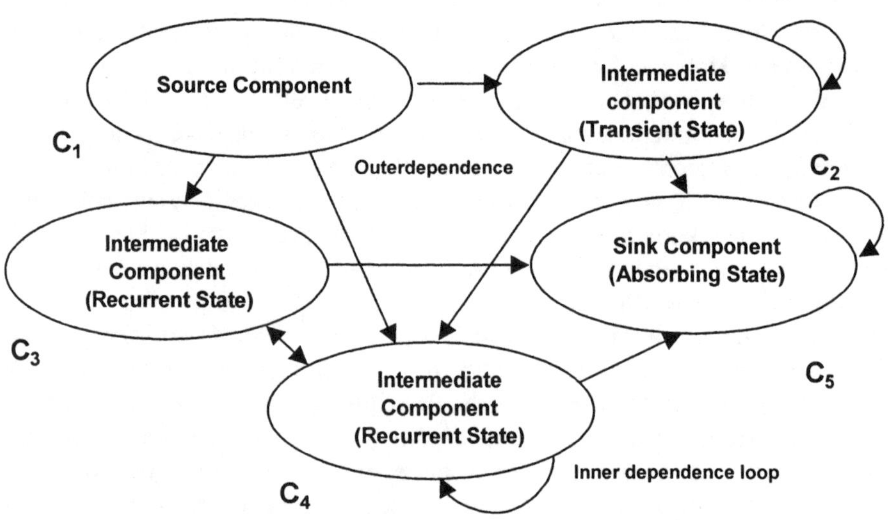

Figure 2-2: Connections in a Network

Having been exposed to the AHP, the reader knows that criteria must be weighted. The weights cannot be meaningfully obtained by simply assigning numbers to them but need to be compared with an objective (or multiple objectives) in mind. Comparisons are not only mathematically necessary, but they are our heritage from our biology. Comparisons require judgments. Judgments are associated with feelings, feelings with intensities, intensities with numbers, numbers with a fundamental scale, and a set of judgments represented by a fundamental scale to priorities. The fundamental scale that represents dominance of one element over another is an absolute scale and the priorities derived from it are normalized or idealized to again yield an absolute scale. Judgments are usually inconsistent. A modicum of inconsistency is a very useful fact because it indicates that our mind has the ability to learn new things that improve and even change our understanding. But large inconsistency can indicate lack of coherent understanding that may lead to a wrong decision. To capture priorities from inconsistent judgments, the transitivity of influence is an essential consideration. It turns out that the principal right eigenvector of the matrix is necessary for capturing transitivities such as A dominates B by an amount x and B dominates C by and amount y, therefore A dominates C by an amount xy, and is the only way to represent priorities. This kind of representation needs to be validated to be credible. It has frequently been validated in the AHP and we have numerous market-share examples (illustrated below) and other full network examples to validate the ANP.

The basic question before us is how to synthesize all possible transitivities to represent overall priorities. A very useful theorem from the path matrix of a graph of a network is that the number of paths of length k between a pair of vertices is obtained from that matrix raised to the kth power. Here we obtain not the number of paths but the influence along paths of a certain length by raising our influence matrix (called the supermatrix below) to powers. We then use Cesaro summability to determine the overall priorities for all the transitivities of different lengths.

2-2. The Supermatrix of a Feedback System

Assume that we have a system of N clusters or components, whereby the elements in each component interact or have an impact on or are themselves influenced by some or all of the elements of that component or of another component with respect to a property governing the interactions of the entire system, such as energy or capital or political influence. Assume that component h, denoted by C_h, $h = 1, ..., N$, has n_h elements, that we denote by $e_{h1}, e_{h2}, \ldots, e_{hn_k}$.

A priority vector derived from paired comparisons in the usual way represents the impact of a given set of elements in a component on another element in the system. When an element has no influence on another element, its influence priority is **assigned** (not derived) as zero.

The priority vectors derived from pairwise comparison matrices are each entered as a part of some column of a supermatrix. The supermatrix represents the influence priority of an element on the left of the matrix on an element at the top of the matrix. A supermatrix along with an example of one of its general entry i, j block are shown in Figure 2-3. The component C_i alongside the supermatrix includes all the priority vectors derived for nodes that are "parent" nodes in the C_i

cluster. Figure 2-4 gives the supermatrix of a hierarchy along with its supermatrix. The entry in the last row and column of the supermatrix of a hierarchy is the identity matrix *I*.

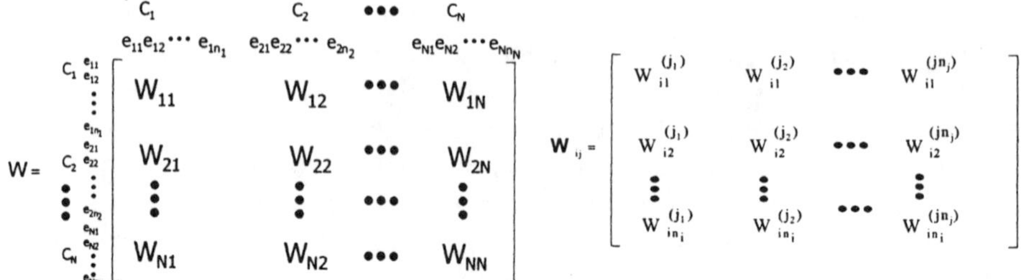

Figure 2-3: The Supermatrix of a Network and Detail of a Matrix in it.

Figure 2-5 shows a holarchy whose bottom level is connected to its top level of criteria along with its supermatrix. Note the difference between the two in the last entry of the top and bottom rows.

$$
W = \begin{bmatrix}
0 & 0 & 0 & \cdots & \bullet & 0 & 0 \\
W_{21} & 0 & 0 & \cdots & \bullet & 0 & 0 \\
0 & W_{32} & 0 & \cdots & \bullet & 0 & 0 \\
\vdots & \vdots & \vdots & \vdots & \vdots & \vdots & \vdots \\
\bullet & \bullet & \bullet & \cdots & W_{n-1,n-2} & \bullet & \bullet \\
0 & 0 & 0 & \cdots & \bullet & W_{n,n-1} & I
\end{bmatrix}
$$

Figure 2-4: The Structure of the Supermatrix of a Hierarchy

$$
W = \begin{bmatrix}
0 & 0 & 0 & \bullet & \bullet & \bullet & 0 & W_{1,n} \\
W_{21} & 0 & 0 & \bullet & \bullet & \bullet & 0 & 0 \\
0 & W_{32} & 0 & \bullet & \bullet & \bullet & 0 & 0 \\
\bullet & \bullet & \bullet & \bullet & \bullet & \bullet & \bullet & \bullet \\
\bullet & \bullet & \bullet & \bullet & \bullet & \bullet & \bullet & \bullet \\
\bullet & \bullet & \bullet & \bullet & \bullet & W_{n-1,n-2} & \bullet & \bullet \\
0 & 0 & 0 & \bullet & \bullet & \bullet & W_{n,n-1} & 0
\end{bmatrix}
$$

Figure 2-5: The Structure of the Supermatrix of a Holarchy

2-3. Why Stochasticity of the Supermatrix is Necessary

Interaction in the supermatrix may be measured according to several different criteria. To display and relate the criteria, we need a separate control hierarchy that includes the criteria and their priorities (see examples below). For each criterion, a different supermatrix of impacts is developed, and in terms of that criterion the components are compared according to their relative impact (or absence of impact) on each other component at the top of the supermatrix, thus developing priorities to weight the block matrices of eigenvector columns under that component in the supermatrix. The resulting stochastic matrix is known as the weighted supermatrix. As we shall see below, it needs to be stochastic to derive meaningful limiting priorities.

Before taking the limit, the supermatrix must first be reduced to a matrix, each of whose columns sums to unity, resulting in what is known as a column stochastic matrix (see below why). In general, a supermatrix is not stochastic. This is because its columns are made up of several eigenvectors whose entries in normalized form sum to one and hence that column sums to the number of nonzero eigenvectors. In order to transform it to a stochastic matrix we need to compare its clusters, according to their impact on each other with respect to the general control criterion we have been considering and thus must do it several times for a decision problem, once for each control criterion, and for that criterion several matrices are needed. Each one is used to compare the influence of all the clusters on a given cluster to which they are connected. This yields an eigenvector of influence of all the clusters on each cluster. Such a vector would have zero components when there is no influence. The priority of a component of such an eigenvector is used to weight all the elements in the block of the supermatrix that corresponds to the elements of both the influencing and the influenced cluster. The result is a stochastic supermatrix. This is not a forced way to make the matrix stochastic. It is natural. Why? Because the elements are compared among themselves and one needs information about the importance of the clusters to which they belong, to determine their relative overall weight among all the elements in the other clusters. Here is an example of why it is necessary to weight the priorities of the elements by those of their clusters: If one shouts into a room, “Ladies and Gentlemen, the president”, everyone is alerted and somewhat awed to expect to see the president of the United States because he is in the news so often. But if the announcement is then followed by, "of the garbage collection association", the priority immediately drops according to the importance of the group to which that president belongs. We cannot avoid such a consideration.

The supermatrix of a hierarchy given above is already column stochastic and its clusters have equal weights. As a result, all the blocks of the matrix are multiplied by the same number. Thus the clusters do not have to be weighted. Its limit matrix shown in Figure 2-6 has a form whose first entry in the bottom row is the well-known hierarchic composition principle. In this case, the limit supermatrix is obtained by raising W to powers, but in this case the kth power ($k \geq n-1$) is sufficient to derive the principle of hierarchic composition in its (k, 1) position.

$$W^k = \begin{bmatrix} 0 & 0 & \cdots & 0 & 0 & 0 \\ 0 & 0 & \cdots & 0 & 0 & 0 \\ \vdots & \vdots & \vdots\vdots\vdots & \vdots & \vdots & \vdots \\ 0 & 0 & \cdots & 0 & 0 & 0 \\ W_{n,n-1}W_{n-1,n-2}\cdots W_{32}W_{21} & W_{n,n-1}W_{n-1,n-2}\cdots W_{32} & \cdots W_{n,n-1}W_{n-1,n-2} & W_{n,n-1} & I \end{bmatrix}$$

Figure 2-6: Limit Matrix Corresponding to Hierarchic Composition

If the supermatrix is stochastic, the limiting priorities depend on its reducibility, primitivity, and cyclicity, with four cases to consider (see Table 2-1 below). Both acyclic cases are illustrated here. A matrix is reducible if on a permutation of rows and columns it can be put in the form $\begin{bmatrix} B_1 & 0 \\ B_2 & B_3 \end{bmatrix}$ where B_1 and B_3 are square submatrices. Otherwise A is irreducible or non-decomposable. It is clear that the supermatrix of a hierarchy is reducible. Its principal eigenvalue λ_{max} is a multiple eigenvalue. A matrix is primitive if some power of it is positive. Otherwise it is called imprimitive. A matrix has to be reducible in order for its powers to cycle which is best illustrated by the following example of successive powers of a matrix and how they shift in an orderly cyclic way the nonzero entries from one power to the next:

$$W = \begin{bmatrix} 0 & W_{12} & 0 \\ 0 & 0 & W_{23} \\ W_{31} & 0 & 0 \end{bmatrix}; \quad W^2 = \begin{bmatrix} 0 & 0 & W_{12}W_{23} \\ W_{23}W_{31} & 0 & 0 \\ 0 & W_{31}W_{12} & 0 \end{bmatrix}$$

$$W^3 = \begin{bmatrix} W_{12}W_{23}W_{31} & 0 & 0 \\ 0 & W_{23}W_{31}W_{12} & 0 \\ 0 & 0 & W_{31}W_{12}W_{23} \end{bmatrix}$$

$$W^{3k} = \begin{bmatrix} (W_{12}W_{23}W_{31})^k & 0 & 0 \\ 0 & (W_{23}W_{31}W_{12})^k & 0 \\ 0 & 0 & (W_{31}W_{12}W_{23})^k \end{bmatrix}$$

$$W^{3k+1} = \begin{bmatrix} 0 & (W_{12}W_{23}W_{31})^k W_{12} & 0 \\ 0 & 0 & (W_{23}W_{31}W_{12})^k W_{23} \\ (W_{31}W_{12}W_{23})^k W_{31} & 0 & 0 \end{bmatrix}$$

$$W^{3k+2} = \begin{bmatrix} 0 & 0 & (W_{12}W_{23}W_{31})^k W_{12}W_{23} \\ (W_{23}W_{31}W_{12})^k W_{23}W_{31} & 0 & 0 \\ 0 & (W_{31}W_{12}W_{23})^k W_{31}W_{12} & 0 \end{bmatrix}$$

Table 2-1: Characterization of W^∞ in Terms of Eigenvalue Multiplicity

	Acyclic	Cyclic
Irreducible	λ_{max} = 1 is a simple root	c other eigenvalues with modulus = 1 (they occur in conjugate pairs)
Reducible	λ_{max} = 1 is a multiple root	c other eigenvalues with modulus = 1 (they occur in conjugate pairs)

Let W be the stochastic matrix for which we wish to obtain $f(W) = W^\infty$. We have

$$\max \sum_{j=1}^{n} a_{ij} \geq \sum_{j=1}^{n} a_{ij} \frac{w_j}{w_i} = \lambda_{max} \quad \text{for max } w_i$$

$$\min \sum_{j=1}^{n} a_{ij} \leq \sum_{j=1}^{n} a_{ij} \frac{w_j}{w_i} = \lambda_{max} \quad \text{for min } w_i$$

For a row stochastic matrix $1=\min\sum_{j=1}^{n} a_{ij} \le \lambda_{max} \le \max\sum_{j=1}^{n} a_{ij} = 1$, thus $\lambda_{max} = 1$.

What we must do now is find a way to derive priorities for these four cases. We will consider the two cases when $\lambda_{max} = 1$ is simple and then again when it is a multiple root.

The following is well known in algebra [22]. According to J.J. Sylvester one can represent an entire function of a (diagonalizable) matrix W whose characteristic roots are distinct as:

$$f(W)=\sum_{i=1}^{n} f(\lambda_i)Z(\lambda_i),$$

where

$$Z(\lambda_i)=\frac{\prod_{j\neq i}(\lambda_j I - W)}{\prod_{j\neq i}(\lambda_j - \lambda_i)}$$

The $Z(\lambda_i)$ can be shown to be complete orthogonal idempotent matrices of W; that is, they have the properties

$$\sum_{i=1}^{k} Z(\lambda_i)=I,\ Z(\lambda_i)Z(\lambda_j)=0,\ i\neq j,\ Z^2(\lambda_i)=Z(\lambda_i),$$

where I and 0 are the identity and null matrices, respectively. Thus for example if one raises a matrix to arbitrarily large powers, it is enough to raise its eigenvalues to these powers and form the above sum involving the sum of polynomials in W. Because the eigenvalues of a stochastic matrix are all less than one, when raised to powers they vanish except when they are equal to one or are complex conjugate roots of one. Because here the eigenvalues are assumed to be distinct, we have the simplest case to deal with, that is $\lambda_{max} = 1$ is a simple eigenvalue. Formally, because the right hand side is a polynomial in W multiplying both sides by W^{∞} each term on the right would be a constant multiplied by W^{∞} and the final outcome is also a constant multiplied by W^{∞}. Because we are only interested in the relative values of the entries in W^{∞} we can ignore the constant and simply raise W to very large powers which the computer program *SuperDecisions* does in this case of distinct eigenvalues.

Next we consider the case where $\lambda_{max} = 1$ is a multiple eigenvalue. For that case we have what is known as the confluent form of Sylvester's theorem:

$$f(W)=\sum_{j=1}^{k}T(\lambda_i)=\sum_{i=1}^{k}\frac{1}{(m_i-1)!}\frac{d^{m_i-1}}{d\lambda^{m_i-1}}f(\lambda)(\lambda I-W)^{-1}\frac{\prod_{i=1}^{n}(\lambda-\lambda_i)}{\prod_{i=m_{i+1}}^{n}(\lambda-\lambda_i)}\Bigg|_{\lambda-\lambda_1}$$

where k is the number of distinct roots and m_i is the multiplicity of the root λ_i. However, as we show below, this too tells us that to obtain the limit priorities it is sufficient to raise W to arbitrarily large power to obtain a satisfactory decimal approximation to W^{∞}.

The only possible nonzero survivors as we raise the matrix to powers are those $\lambda's$ that are equal to one or are roots of one [56]. If the multiplicity of the largest real eigenvalue $\lambda_{\max}=1$ is n_1, then we have

$$W^{\infty}=n_1\frac{\frac{d^{(n_1-1)}}{d\lambda^{(n_1-1)}}\left[(\lambda I-W)^{-1}\Delta(\lambda)\right]}{\Delta^{(n_1)}(\lambda)}\Bigg|_{\lambda=1}$$

where one takes derivatives of the characteristic polynomial of the matrix W, and $\Delta(\lambda)=\det(\lambda I-W)=\lambda^{n}+p_1\lambda^{n-1}+\ldots+p_n$. Also $(\lambda I-W)^{-1}=F(\lambda)/\Delta(\lambda)$ and $F(\lambda)=W^{n-1}+(\lambda+p_1)W^{n-2}+(\lambda^2+p\lambda_1+p_2)W^{n-3}+\ldots$
$+(\lambda^{n-1}+p_1\lambda^{n-2}+\ldots+p_{n-1})I$ is the adjoint of $(\lambda I-W)$.

Now the right side is a polynomial in W. Again, if we multiply both sides by W^{∞}, we would have on the right a constant multiplied by W^{∞} which means that we can obtain W^{∞} by raising W to large powers.

For the cases of roots of one when $\lambda_{\max}=1$ is a simple or a multiple root let us again formally see what happens to our polynomial expressions on the right in both of Sylvester's formulas as we now multiply both on the left and on the right first by $\left(W^{c}\right)^{\infty}$ obtaining one equation and then again by $\left(W^{c+1}\right)^{\infty}$ obtaining another and so on c times, finally multiplying both sides by $\left(W^{c+c-1}\right)^{\infty}$. We then sum these equations and take their average on both sides. The left side of each of the equations reduces to W^{∞} and the average is $\frac{1}{c}W^{\infty}$. On the right side the sum for each eigenvalue that is a root of unity is simply a constant times the sum $\left(W^{c}\right)^{\infty}+\left(W^{c+1}\right)^{\infty}+\cdots+\left(W^{c+c-1}\right)^{\infty}$. Also, because this sum is common to all the eigenvalues, it factors out and their different constants sum to a new constant multiplied by (1/c). This is true whether one is a simple or a multiple eigenvalue because the same process applies to accumulating its constants. In the very end we simply have

$$\frac{1}{c}\left[\left(W^{c}\right)^{\infty}+\left(W^{c+1}\right)^{\infty}+\cdots+\left(W^{c+c-1}\right)^{\infty}\right]=\frac{1}{c}\left(1+W+\cdots+W^{c-1}\right)\left(W^{c}\right)^{\infty} \quad c\geq 2 \ ,$$

which amounts to averaging over a cycle of length c obtained in raising W to infinite power. The cyclicity c can be determined, among others, by noting the return of the form of the matrix of powers of W to the original form of blocks of zero in W.

Caution: Some interesting things can happen in the limit supermatrix when it is reducible. For example if we have multiple goals in a hierarchy that are not connected to a higher goal, that is if we have multiple sources, we may have several limit vectors for the alternatives and these must be synthesized somehow to give a unique answer. To do that, the sources need to be connected to a higher goal and prioritized with respect to it. Otherwise, the outcome would not be unique and we would obtain nothing that is meaningful in a cooperative decision (but may be useful in a non-cooperative problem where the goals for example, are different ways of facing an opponent). It is significant to note that a hierarchy always has a single source node (the goal) and a single sink cluster (the alternatives), yet its supermatrix is reducible. Only when the supermatrix is irreducible and thus its graph is strongly connected with a path from any node or cluster to any other node or cluster that the columns of the supermatrix would be identical. It is rare that the supermatrix of a decision problem is irreducible. If the source clusters do not have sufficient interaction to serve as a single source, one could take the average of the alternatives relating to the several sources as if they are equally important to obtain a single overall outcome.

2-4. Why Dominance Gives Rise to the Principal Eigenvector-Cesaro Summability

In the field of decision-making, the concept of priority is quintessential and how priorities are derived influences the choices one makes. Priorities should be unique and not one of many possibilities, and they must also capture the dominance of the order expressed in the judgments of the pairwise comparison matrix. The idea of a priority vector has much less validity for an arbitrary positive reciprocal matrix than for a consistent and a near consistent matrix. A matrix is near consistent if it is a small perturbation of a consistent matrix. The custom is to look for a vector $w = (w_1, \ldots, w_n)$ such that the matrix $W = (w_i/w_j)$ is "close" to $A = (a_{ij})$ by minimizing a metric. Metric closeness to the numerical values of the a_{ij} by itself says little about the numerical precision with which one element dominates another directly as in the matrix itself and indirectly through other elements as represented by the powers of the matrix. We now show that with the idea of dominance, the **principal eigenvector,** known to be unique to within a positive multiplicative constant (thus defining a ratio scale), and made unique through normalization, is the **only plausible candidate for representing priorities derived from a positive reciprocal near consistent pairwise comparison matrix.**

Let a_{ij} be the relative dominance of A_i over A_j in the paired comparisons process. Let the matrix corresponding to the reciprocal pairwise relation be denoted by (a_{ij}). The relative dominance of A_i over A_j along paths of length k is given by

$$\frac{\sum_{j=1}^{n} a_{ij}^{(k)}}{\sum_{i=1}^{n}\sum_{j=1}^{n} a_{ij}^{(k)}}$$

where $a_{ij}^{(k)}$ is the (i,j) entry of the kth power of the matrix (a_{ij}).

A consistent matrix A of order n satisfies the relation $a_{ij} = a_{ik} / a_{jk}$ for all $i, j, k = 1, \ldots, n.$ Thus $A^m = n^{m-1}A$. Note that a consistent matrix is reciprocal with $a_{ji} = 1/a_{ij}$. Because a consistent matrix is always of the form $A = (w_i / w_j)$, we immediately have on using $e = (1, \ldots 1)^T$ with T indicating the transpose vector (all other vectors are column vectors):

$$\lim_{k\to\infty} \frac{\sum_{m=1}^{k} A^m e}{\sum_{m=1}^{k} e^T A^m e} = \lim_{h\to\infty} \frac{Ae}{e^T Ae} = cw$$

where, because A has rank one, n is its principal eigenvalue and $w = (w_1, \ldots, w_n)$ is its corresponding principal right eigenvector and c is a positive constant.

For an inconsistent matrix, the sum of all the dominances along paths of length 1, 2, and so on has a limit determined as a Cesaro sum. That limit is the principal eigenvector of the matrix of judgments. The total dominance $w(A_i)$, of alternative i over all other alternatives along paths of all lengths is given by the infinite series

$$w(A_i)=\sum_{k=1}^{\infty}\frac{\sum_{j=1}^{n}a_{ij}^{(k)}}{\sum_{i=1}^{n}\sum_{j=1}^{n}a_{ij}^{(k)}}$$

whose sum is the Cesaro sum

$$\lim_{M\to\infty}\frac{1}{M}\sum_{k=1}^{M}\frac{\sum_{j=1}^{n}a_{ij}^{(k)}}{\sum_{i=1}^{n}\sum_{j=1}^{n}a_{ij}^{(k)}}.$$

Why? Note that the sums of different sets with k numbers in each, determines their ranks according to their total value. The average of each sum is obtained by dividing by k. The averages give the same ranks because they only differ by the same constant from the original sums. Often the sum of an infinite series of numbers is infinite but if we form the average, that average as k tends to infinity may converge. In that case it converges to the same limit as that of the kth term of the infinite sum. Thus taking the limit of the averages gives us a meaningful ranking of the objects. This is a profound observation proved by the Italian Mathematician Ernesto Cesaro (1859-1906).

Cesaro Summability: Let us prove that if a sequence of numbers converges then the sequence of arithmetic means formed from that sequence also converges to the same limit as the sequence.

Proof: Let s_n denote the nth term of the sequence and let

$\sigma_n=\frac{s_1+...+s_n}{n}$, if $\lim_{n\to\infty}\sigma_n=S$, then S is called the Cesaro sum of s_n.

Let $t_n=s_n-S, \tau_n=\sigma_n-S$, and thus $\tau_n=\frac{t_1+...+t_n}{n}$. We prove that $\tau_n\to 0$ as $n\to\infty$. Choose $a>0$, so that each $|t_n|<a$. Given $\varepsilon>0$, choose N so that for $n>N, |t_n|<\varepsilon$.

Now for $n > N$, $|\tau_n| \le \frac{|t_1|+...+|t_N|}{n} + \frac{|t_{N+1}|+...+|t_n|}{n} < \frac{Na}{n} + \varepsilon$. Since ε is arbitrary, it follows that $\lim_{n\to\infty} |\tau_n| = 0$ and $\sigma_n \to S$.

Cesaro' summability ensures that

$$w(A_i) = \sum_{k=1}^{\infty} \frac{\sum_{j=1}^{n} a_{ij}^{(k)}}{\sum_{i=1}^{n}\sum_{j=1}^{n} a_{ij}^{(k)}} = \lim_{M\to\infty} \frac{1}{M} \sum_{k=1}^{M} \frac{\sum_{j=1}^{n} a_{ij}^{(k)}}{\sum_{i=1}^{n}\sum_{j=1}^{n} a_{ij}^{(k)}} = \lim_{k\to\infty} \frac{\sum_{j=1}^{n} a_{ij}^{(k)}}{\sum_{i=1}^{n}\sum_{j=1}^{n} a_{ij}^{(k)}}.$$

This approach to the idea of derived overall dominance is a variant of the well-known theorem of Oskar Perron for positive matrices in which it is demonstrated that the limit converges to the principal right eigenvector of the matrix. Thus a reciprocal pairwise comparisons reciprocal matrix $A = (a_{ij})$, satisfies the system of homogeneous equations $\sum_{j=1}^{n} a_{ij} w_j = \lambda_{\max} w_i$, $i = 1,...,n$, where $\lambda_{\max}$ is the principal eigenvalue of the matrix A and w is its corresponding principal right eigenvector.

2-5. The Control Hierarchy

Although in this part we only illustrate the use of a single control criterion and a single decision network and supermatrix, in the next session the idea of a hierarchy of control criteria for thinking about the spread of influence is essential for decision-making. What is a control hierarchy? It is a hierarchy with criteria, called control criteria that serve as a basis for making pairwise comparisons about influence. Examples are: economic influence, social influence and environmental influence and so on. For each of these control criteria, one obtains priorities from a limit supermatrix and then combines the several sets of priorities by weighting them by the priorities of the control criteria to obtain an overall outcome.

Analysis of priorities in a system can be thought of in terms of a control hierarchy with dependence among its bottom-level subsystem arranged as a network. Dependence can occur within the clusters and between them. A control network can replace a control hierarchy at the top with dependence among its clusters. More generally, one can have a cascading set of control networks the outcome of one network is used to synthesize the outcomes of what it controls.

For obvious reasons relating to the complexity of exposition, apart from a control hierarchy, we will not discuss such complex control structures here. A control hierarchy can also be involved in the network itself with feedback involved from the criteria to the elements of the network and back to the criteria to modify their influence. This kind of closed-circuit interaction between the operating parts and the criteria that drive the parts is likely to be prevalent in the brain.

A component or cluster in the ANP is a collection of elements whose function derives from the synergy of their interaction and hence has a higher-order function not found in any single element. A component is like the audio or visual component of a television set or like an arm or a leg, consisting of muscle and bone, in the human body. The clusters of the system should generally be synergistically different from the elements themselves. Otherwise they would be a mechanical collection with no intrinsic meaning.

The criteria in the control hierarchy that are used for comparing the components are usually the major parent criteria whose subcriteria are used to compare the elements in the component. Thus the criteria for comparison of the components need to be more general than those of the elements because of the greater functional complexity of the components. Sometimes for convenience, interactions of both components and elements are examined in terms of the same criteria in the control hierarchy. Although one does that to economize on the effort spent, it is more meaningful to compare the clusters with respect to control criteria and to compare the elements with respect to subcriteria of the control criteria. Otherwise the process can lead to asking difficult questions in making the paired comparisons.

The control hierarchy, critical for ANP analysis, provides overriding criteria for comparing each type of interaction that is intended by the network representation. There are two types of control criteria (subcriteria). A control criterion may be directly connected to the structure as the goal of a hierarchy if the structure is in fact a hierarchy. In this case the control criterion is called a comparison-"linking" criterion. Otherwise a control criterion does not connect directly to the structure but "induces" comparisons in a network. In that case the control criterion is called a comparison-"inducing" criterion. Note that the structure is the same, but how we think in terms of criteria is different.

An example of dependence between the elements in a component which corresponds to a loop within the component is the input-output of materials among industries. The electric industry supplies electricity to other industries including itself. But it depends more on the coal industry than on its own electricity for operation and also more on the steel industry for its turbines.

To summarize, a control hierarchy is a hierarchy of criteria and subcriteria that help us think about the spread of influence. Priorities are derived for the control criteria with benefits, or opportunities or costs or risks in mind. It is sometimes easier to use the criteria to compare the components of a system, and the subcriteria to compare the elements in the components. The generic question is: given an element in any component, how much more does a given element of a pair influence that element with respect to a control subcriterion (criterion)? The same kind of question is asked about the comparison of components. The weights of the components are used to weight the blocks of the supermatrix corresponding to the component being influenced. The limiting priorities in each supermatrix are weighted by the priority of the corresponding subcriterion and the results are synthesized for all the subcriteria. If it should happen that an element or a component has no input, a zero is entered in the corresponding priority vector.

In each block of the supermatrix, a column is either a normalized eigenvector with possibly some zero entries, or all of its elements are equal to zero. In either case it is weighted by the priority of the corresponding cluster on the left. If it is zero, that column of the supermatrix must be normalized after weighting by the cluster's weights. This operation is equivalent to assigning a zero value to the cluster on the left when weighting a column of a block with zero entries and then renormalizing the weights of the remaining clusters.

2-6. Three Market Share Examples – A Way to Validate the ANP

People who work in decision making often overlook the fact that the human mind is a composite of at least two parts, thinking and feeling, and that our attempt to separate these two is not always to our advantage. In addition, what we think about is a matter of taste which belongs to the domain of feeling and thus we cannot separate the subjects of thinking and feeling. We deceive ourselves in assuming that rational, logical thinking is divorced from feeling. Every time we think, our feelings and intuition are hidden behind as a coach of our thinking process because they provide the underlying meaning and the intensity or emphasis we place on what we think about. In attempting to suppress feelings we lose our real understanding of the world around us. Subjectivity and objectivity cannot be separated with the surgical knife of "logical thinking". How to combine the two is by transforming feelings into judgment expressed numerically within elaborate and carefully thought out structures. We have a large number of examples where users of the ANP have obtained surprisingly close answers to what is known in the real world. Many of these examples are done in a little over an hour in class, as in short two and a half day courses on the ANP in Sao Paulo, Prague, Jakarta, Hawaii and other places. When properly laid out within a structure and judgments are carefully used, intuition, which usually is not very reliable, turns out to be a powerful and accurate part of the working of the nervous system.

2-6.1 Market Share in the Hamburger Industry

The Encyclopedia Americana says that intuition is a way of knowing directly excluding inference, discursive reasoning, logic and the employment of symbols and ideas. It is also a direct acquaintance with oneself that cannot be put into words, or a similar sensitivity to the thoughts and feelings of others. The dictionary defines a hunch as a feeling based on intuition. One reason that science does not trust intuition is because hunches that are discrete instances of intuition can often be wrong. Intuition represents a special type of thought whose separate links run more or less imperceptibly through the consciousness, making it possible to perceive truth (the result of thought) with utmost clarity. Descartes wrote about intuition, "Thanks to its simplicity it is more reliable than deduction itself". Until the AHP/ANP there has been no formal mathematical way to lay down exhaustively and as best as one can all the factors relating to a problem and establish intensities of hunches in paired comparisons to put all the relevant intuition scientifically together and discover what intuition really says. Intuition drives reason and has in it the meaning behind what reason works on. The ANP combines intuition and judgment with reason. It asks that one do one's best to lay down all the factors and all the numerically expressed relations among these factors. It works very well. We now have dozens, literally dozens of examples whereby students and other people who know their problem can determine the relative market share of several companies without knowing or using numerical data about them but only judgments. The reader needs to see it happen to believe it because it is done all in class in about an hour without having anticipated the subject from the instructor at all.

This example applies ANP to the problem of predicting the market share for the big three companies in the hamburger fast food industry: McDonald's, Burger King and Wendy's (1996). These three firms are very competitive and offer a similar menu of hamburgers and other food items. To attract new customers and to retain their own, they have to compete by setting reasonable prices, making quality hamburgers, and promoting support of the community by sponsoring charity events and other public services.

The ANP model consists of clusters of elements connected by their dependence to one another. A cluster therefore allows one to think about grouping elements that share a set of attributes. The marketing mix is an example of a cluster whose elements are: price, product, promotion and location. The basic requirement when identifying clusters and their elements is that the elements are similar.

For this simple network model, we consider a single control criterion: economic influence. Figure 2-7 below shows the connections between clusters; a cluster is connected to another cluster when at least one element in it is connected to at least two elements in another cluster. The elements themselves are not shown in this figure. Except for the customer group cluster, inner dependence exists for all other clusters. In that case, the connections between elements are in the same cluster.

Structure

The structure of the model is described by its clusters and elements, and by the connection between them. These connections indicate the flow of influence between the elements. For example, with respect to promotion is nutrition more or less important than packaging, and if so, by how much. In other words, given a limited budget, the company has to prioritize spending on promoting one message over others. The importance of this comparison is the basis for connecting Promotion (in the *Marketing Mix* cluster) to elements in the *Contemporary Issues* cluster (packaging, nutrition, waste disposal and recycling). The reverse connection is also important because management is aware of themes in the *contemporary* cluster influence elements in the *marketing mix* differently. For example, using more costly materials that can be recycled may raise prices more than the promotion of this fact to the public may bring in new business. Through this process of analyzing dependencies, the prevailing understanding of the marketplace is mapped out in the ANP model.

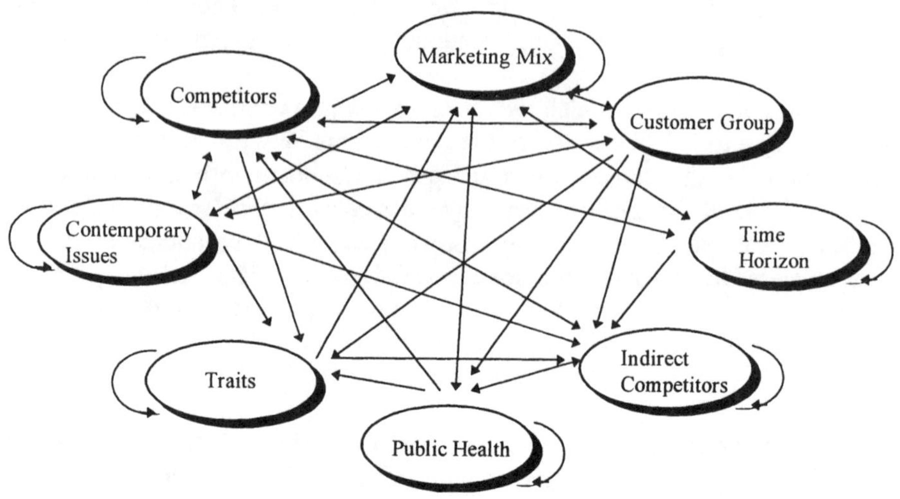

Figure 2-7: Overall Goal: Market Share of Competitor Group

Direct Competitors Cluster

The big three companies - McDonald's, Burger King and Wendy's - are elements in the *Competitors* cluster. Each is a significant competitor with the other competitors warranting continuous monitoring and quick responses. Pairwise comparisons allow us to evaluate the importance of the two competitors with respect to their influence on each cluster's market share.

Indirect Competitors Cluster

These are companies offering alternatives to hamburgers but competing for the same overall customer base. They include: subs (Miami, Subway, corner sandwich), fried chicken (KFC, BC), Pizza (Pizza Hut), Mexican (Taco Bell), Chinese, Steak (Ponderosa), and Diners (Full service and formal). Companies in this cluster compete indirectly against the big three by offering customers alternate foods and tastes and like the direct competitors, also compete and influence one another for market share.

Customer Cluster

Four basic consumer groups considered include: the white collar professional, the blue collar laborer, the student and the family. These segments help us evaluate the influence other elements may have on each of them. For example, price may influence each segment differently. Students and families on a tight budget may be more concerned with price but the working individual may instead be more concerned with convenience. This is the only cluster without inner dependence as customer segments are perceived not to influence one another.

Marketing Mix Cluster

Price in this model refers to the average price of the typical product, for example, the price of a Big Mac. However, the model could be extended to include other products and their prices. The typical product is that which the company sells the most. For location, we consider the number of established outlets, and for promotion we consider specially packaged lunch deals that would usually be more expensive when bought separately.

Contemporary Concerns Cluster

This cluster includes issues the public is aware of about the fast food industry. For example, CNN raised questions about the nutritional value of fast foods in a news report. Also, environmental groups pressure companies into paying more attention to preserving Nature and the environment by practicing recycling, properly disposing of waste, and by not over-packaging their product. These factors help raise the cost and change the routine of doing business but may also attract more customers.

Public Health Concerns Cluster

Periodic outbreak of meat contamination always serves to create panic as to the safety of the meat supply channels and the adequacy of regulation and inspection. Consumers have also become highly sensitized to other evidence of hygiene related to for example, the site (clean tables, floors) and the personnel (uniforms, hats, gloves, and the handling of money together with food).

Traits Cluster

The elements of this cluster consist of attributes customers may use or recall when judging one eatery over another. They are 1) the speed of service, 2) available seating and parking, 3) whether there is a delivery service and 4) the presence or absence of a drive through facility.

Time Horizon Cluster

This cluster makes managers think about short and medium term measures to improve market share by connecting other elements to this cluster.

Paired Comparisons

In making paired comparisons of homogeneous elements, ratios are estimated by using a 1 to 9 fundamental scale of absolute numbers to compare two alternatives with respect to an attribute, with the smaller or lesser alternative as the unit for that attribute. To estimate the larger one as a multiple of that unit, one assigns to it an absolute number from the fundamental scale. This process is done for every pair. Rather than assigning two numbers w_i and w_j and forming the ratio w_i/w_j, we assign a single number from 1 to 9 to represent the ratio $(w_i / w_j)/1$. The absolute number from the scale is an approximation to the ratio w_i / w_j. The derived scale gives us w_i and w_j. This is the central point in the relative measurement approach of the AHP.

Paired comparisons are needed for all the connections in the model. For example, Burger King is connected to elements in the *Customer Group* cluster. There would be a set of numerical judgments and the derived priority weights from these judgments, represented in the reciprocal matrix shown in Table 2-2 below.

Table 2-2: Pairwise judgments of the Customer Group for Burger King

Burger King	White Collar	Blue Collar	Student	Family	Priorities
White collar	1	4	5	1 / 3	0.299
Blue collar	1 / 4	1	4	1 / 3	0.138
Student	1 / 5	1 / 4	1	1/ 7	0.051
Family	3	3	7	1	0.512

The judgments in the first row of this reciprocal matrix say that in considering the market share of Burger King, White Collar workers are four times more important than Blue Collar workers, White Collar workers are 5 times more important than Students but only a third as important as Family. The derived priorities in the last column are computed by raising the reciprocal matrix to arbitrarily large powers and then normalizing their row sums. Each priority vector's entries sum to one and are placed in their appropriate location in the supermatrix. This vector will be placed in the Burger King column in the rows labeled White collar, Blue collar, etc.

The Supermatrix

A supermatrix is a two-dimensional matrix of elements by elements. The priority vectors from the paired comparisons appear in the appropriate column of the supermatrix. In the supermatrix of Tables 2-3a and 2-3b (b is the continuation of a because it is to long to put in a single page), the sum of each column corresponds to the number of comparison sets. If Burger King only had two comparison sets, then the column under Burger King (BURG) would sum to 2 because each priority vector sums to 1. In Table 2-6 we give priorities, derived from paired comparisons, for the clusters as they impact each cluster according to market share. All the numbers in the *i,j* block of Tables 2-3a and b which correspond to the influence of the C_i cluster on the left on the C_j cluster at the top are multiplied by the weight of the cluster C_i. For example, the 9 numbers in the upper left hand corner of the matrix in the (Competitors, Competitors) component that contains nodes McDonald's, Burger King and Wendy's are multiplied by the first number in the cluster matrix, 0.169. Applying the cluster matrix numbers to their respective blocks in the unweighted supermatrix yields the weighted matrix that is column stochastic, shown in Table 2-4a and 2-4b. Raising this matrix to powers gives the limiting matrix shown in Table 2-5a and 2-5b that represents all possible interactions in the system.

Table 2-3a: The Initial Supermatrix for the Hamburger Model

Initial	MCDO	BURG	WEND	WHIT	BLUE	STUD	FAMI	PRIC	PROD	LOCA	DEAL	NUTR	RECY	WAST	OVER	PERS
McDonald	0.0000	0.9000	0.8330	0.7560	0.7350	0.7350	0.6990	0.6960	0.7050	0.7050	0.6910	0.7170	0.7700	0.7310	0.6910	0.7420
Burger K	0.5000	0.0000	0.1670	0.1880	0.2070	0.2070	0.2370	0.2290	0.2110	0.2110	0.2180	0.2050	0.1620	0.1880	0.2180	0.1830
Wendy's	0.5000	0.1000	0.0000	0.0560	0.0580	0.0580	0.0640	0.0750	0.0840	0.0840	0.0910	0.0780	0.0680	0.0810	0.0910	0.0750
White Co	0.3080	0.2990	0.1420	0.0000	0.0000	0.0000	0.0000	0.0840	0.2570	0.1720	0.1090	0.2390	0.1680	0.2000	0.2000	0.2760
Blue Col	0.1010	0.1380	0.2760	0.0000	0.0000	0.0000	0.0000	0.1470	0.1980	0.3170	0.1890	0.2810	0.1980	0.2000	0.2000	0.1180
Students	0.0540	0.0510	0.0600	0.0000	0.0000	0.0000	0.0000	0.4760	0.0940	0.3890	0.3510	0.1400	0.3950	0.4000	0.4000	0.1180
Families	0.5370	0.5120	0.5220	0.0000	0.0000	0.0000	0.0000	0.2930	0.4510	0.1220	0.3510	0.3400	0.2390	0.2000	0.2000	0.4880
Price	0.3440	0.2600	0.3010	0.1930	0.2370	0.2150	0.1970	0.0000	1.0000	0.0000	0.2500	0.6670	0.7500	0.7500	0.5000	0.0000
Product	0.1920	0.2600	0.3680	0.4520	0.1370	0.1060	0.1580	0.2500	0.0000	0.0000	0.5000	0.3330	0.2500	0.2500	0.5000	1.0000
Location	0.3900	0.3810	0.2000	0.1430	0.0790	0.1890	0.0900	0.2500	0.0000	0.0000	0.2500	0.0000	0.0000	0.0000	0.0000	0.0000
Deals	0.0740	0.0990	0.1310	0.2120	0.5470	0.4910	0.5540	0.5000	0.0000	0.0000	0.0000	0.0000	0.0000	0.0000	0.0000	0.0000
Nutrition	0.6260	0.6850	0.6740	0.6380	0.5620	0.4830	0.5990	0.2500	1.0000	0.0000	1.0000	0.0000	0.0000	0.0000	0.0000	0.0000
Recycling	0.1990	0.1070	0.1920	0.1720	0.1990	0.2760	0.1800	0.2500	0.0000	0.0000	0.0000	0.0000	0.0000	0.5000	0.3330	0.0000
Waste Di	0.0640	0.0570	0.0650	0.0640	0.1400	0.1410	0.1330	0.2500	0.0000	0.0000	0.0000	0.0000	0.3330	0.0000	0.6670	0.0000
Over Pac	0.1110	0.1500	0.0690	0.1260	0.0990	0.1010	0.0880	0.2500	0.0000	0.0000	0.0000	0.0000	0.6670	0.5000	0.0000	0.0000
Personnel	0.4930	0.5280	0.5280	0.4930	0.4930	0.5280	0.5280	0.3330	0.2680	0.0000	0.0000	0.0000	0.0000	0.0000	0.0000	0.0000
Food Hyg	0.3110	0.3330	0.3330	0.3110	0.3110	0.3330	0.3330	0.3330	0.6150	0.0000	0.0000	0.0000	0.0000	0.0000	0.0000	0.5000
Site Hyg	0.1960	0.1400	0.1400	0.1960	0.1960	0.1400	0.1400	0.3330	0.1170	0.0000	0.0000	0.0000	0.0000	0.0000	0.0000	0.5000
Speed Of	0.6740	0.6960	0.5940	0.3490	0.4540	0.4290	0.2110	0.2000	1.0000	0.0000	1.0000	0.0000	0.0000	0.0000	0.5000	0.0000
Seating	0.2260	0.2290	0.2490	0.1640	0.2040	0.2580	0.2160	0.2000	0.0000	0.0000	0.0000	0.0000	0.0000	0.0000	0.0000	0.0000
Parking	0.1010	0.0750	0.1570	0.1410	0.0910	0.0870	0.1660	0.2000	0.0000	0.2400	0.0000	0.0000	0.0000	0.0000	0.0000	0.0000
Delivery	0.0000	0.0000	0.0000	0.1070	0.1950	0.1560	0.1170	0.2000	0.0000	0.5500	0.0000	0.0000	0.0000	0.0000	0.2500	0.0000
Drive Th	0.0000	0.0000	0.0000	0.2400	0.0560	0.0700	0.2890	0.2000	0.0000	0.2100	0.0000	0.0000	0.0000	0.0000	0.2500	0.0000
Subs	0.2560	0.1310	0.2800	0.0570	0.2260	0.2360	0.0680	0.0540	0.1080	0.0950	0.0600	0.0800	0.1430	0.1430	0.1430	0.1430
Chicken	0.1370	0.2340	0.1800	0.1780	0.1620	0.1790	0.1810	0.1150	0.1790	0.0740	0.0950	0.1420	0.1430	0.1430	0.1430	0.1430
Pizza	0.3720	0.3560	0.2830	0.1060	0.3810	0.2870	0.0690	0.0840	0.1330	0.1270	0.1090	0.0810	0.1430	0.1430	0.1430	0.1430
Mexican	0.1050	0.1440	0.1000	0.0780	0.0520	0.1140	0.0560	0.0540	0.0640	0.0680	0.0740	0.0860	0.1430	0.1430	0.1430	0.1430
Chinese	0.0460	0.0600	0.0690	0.1970	0.0670	0.0920	0.2300	0.1740	0.2490	0.1580	0.1700	0.2040	0.1430	0.1430	0.1430	0.1430
Steak	0.0440	0.0420	0.0500	0.2300	0.0730	0.0520	0.2210	0.1890	0.2670	0.2390	0.2100	0.2040	0.1430	0.1430	0.1430	0.1430
Diners	0.0390	0.0330	0.0370	0.1540	0.0390	0.0410	0.1750	0.3290	0.0000	0.2390	0.2820	0.2040	0.1430	0.1430	0.1430	0.1430
Short Te	0.0000	0.0000	0.0000	0.0000	0.0000	0.0000	0.0000	0.0000	0.0000	0.0000	0.5000	0.0000	0.0000	0.0000	0.0000	0.0000
Medium T	0.0000	0.0000	0.0000	0.0000	0.0000	0.0000	0.0000	0.0000	0.0000	0.0000	0.5000	0.0000	0.0000	0.0000	0.0000	0.0000

Table 2-3b: The Initial Supermatrix for the Hamburger Model

Initial	FOOD	SITE	SPEE	SEAT	PARK	DELI	DRIV	SUBS	CHIC	PIZZ	MEXI	CHIN	STEA	DINE	SHOR	MEDI
McDonald	0.7310	0.6670	0.6250	0.0000	0.0000	0.0000	0.5400	0.7050	0.7010	0.6740	0.6250	0.6740	0.6250	0.6140	0.6370	0.6960
Burger K	0.1880	0.2220	0.2380	0.0000	0.0000	0.0000	0.2970	0.2110	0.1930	0.2260	0.2380	0.2260	0.2380	0.2680	0.2580	0.2290
Wendy's	0.0810	0.1110	0.1360	0.0000	0.0000	0.0000	0.1630	0.0840	0.1060	0.1010	0.1360	0.1010	0.1360	0.1170	0.1050	0.0750
White Co	0.2660	0.2930	0.4000	0.0000	0.0000	0.2500	0.2980	0.1670	0.2450	0.1110	0.2000	0.2820	0.3070	0.2890	0.0000	0.0000
Blue Col	0.0910	0.0940	0.2000	0.0000	0.0000	0.2500	0.2100	0.3330	0.1760	0.2720	0.2000	0.1490	0.1190	0.1290	0.0000	0.0000
Students	0.0910	0.0940	0.2000	0.0000	0.0000	0.2500	0.2460	0.3330	0.2810	0.3620	0.4000	0.0750	0.0690	0.0710	0.0000	0.0000
Families	0.5520	0.5180	0.2000	0.0000	0.0000	0.2500	0.2460	0.1670	0.2980	0.2550	0.2000	0.4930	0.5050	0.5100	0.0000	0.0000
Price	0.0000	0.0000	0.0000	0.0000	0.0000	0.1590	0.1250	0.3500	0.2050	0.1680	0.1520	0.2400	0.2120	0.1630	0.2500	0.1960
Product	1.0000	1.0000	1.0000	0.2000	0.2500	0.0750	0.1250	0.2160	0.1880	0.1980	0.1170	0.1160	0.1930	0.4900	0.2500	0.3110
Location	0.0000	0.0000	0.0000	0.8000	0.7500	0.5670	0.7500	0.1120	0.1440	0.2390	0.2900	0.1850	0.1430	0.2310	0.0000	0.0000
Deals	0.0000	0.0000	0.0000	0.0000	0.0000	0.1990	0.0000	0.3220	0.4630	0.3950	0.4410	0.4580	0.4520	0.1160	0.5000	0.4930
Nutrition	0.0000	0.0000	0.0000	0.0000	0.0000	0.0000	0.0000	0.5190	0.5000	0.5710	0.5710	0.5000	0.5710	0.5710	0.0000	0.0000
Recycling	0.0000	0.0000	0.0000	0.0000	0.0000	0.0000	0.0000	0.1500	0.1670	0.1430	0.1430	0.1670	0.1430	0.1430	0.0000	0.0000
Waste Di	0.0000	0.0000	0.0000	0.0000	0.0000	0.0000	0.0000	0.1940	0.1670	0.1430	0.1430	0.1670	0.1430	0.1430	0.0000	0.0000
Over Pac	0.0000	0.0000	0.0000	0.0000	0.0000	0.0000	0.0000	0.1370	0.1670	0.1430	0.1430	0.1670	0.1430	0.1430	0.0000	0.0000
Personnel	1.0000	0.0000	0.0000	0.0000	0.0000	0.0000	0.0000	0.3270	0.3330	0.3330	0.3330	0.3330	0.3330	0.3330	0.0000	0.0000
Food Hyg	0.0000	0.0000	0.0000	0.0000	0.0000	0.0000	0.0000	0.4130	0.3330	0.3330	0.3330	0.3330	0.3330	0.3330	0.0000	0.0000
Site Hyg	0.0000	0.0000	0.0000	0.0000	0.0000	0.0000	0.0000	0.2600	0.3330	0.3330	0.3330	0.3330	0.3330	0.3330	0.0000	0.0000
Speed Of	0.0000	0.0000	0.0000	0.1670	0.0000	0.1270	0.2500	0.2770	0.3620	0.3260	0.3520	0.2840	0.2730	0.2730	0.0000	0.0000
Seating	0.0000	0.7500	0.0000	0.0000	0.0000	0.2230	0.2500	0.2470	0.2270	0.1180	0.1330	0.2480	0.2730	0.2730	0.0000	0.0000
Parking	0.0000	0.0000	0.0000	0.4040	0.0000	0.4880	0.2500	0.1920	0.1370	0.1520	0.1630	0.1860	0.2730	0.2730	0.0000	0.0000
Delivery	0.0000	0.1250	0.0000	0.1910	0.5000	0.0000	0.2500	0.1270	0.1370	0.2670	0.1890	0.1810	0.0910	0.0910	0.0000	0.0000
Drive Th	0.0000	0.1250	0.0000	0.2390	0.5000	0.1620	0.0000	0.1570	0.1370	0.1370	0.1630	0.1010	0.0910	0.0910	0.0000	0.0000
Subs	0.2830	0.1430	0.1430	0.0000	0.0000	0.0000	0.1430	0.2870	0.1670	0.1290	0.1640	0.0880	0.0640	0.0750	0.1430	0.1430
Chicken	0.1480	0.1430	0.1430	0.0000	0.0000	0.0000	0.1430	0.1560	0.2200	0.2150	0.1610	0.1860	0.1140	0.0750	0.1430	0.1430
Pizza	0.3270	0.1430	0.1430	0.0000	0.0000	0.0000	0.1430	0.1900	0.2020	0.2150	0.1840	0.1630	0.0850	0.0750	0.1430	0.1430
Mexican	0.0580	0.1430	0.1430	0.0000	0.0000	0.0000	0.1430	0.1030	0.0900	0.0830	0.2250	0.0750	0.0620	0.0750	0.1430	0.1430
Chinese	0.0530	0.1430	0.1430	0.0000	0.0000	0.0000	0.1430	0.1020	0.1250	0.1370	0.0880	0.1620	0.2280	0.2070	0.1430	0.1430
Steak	0.0490	0.1430	0.1430	0.0000	0.0000	0.0000	0.1430	0.0810	0.0980	0.1100	0.0880	0.1630	0.2190	0.2070	0.1430	0.1430
Diners	0.0830	0.1430	0.1430	0.0000	0.0000	0.0000	0.1430	0.0810	0.0980	0.1100	0.0880	0.1630	0.2280	0.2850	0.1430	0.1430
Short Te	0.0000	0.0000	0.0000	0.0000	0.0000	0.0000	0.0000	0.0000	0.0000	0.0000	0.0000	0.0000	0.0000	0.0000	0.0000	1.0000
Medium T	0.0000	0.0000	0.0000	0.0000	0.0000	0.0000	0.0000	0.0000	0.0000	0.0000	0.0000	0.0000	0.0000	0.0000	1.0000	0.0000

Table 2-4a: The Weighted Supermatrix for the Hamburger Model

Weighted	Mcdo	Burg	Wend	Whit	Blue	Stud	Fami	Pric	Prod	Loca	Deal	Nutr	Recy	Wast	Over	Pers
McDonald	0.0000	0.1521	0.1408	0.1512	0.1470	0.1470	0.1398	0.1051	0.1065	0.1065	0.1043	0.1592	0.1709	0.1623	0.1534	0.1848
Burger K	0.0845	0.0000	0.0282	0.0376	0.0414	0.0414	0.0474	0.0346	0.0319	0.0319	0.0329	0.0455	0.0360	0:0417	0.0484	0.0456
Wendy's	0.0845	0.0169	0.0000	0.0112	0.0116	0.0116	0.0128	0.0113	0.0127	0.0127	0.0137	0.0173	0.0151	0.0180	0.0202	0.0187
White Co	0.0573	0.0556	0.0264	0.0000	0.0000	0.0000	0.0000	0.0151	0.0463	0.0310	0.0196	0.0531	0.0373	0.0444	0.0444	0.0483
Blue Col	0.0188	0.0257	0.0513	0.0000	0.0000	0.0000	0.0000	0.0265	0.0356	0.0571	0.0340	0.0624	0.0440	0.0444	0.0444	0.0207
Students	0.0100	0.0095	0.0112	0.0000	0.0000	0.0000	0.0000	0.0857	0.0169	0.0700	0.0632	0.0311	0.0877	0.0888	0.0888	0.0207
Families	0.0999	0.0952	0.0971	0.0000	0.0000	0.0000	0.0000	0.0527	0.0812	0.0220	0.0632	0.0755	0.0531	0.0444	0.0444	0.0854
Price	0.0478	0.0361	0.0418	0.0349	0.0429	0.0389	0.0357	0.0000	0.1620	0.0000	0.0405	0.1341	0.1508	0.1508	0.1005	0.0000
Product	0.0267	0.0361	0.0512	0.0818	0.0248	0.0192	0.0286	0.0405	0.0000	0.0000	0.0810	0.0669	0.0503	0.0503	0.1005	0.1570
Location	0.0542	0.0530	0.0278	0.0259	0.0143	0.0342	0.0163	0.0405	0.0000	0.0000	0.0405	0.0000	0.0000	0.0000	0.0000	0.0000
Deals	0.0103	0.0138	0.0182	0.0384	0.0990	0.0889	0.1003	0.0810	0.0000	0.0000	0.0000	0.0000	0.0000	0.0000	0.0000	0.0000
Nutrition	0.0645	0.0706	0.0694	0.0721	0.0635	0.0546	0.0677	0.0243	0.0970	0.0000	0.0970	0.0000	0.0000	0.0000	0.0000	0.0000
Recycling	0.0205	0.0110	0.0198	0.0194	0.0225	0.0312	0.0203	0.0243	0.0000	0.0000	0.0000	0.0000	0.0000	0.0635	0.0423	0.0000
Waste Di	0.0066	0.0059	0.0067	0.0072	0.0158	0.0159	0.0150	0.0243	0.0000	0.0000	0.0000	0.0000	0.0423	0.0000	0.0847	0.0000
Over Pac	0.0114	0.0155	0.0071	0.0142	0.0112	0.0114	0.0099	0.0243	0.0000	0.0000	0.0000	0.0000	0.0847	0.0635	0.0000	0.0000
Personnel	0.0823	0.0882	0.0882	0.0804	0.0804	0.0861	0.0861	0.0566	0.0456	0.0000	0.0000	0.0000	0.0000	0.0000	0.0000	0.0000
Food Hyg	0.0519	0.0556	0.0556	0.0507	0.0507	0.0543	0.0543	0.0566	0.1046	0.0000	0.0000	0.0000	0.0000	0.0000	0.0000	0.1100
Site Hyg	0.0327	0.0234	0.0234	0.0319	0.0319	0.0228	0.0228	0.0566	0.0199	0.0000	0.0000	0.0000	0.0000	0.0000	0.0000	0.1100
Speed Of	0.0499	0.0515	0.0440	0.0394	0.0513	0.0485	0.0238	0.0142	0.0710	0.0000	0.0710	0.0000	0.0000	0.0000	0.0505	0.0000
Seating	0.0167	0.0169	0.0184	0.0185	0.0231	0.0292	0.0244	0.0142	0.0000	0.0000	0.0000	0.0000	0.0000	0.0000	0.0000	0.0000
Parking	0.0075	0.0055	0.0116	0.0159	0.0103	0.0098	0.0188	0.0142	0.0000	0.0170	0.0000	0.0000	0.0000	0.0000	0.0000	0.0000
Delivery	0.0000	0.0000	0.0000	0.0121	0.0220	0.0176	0.0132	0.0142	0.0000	0.0391	0.0000	0.0000	0.0000	0.0000	0.0253	0.0000
Drive Th	0.0000	0.0000	0.0000	0.0271	0.0063	0.0079	0.0327	0.0142	0.0000	0.0149	0.0000	0.0000	0.0000	0.0000	0.0253	0.0000
Subs	0.0415	0.0212	0.0454	0.0131	0.0518	0.0540	0.0156	0.0057	0.0114	0.0101	0.0064	0.0102	0.0182	0.0182	0.0182	0.0160
Chicken	0.0222	0.0379	0.0292	0.0408	0.0371	0.0410	0.0414	0.0122	0.0190	0.0078	0.0101	0.0180	0.0182	0.0182	0.0182	0.0160
Pizza	0.0603	0.0577	0.0458	0.0243	0.0872	0.0657	0.0158	0.0089	0.0141	0.0135	0.0116	0.0103	0.0182	0.0182	0.0182	0.0160
Mexican	0.0170	0.0233	0.0162	0.0179	0.0119	0.0261	0.0128	0.0057	0.0068	0.0072	0.0078	0.0109	0.0182	0.0182	0.0182	0.0160
Chinese	0.0075	0.0097	0.0112	0.0451	0.0153	0.0211	0.0527	0.0184	0.0264	0.0167	0.0180	0.0259	0.0182	0.0182	0.0182	0.0160
Steak	0.0071	0.0068	0.0081	0.0527	0.0167	0.0119	0.0506	0.0200	0.0283	0.0253	0.0223	0.0259	0.0182	0.0182	0.0182	0.0160
Diners	0.0063	0.0053	0.0060	0.0353	0.0089	0.0094	0.0401	0.0349	0.0000	0.0253	0.0299	0.0259	0.0182	0.0182	0.0182	0.0160
Short Te	0.0000	0.0000	0.0000	0.0000	0.0000	0.0000	0.0000	0.0000	0.0000	0.0000	0.0320	0.0000	0.0000	0.0000	0.0000	0.0000
Medium T	0.0000	0.0000	0.0000	0.0000	0.0000	0.0000	0.0000	0.0000	0.0000	0.0000	0.0320	0.0000	0.0000	0.0000	0.0000	0.0000

Table 2-4b: The Weighted Supermatrix for the Hamburger Model

Weighted	Food	Site	Spee	Seat	Park	Deli	Driv	Subs	Chic	Pizz	Mexi	Chin	Stea	Dine	Shor	Medi
McDonald	0.1820	0.1661	0.1575	0.0000	0.0000	0.0000	0.1361	0.1361	0.1353	0.1301	0.1206	0.1301	0.1206	0.1185	0.2491	0.2721
BurgerK	0.0468	0.0553	0.0600	0.0000	0.0000	0.0000	0.0748	0.0407	0.0372	0.0436	0.0459	0.0436	0.0459	0.0517	0.1009	0.0895
Wendy's	0.0202	0.0276	0.0343	0.0000	0.0000	0.0000	0.0411	0.0162	0.0205	0.0195	0.0262	0.0195	0.0262	0.0226	0.0411	0.0293
White Co	0.0466	0.0513	0.1008	0.0000	0.0000	0.0630	0.0751	0.0297	0.0436	0.0198	0.0356	0.0502	0.0546	0.0514	0.0000	0.0000
Blue Col	0.0159	0.0165	0.0504	0.0000	0.0000	0.0630	0.0529	0.0593	0.0313	0.0484	0.0356	0.0265	0.0212	0.0230	0.0000	0.0000
Students	0.0159	0.0165	0.0504	0.0000	0.0000	0.0630	0.0620	0.0593	0.0500	0.0644	0.0712	0.0134	0.0123	0.0126	0.0000	0.0000
Families	0.0966	0.0906	0.0504	0.0000	0.0000	0.0630	0.0620	0.0297	0.0530	0.0454	0.0356	0.0878	0.0899	0.0908	0.0000	0.0000
Price	0.0000	0.0000	0.0000	0.0000	0.0000	0.0347	0.0273	0.0392	0.0230	0.0188	0.0170	0.0269	0.0237	0.0183	0.0488	0.0382
Product	0.1570	0.1570	0.2180	0.3436	0.0545	0.0164	0.0273	0.0242	0.0211	0.0222	0.0131	0.0130	0.0216	0.0549	0.0488	0.0606
Location	0.0000	0.0000	0.0000	0.1744	0.1635	0.1236	0.1635	0.0125	0.0161	0.0268	0.0325	0.0207	0.0160	0.0259	0.0000	0.0000
Deals	0.0000	0.0000	0.0000	0.0000	0.0000	0.0434	0.0000	0.0361	0.0519	0.0442	0.0494	0.0513	0.0506	0.0130	0.0975	0.0961
Nutrition	0.0000	0.0000	0.0000	0.0000	0.0000	0.0000	0.0000	0.0477	0.0460	0.0525	0.0525	0.0460	0.0525	0.0525	0.0000	0.0000
Recycling	0.0000	0.0000	0.0000	0.0000	0.0000	0.0000	0.0000	0.0138	0.0154	0.0132	0.0132	0.0154	0.0132	0.0132	0.0000	0.0000
Waste Di	0.0000	0.0000	0.0000	0.0000	0.0000	0.0000	0.0000	0.0178	0.0154	0.0132	0.0132	0.0154	0.0132	0.0132	0.0000	0.0000
Over Pac	0.0000	0.0000	0.0000	0.0000	0.0000	0.0000	0.0000	0.0126	0.0154	0.0132	0.0132	0.0154	0.0132	0.0132	0.0000	0.0000
Personnel	0.2200	0.0000	0.0000	0.0000	0.0000	0.0000	0.0000	0.0713	0.0726	0.0726	0.0726	0.0726	0.0726	0.0726	0.0000	0.0000
Food Hyg	0.0000	0.0000	0.0000	0.0000	0.0000	0.0000	0.0000	0.0900	0.0726	0.0726	0.0726	0.0726	0.0726	0.0726	0.0000	0.0000
Site Hyg	0.0000	0.0000	0.0000	0.0000	0.0000	0.0000	0.0000	0.0567	0.0726	0.0726	0.0726	0.0726	0.0726	0.0726	0.0000	0.0000
Speed Of	0.0000	0.0000	0.0000	0.0182	0.0000	0.0138	0.0273	0.0230	0.0300	0.0271	0.0292	0.0236	0.0227	0.0227	0.0000	0.0000
Seating	0.0000	0.0660	0.0000	0.0000	0.0000	0.0243	0.0273	0.0205	0.0188	0.0098	0.0110	0.0206	0.0227	0.0227	0.0000	0.0000
Parking	0.0000	0.0000	0.0000	0.0440	0.0000	0.0532	0.0273	0.0159	0.0114	0.0126	0.0135	0.0154	0.0227	0.0227	0.0000	0.0000
Delivery	0.0000	0.0110	0.0000	0.0208	0.0545	0.0000	0.0273	0.0105	0.0114	0.0222	0.0157	0.0150	0.0076	0.0076	0.0000	0.0000
Drive Th	0.0000	0.0110	0.0000	0.0261	0.0545	0.0177	0.0000	0.0130	0.0114	0.0114	0.0135	0.0084	0.0076	0.0076	0.0000	0.0000
Subs	0.0317	0.0160	0.0242	0.0000	0.0000	0.0000	0.0242	0.0359	0.0209	0.0161	0.0205	0.0110	0.0080	0.0094	0.0395	0.0395
Chicken	0.0166	0.0160	0.0242	0.0000	0.0000	0.0000	0.0242	0.0195	0.0275	0.0269	0.0201	0.0233	0.0143	0.0094	0.0395	0.0395
Pizza	0.0366	0.0160	0.0242	0.0000	0.0000	0.0000	0.0242	0.0238	0.0253	0.0269	0.0230	0.0204	0.0106	0.0094	0.0395	0.0395
Mexican	0.0065	0.0160	0.0242	0.0000	0.0000	0.0000	0.0242	0.0129	0.0113	0.0104	0.0281	0.0094	0.0078	0.0094	0.0395	0.0395
Chinese	0.0059	0.0160	0.0242	0.0000	0.0000	0.0000	0.0242	0.0128	0.0156	0.0171	0.0110	0.0203	0.0285	0.0259	0.0395	0.0395
Steak	0.0055	0.0160	0.0242	0.0000	0.0000	0.0000	0.0242	0.0101	0.0123	0.0138	0.0110	0.0204	0.0274	0.0259	0.0395	0.0395
Diners	0.0093	0.0160	0.0242	0.0000	0.0000	0.0000	0.0242	0.0101	0.0123	0.0138	0.0110	0.0204	0.0285	0.0356	0.0395	0.0395
Short Te	0.0000	0.0000	0.0000	0.0000	0.0000	0.0000	0.0000	0.0000	0.0000	0.0000	0.0000	0.0000	0.0000	0.0000	0.0000	0.1380
Medium T	0.0000	0.0000	0.0000	0.0000	0.0000	0.0000	0.0000	0.0000	0.0000	0.0000	0.0000	0.0000	0.0000	0.0000	0.1380	0.0000

Table 2-5a: The Synthesized or Limiting Global Supermatrix for the Hamburger Model

Global	Mcdo	Burg	Wend	Whit	Blue	Stud	Fami	Pric	Prod	Loca	Deal	Nutr	Recy	Wast	Over	Pers
McDonald	0.1298	0.1298	0.1298	0.1298	0.1298	0.1298	0.1298	0.1298	0.1298	0.1298	0.1298	0.1298	0.1298	0.1298	0.1298	0.1298
Burger K	0.0478	0.0478	0.0478	0.0478	0.0478	0.0478	0.0478	0.0478	0.0478	0.0478	0.0478	0.0478	0.0478	0.0478	0.0478	0.0478
Wendy's	0.0266	0.0266	0.0266	0.0266	0.0266	0.0266	0.0266	0.0266	0.0266	0.0266	0.0266	0.0266	0.0266	0.0266	0.0266	0.0266
White Co	0.0414	0.0414	0.0414	0.0414	0.0414	0.0414	0.0414	0.0414	0.0414	0.0414	0.0414	0.0414	0.0414	0.0414	0.0414	0.0414
Blue Col	0.0312	0.0312	0.0312	0.0312	0.0312	0.0312	0.0312	0.0312	0.0312	0.0312	0.0312	0.0312	0.0312	0.0312	0.0312	0.0312
Students	0.0323	0.0323	0.0323	0.0323	0.0323	0.0323	0.0323	0.0323	0.0323	0.0323	0.0323	0.0323	0.0323	0.0323	0.0323	0.0323
Families	0.0654	0.0654	0.0654	0.0654	0.0654	0.0654	0.0654	0.0654	0.0654	0.0654	0.0654	0.0654	0.0654	0.0654	0.0654	0.0654
Price	0.0447	0.0447	0.0447	0.0447	0.0447	0.0447	0.0447	0.0447	0.0447	0.0447	0.0447	0.0447	0.0447	0.0447	0.0447	0.0447
Product	0.0647	0.0647	0.0647	0.0647	0.0647	0.0647	0.0647	0.0647	0.0647	0.0647	0.0647	0.0647	0.0647	0.0647	0.0647	0.0647
Location	0.0386	0.0386	0.0386	0.0386	0.0386	0.0386	0.0386	0.0386	0.0386	0.0386	0.0386	0.0386	0.0386	0.0386	0.0386	0.0386
Deals	0.0281	0.0281	0.0281	0.0281	0.0281	0.0281	0.0281	0.0281	0.0281	0.0281	0.0281	0.0281	0.0281	0.0281	0.0281	0.0281
Nutrition	0.0435	0.0435	0.0435	0.0435	0.0435	0.0435	0.0435	0.0435	0.0435	0.0435	0.0435	0.0435	0.0435	0.0435	0.0435	0.0435
Recycling	0.0118	0.0118	0.0118	0.0118	0.0118	0.0118	0.0118	0.0118	0.0118	0.0118	0.0118	0.0118	0.0118	0.0118	0.0118	0.0118
Waste Di	0.0083	0.0083	0.0083	0.0083	0.0083	0.0083	0.0083	0.0083	0.0083	0.0083	0.0083	0.0083	0.0083	0.0083	0.0083	0.0083
Overpac	0.0093	0.0093	0.0093	0.0093	0.0093	0.0093	0.0093	0.0093	0.0093	0.0093	0.0093	0.0093	0.0093	0.0093	0.0093	0.0093
Personnel	0.0601	0.0601	0.0601	0.0601	0.0601	0.0601	0.0601	0.0601	0.0601	0.0601	0.0601	0.0601	0.0601	0.0601	0.0601	0.0601
Food Hyg	0.0485	0.0485	0.0485	0.0485	0.0485	0.0485	0.0485	0.0485	0.0485	0.0485	0.0485	0.0485	0.0485	0.0485	0.0485	0.0485
Site Hyg	0.0326	0.0326	0.0326	0.0326	0.0326	0.0326	0.0326	0.0326	0.0326	0.0326	0.0326	0.0326	0.0326	0.0326	0.0326	0.0326
Speedof	0.0302	0.0302	0.0302	0.0302	0.0302	0.0302	0.0302	0.0302	0.0302	0.0302	0.0302	0.0302	0.0302	0.0302	0.0302	0.0302
Seating	0.0145	0.0145	0.0145	0.0145	0.0145	0.0145	0.0145	0.0145	0.0145	0.0145	0.0145	0.0145	0.0145	0.0145	0.0145	0.0145
Parking	0.0119	0.0119	0.0119	0.0119	0.0119	0.0119	0.0119	0.0119	0.0119	0.0119	0.0119	0.0119	0.0119	0.0119	0.0119	0.0119
Delivery	0.0122	0.0122	0.0122	0.0122	0.0122	0.0122	0.0122	0.0122	0.0122	0.0122	0.0122	0.0122	0.0122	0.0122	0.0122	0.0122
Driveth	0.0113	0.0113	0.0113	0.0113	0.0113	0.0113	0.0113	0.0113	0.0113	0.0113	0.0113	0.0113	0.0113	0.0113	0.0113	0.0113
Subs	0.0230	0.0230	0.0230	0.0230	0.0230	0.0230	0.0230	0.0230	0.0230	0.0230	0.0230	0.0230	0.0230	0.0230	0.0230	0.0230
Chicken	0.0237	0.0237	0.0237	0.0237	0.0237	0.0237	0.0237	0.0237	0.0237	0.0237	0.0237	0.0237	0.0237	0.0237	0.0237	0.0237
Pizza	0.0306	0.0306	0.0306	0.0306	0.0306	0.0306	0.0306	0.0306	0.0306	0.0306	0.0306	0.0306	0.0306	0.0306	0.0306	0.0306
Mexican	0.0144	0.0144	0.0144	0.0144	0.0144	0.0144	0.0144	0.0144	0.0144	0.0144	0.0144	0.0144	0.0144	0.0144	0.0144	0.0144
Chinese	0.0209	0.0209	0.0209	0.0209	0.0209	0.0209	0.0209	0.0209	0.0209	0.0209	0.0209	0.0209	0.0209	0.0209	0.0209	0.0209
Steak	0.0213	0.0213	0.0213	0.0213	0.0213	0.0213	0.0213	0.0213	0.0213	0.0213	0.0213	0.0213	0.0213	0.0213	0.0213	0.0213
Diners	0.0187	0.0187	0.0187	0.0187	0.0187	0.0187	0.0187	0.0187	0.0187	0.0187	0.0187	0.0187	0.0187	0.0187	0.0187	0.0187
Short Te	0.0013	0.0013	0.0013	0.0013	0.0013	0.0013	0.0013	0.0013	0.0013	0.0013	0.0013	0.0013	0.0013	0.0013	0.0013	0.0013
Medium T	0.0013	0.0013	0.0013	0.0013	0.0013	0.0013	0.0013	0.0013	0.0013	0.0013	0.0013	0.0013	0.0013	0.0013	0.0013	0.0013

Table 2-5b: The Synthesized or Limiting Global Supermatrix for the Hamburger Model

Global	Food	Site	Spee	Seat	Park	Deli	Driv	Subs	Chic	Pizz	Mexi	Chin	Stea	Dine	Shor	Medi
McDonald	0.1298	0.1298	0.1298	0.1298	0.1298	0.1298	0.1298	0.1298	0.1298	0.1298	0.1298	0.1298	0.1298	0.1298	0.1298	0.1298
Burger K	0.0478	0.0478	0.0478	0.0478	0.0478	0.0478	0.0478	0.0478	0.0478	0.0478	0.0478	0.0478	0.0478	0.0478	0.0478	0.0478
Wendy's	0.0266	0.0266	0.0266	0.0266	0.0266	0.0266	0.0266	0.0266	0.0266	0.0266	0.0266	0.0266	0.0266	0.0266	0.0266	0.0266
White Co	0.0414	0.0414	0.0414	0.0414	0.0414	0.0414	0.0414	0.0414	0.0414	0.0414	0.0414	0.0414	0.0414	0.0414	0.0414	0.0414
Blue Col	0.0312	0.0312	0.0312	0.0312	0.0312	0.0312	0.0312	0.0312	0.0312	0.0312	0.0312	0.0312	0.0312	0.0312	0.0312	0.0312
Students	0.0323	0.0323	0.0323	0.0323	0.0323	0.0323	0.0323	0.0323	0.0323	0.0323	0.0323	0.0323	0.0323	0.0323	0.0323	0.0323
Families	0.0654	0.0654	0.0654	0.0654	0.0654	0.0654	0.0654	0.0654	0.0654	0.0654	0.0654	0.0654	0.0654	0.0654	0.0654	0.0654
Price	0.0447	0.0447	0.0447	0.0447	0.0447	0.0447	0.0447	0.0447	0.0447	0.0447	0.0447	0.0447	0.0447	0.0447	0.0447	0.0447
Product	0.0647	0.0647	0.0647	0.0647	0.0647	0.0647	0.0647	0.0647	0.0647	0.0647	0.0647	0.0647	0.0647	0.0647	0.0647	0.0647
Location	0.0386	0.0386	0.0386	0.0386	0.0386	0.0386	0.0386	0.0386	0.0386	0.0386	0.0386	0.0386	0.0386	0.0386	0.0386	0.0386
Deals	0.0281	0.0281	0.0281	0.0281	0.0281	0.0281	0.0281	0.0281	0.0281	0.0281	0.0281	0.0281	0.0281	0.0281	0.0281	0.0281
Nutrition	0.0435	0.0435	0.0435	0.0435	0.0435	0.0435	0.0435	0.0435	0.0435	0.0435	0.0435	0.0435	0.0435	0.0435	0.0435	0.0435
Recycling	0.0118	0.0118	0.0118	0.0118	0.0118	0.0118	0.0118	0.0118	0.0118	0.0118	0.0118	0.0118	0.0118	0.0118	0.0118	0.0118
Waste Di	0.0083	0.0083	0.0083	0.0083	0.0083	0.0083	0.0083	0.0083	0.0083	0.0083	0.0083	0.0083	0.0083	0.0083	0.0083	0.0083
Overpac	0.0093	0.0093	0.0093	0.0093	0.0093	0.0093	0.0093	0.0093	0.0093	0.0093	0.0093	0.0093	0.0093	0.0093	0.0093	0.0093
Personnel	0.0601	0.0601	0.0601	0.0601	0.0601	0.0601	0.0601	0.0601	0.0601	0.0601	0.0601	0.0601	0.0601	0.0601	0.0601	0.0601
Food Hyg	0.0485	0.0485	0.0485	0.0485	0.0485	0.0485	0.0485	0.0485	0.0485	0.0485	0.0485	0.0485	0.0485	0.0485	0.0485	0.0485
Site Hyg	0.0326	0.0326	0.0326	0.0326	0.0326	0.0326	0.0326	0.0326	0.0326	0.0326	0.0326	0.0326	0.0326	0.0326	0.0326	0.0326
Speedof	0.0302	0.0302	0.0302	0.0302	0.0302	0.0302	0.0302	0.0302	0.0302	0.0302	0.0302	0.0302	0.0302	0.0302	0.0302	0.0302
Seating	0.0145	0.0145	0.0145	0.0145	0.0145	0.0145	0.0145	0.0145	0.0145	0.0145	0.0145	0.0145	0.0145	0.0145	0.0145	0.0145
Parking	0.0119	0.0119	0.0119	0.0119	0.0119	0.0119	0.0119	0.0119	0.0119	0.0119	0.0119	0.0119	0.0119	0.0119	0.0119	0.0119
Delivery	0.0122	0.0122	0.0122	0.0122	0.0122	0.0122	0.0122	0.0122	0.0122	0.0122	0.0122	0.0122	0.0122	0.0122	0.0122	0.0122
Driveth	0.0113	0.0113	0.0113	0.0113	0.0113	0.0113	0.0113	0.0113	0.0113	0.0113	0.0113	0.0113	0.0113	0.0113	0.0113	0.0113
Subs	0.0230	0.0230	0.0230	0.0230	0.0230	0.0230	0.0230	0.0230	0.0230	0.0230	0.0230	0.0230	0.0230	0.0230	0.0230	0.0230
Chicken	0.0237	0.0237	0.0237	0.0237	0.0237	0.0237	0.0237	0.0237	0.0237	0.0237	0.0237	0.0237	0.0237	0.0237	0.0237	0.0237
Pizza	0.0306	0.0306	0.0306	0.0306	0.0306	0.0306	0.0306	0.0306	0.0306	0.0306	0.0306	0.0306	0.0306	0.0306	0.0306	0.0306
Mexican	0.0144	0.0144	0.0144	0.0144	0.0144	0.0144	0.0144	0.0144	0.0144	0.0144	0.0144	0.0144	0.0144	0.0144	0.0144	0.0144
Chinese	0.0209	0.0209	0.0209	0.0209	0.0209	0.0209	0.0209	0.0209	0.0209	0.0209	0.0209	0.0209	0.0209	0.0209	0.0209	0.0209
Steak	0.0213	0.0213	0.0213	0.0213	0.0213	0.0213	0.0213	0.0213	0.0213	0.0213	0.0213	0.0213	0.0213	0.0213	0.0213	0.0213
Diners	0.0187	0.0187	0.0187	0.0187	0.0187	0.0187	0.0187	0.0187	0.0187	0.0187	0.0187	0.0187	0.0187	0.0187	0.0187	0.0187
Short Te	0.0013	0.0013	0.0013	0.0013	0.0013	0.0013	0.0013	0.0013	0.0013	0.0013	0.0013	0.0013	0.0013	0.0013	0.0013	0.0013
Medium T	0.0013	0.0013	0.0013	0.0013	0.0013	0.0013	0.0013	0.0013	0.0013	0.0013	0.0013	0.0013	0.0013	0.0013	0.0013	0.0013

Table 2-6: Cluster Weights with Respect to Economic Impact Control Criterion of the Hamburger Model

	Competitors	Customer Groups	Marketing Mix	Contemporary Issues	Public Health	Traits	Indirect Competitors	Time Horizon
Competitors	0.169	0.200	0.151	0.222	0.249	0.252	0.193	0.454
Customer Group	0.186	0.000	0.180	0.222	0.175	0.252	0.178	0.000
Marketing Mix	0.139	0.181	0.162	0.201	0.157	0.218	0.112	0.226
Contemporary Issues	0.103	0.113	0.097	0.127	0.000	0.000	0.092	0.000
Public Health	0.167	0.163	0.170	0.000	0.220	0.000	0.218	0.000
Traits	0.074	0.113	0.071	0.101	0.088	0.109	0.083	0.000
Indirect Competitors	0.162	0.229	0.106	0.127	0.112	0.169	0.125	0.320
Time Horizon	0.000	0.000	0.064	0.000	0.000	0.000	0.000	0.000

The predicted relative market share is obtained in the column corresponding to the clusters of direct and indirect in the limiting supermatrix. These predictions and the actual market shares as appeared in the Market Share Reporter (Darney and Reddy, 1992) are shown in Table 2-7.

Table 2-7: Predicted and Actual Market Shares for Direct Competitors

	Market	Share
Company	Predicted %	Actual %
McDonald's	62.9	58.2
Burger King	23.9	28.6
Wendy's	13.2	13.2

We also found for the indirect competitor the following result in Table 2-8:

Table 2-8: Predicted and Actual Market Shares for Indirect Competitors

Company	Market Predicted %	Share Actual %
PIZZA	33.7	37.0
CHICKEN	26.0	28.4
MEXICAN	15.2	22.8
SUBS	25.0	11.7

In addition to the priorities for the Competitors, limiting priorities for each node in the model are obtained as shown in Table 2-9.

Table 2-9: Priorities Obtained from Limit Supermatrix

		Priorities from Limit Matrix	Priorities Normalized by Cluster
1 Alternatives	1 McDonald's	0.1749	0.5549
	2 Burger King	0.0883	0.2801
	3 Wendy's	0.0520	0.1650
2 Advertising	1 Creativity	0.0727	0.2071
	2 Promotion	0.0878	0.2501
	3 Frequency	0.1905	0.5427
3 Quality of food	1 Nutrition	0.0087	0.2825
	2 Taste	0.0076	0.2468
	3 Portion	0.0145	0.4708
4 Other	1 Price	0.0462	0.1523
	2 Location	0.0681	0.2245
	3 Service	0.0091	0.0300
	4 Speed	0.0248	0.0818
	5 Cleanliness	0.0271	0.0894
	6 Menu Item	0.0474	0.1563
	7 Take-out	0.0210	0.0692
	8 Reputation	0.0596	0.1965

This limit supermatrix predicts the market share for three fast-food restaurant chains. Based on the outcome, companies should be able to improve on the dominant factors in the model to gain market share over their competitors. Sensitivity analysis can be performed to plan various strategies depending on market responses.

Market share for the fast food restaurants as determined by the supermatrix model is as follows:

McDonald's	55.9%
Burger King	28.4%
Wendy's	15.6%

Normalized industry statistics for these restaurant chains in terms of sales in dollars reported March 1993 (published in the Market Share Reporter 1994) reflect market share as follows:

McDonald's	61.4%
Burger King	25.1%
Wendy's	13.5%

For the market of the top 15 restaurant chain industries, early 1994 statistics reported the following:

McDonald's	32.3%
Burger King	13.2%
Wendy's	7.1%
Indirect	47.4%

These figures show that McDonald's has nearly one-third the share of the entire fast-food market.

2-6.2 AIRLINE EXAMPLE (2001)

James Nagy did the following study of the market share of eight US airlines. Nowhere did he use numerical data, but only his knowledge of the airlines and how good each is relative to the others on the factors mentioned below. Note that in three of the clusters there is an inner dependence loop which indicates that the elements in that cluster depend on each other with respect to market share. Figure 2-8 shows the clusters and their inner and outer dependence connections. Included are the unweighted, weighted and limit supermatrices. Sample pairwise comparison matrices are included along with the question asked to which the judgments responded. In particular we have also included the matrix of eigenvectors derived from comparing the influence with respect to market share of all the clusters on each of them. The entry of each eigenvector is used to weigh all the elements in the block of the unweighted supermatrix that corresponds to it. The outcome of this weighting is the weighted supermatrix that is then raised to limit powers to obtain the final priorities for the alternatives, which are the airlines. When these priorities are normalized we obtain the outcome of the model that is then compared with the actual dollar market share of each airline normalized to sum to one. The two are amazingly close. See the results in Table 2-10. Nagy writes:

> "I initially chose the airline industry for the assignment because I was a frequent traveler. My study group at Katz helped me make the comparisons between airlines that I did not have first hand experience as a passenger. Otherwise, I used my personal experience and perception of consumer sentiment towards the airlines to make the comparison. I was equally surprised at the results. In fact, I initially questioned how they could be so close. I would like to see the results of a study using today's consumer perception. A lot has changed in the industry since the 9/11 tragedy in the year 2001. You could divide the class up into 4 to 5 small groups and let them do the comparisons as individual groups and compare the results."

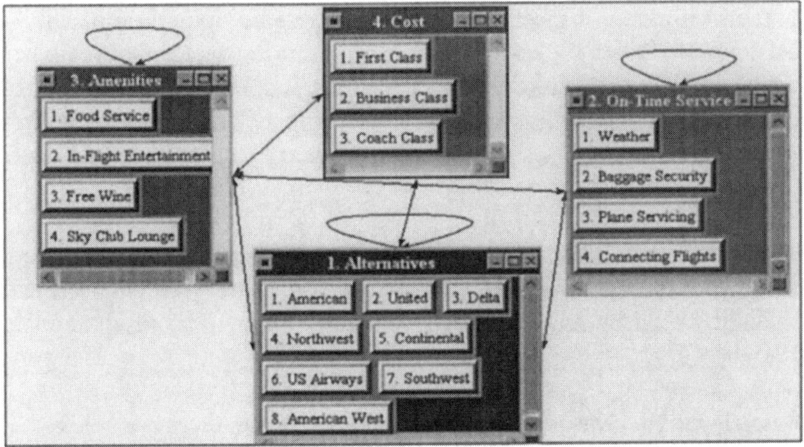

Figure 2-8: Airline Model from the ANP Super Decisions Software [15]

Table 2-10: Market Share of Airlines, Actual and Predicted.

	Actual (yr 2000)	Model Estimate
American	23.9	24.0
United	18.7	19.7
Delta	18.0	18.0
Northwest	11.4	12.4
Continental	9.3	10.0
US Airways	7.5	7.1
Southwest	5.9	6.4
American West	4.4	2.9

2-6.3 CELLULAR PHONE CARRIERS (Done by my graduate students from Germany: Anabel Hengelmann and Andreas Neuhierl and from Chile, Fernandez Rodriguez, March 2004)

All the companies that were compared in the analysis represented in Figure 2-9 are cellular network operators. They run and maintain a wireless network all over Germany. Comparable companies in the US are hard to find as most cellular operators in the US, such as Verizon or AT&T also offer internet services and regular phone technology. If one made a separate company out of Verizon Wireless, this would resemble one of the companies that are compared. I believe there are actually no companies that operate a nation-wide network as all the four companies in the analysis do in Germany, which is of course much easier as Germany is much smaller than the United States of America.

While the American market had been deregulated long before the German market, deregulation in the early 90's was the driving factor that really triggered the development in the market out of which these companies actually evolved. It is also logical that the development of more competitive markets occurred first in the wireless market as there are fewer property rights involved than when building a wire network.

There are only these four companies competing in the German market, which makes the market relatively easy to oversee. If there were many local small companies it would be much harder to compare them. The results are shown in Table 2-11.

T-Mobile: T-Mobile was started as a subsidiary of the German Telekom, former a monopoly and the first to operate a wireless network in Germany. The German Telekom is now a private company but when it was a monopoly it was owned by the Federal Republic. A year ago, T-Mobile bought Voicestream to establish a position in the American market and it actually have stores in Pittsburgh.

Vodafone: Vodafone is actually a British company, but bought Mannesmann Mobilfunk in 2001. Mannesmann Mobilfunk was a German company that started operating a wireless network with T-Mobile and was actually the first private telecommunications company in Germany. With the acquisition of Mannesmann Mobilfunk, Vodafone was able to gain a very strong position in the German market.

O2: O2 used to be called Viag Interkom and was actually started as a privatization project of the state of Bavaria. Today it fully privately owned. While they used to buy communication slots from T-Mobile and Vodafone when they originally started their network, they are now fully operating their own network and do not have to rely on the other companies in the market.

E-Plus: E-Plus is the German entity of the Japanese telecom giant NTTDOCOMO. E-Plus was the third player in the German market and was the first to operate on a new standard (GSM 1800). GSM 1800 allows more cellular users per cellular transmission station but has less sending performance and thus requires the placement of more transmission stations. This was a drawback in the early development of the companies as it took them longer to build up a fully covering network. O2 is also operating on this standard, yet had learned out of E-Plus' experience and was able to build up its network comparably quickly.

Table 2-11: Actual and Predicted Relative MarketShare of Cell-phone Providers

	Actual	Predicted
T-Mobile	42.5%	42.17%
Vodafone	38.5%	38.05%
E-Plus	11.8%	12.17%
O2	7.2%	7.61%

Source: http://www.t-mobile.de/downloads/company/roadshows/strategie.pdf

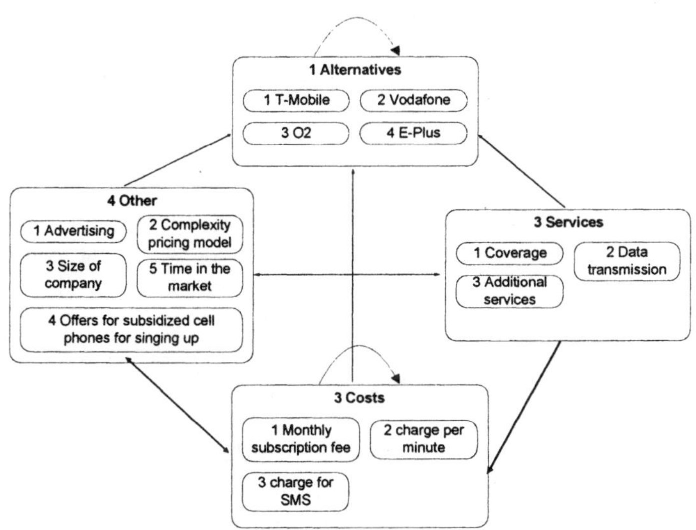

Figure 2-9: Cellular Phones

Andreas Neuhierl wrote the following:

"I started with the easiest part in this example which is choosing the alternatives. As there are only four competitors this was taken care of pretty quickly. After that I started to try to identify a number of factors that influence the market share of a company. I had no knowledge of the actual numbers, only a rough idea that the providers would fall into two groups just by the age of the company. I did not think directly of market share as this was a little too abstract for me, rather I thought of what makes me decide on a certain provider. So technically I used myself and my judgment as a proxy to predict what other people would do, as I measured market share by subscribers.

Usually in Germany cellular contracts run for at least two years so before deciding who you are going to sign up with, you do quite a bit of research on what's better, what do I like more. I've been using a cell phone for about 7 years now and I have been a customer of three of the four providers. I've gone through the "research experience" of choosing a cellular provider three times now and I basically just used the criteria I always look for when making a decision. Advertising is certainly not a factor that I actively look for when deciding on a provider, but I suppose that I am at least subconsciously biased by it, so I accounted for that. When doing the pairwise comparisons, I only used what I had learned from deciding on a provider for myself. I believe that I have a pretty good idea of most of the factors as I had last decided on a provider in October of 2003.

NOTE: While I built the model at home over the weekend, I did the pairwise comparisons in class and actually obtained the chart showing the actual market share during the break in class.

Then I just had the software calculate the numbers. I then wrote up the report and did not even have any numbers of the actual market share in there, just the numbers obtained from the SuperDecisions software and the chart. That's what I submitted. To that point I knew that the model was really good and by looking at the chart I could tell that my numbers were really close, but I could not quantify the difference between the actual and the predicted values. After I submitted the model, I did not change anything at all, had Rozann not asked me to include a table, I probably would have never found out the difference between the relative actual and the predicted numbers. I had to get the numbers from a different source as my first source only had the chart. So there was virtually no chance that I could have adjusted the model afterwards. In addition it could not be verified if I did. Rozann has the first version that I submitted and the second version in which I included the table. So if there were a difference in my numbers, Rozann would have seen it." Rozann is this author's wife.

2-7. Conclusions

The outcomes of the market share examples show us that in the system of input-process-output, with the structure and judgments as input, synthesis as throughput, we obtain overall priorities as output. The relative numerical values of this output correspond very closely to actual relative values measured by money. This is an extension of validating the AHP measurement process using a single paired comparison matrix (area, weights, distances, amount of protein in foods, drink consumption, electric appliance energy consumption, relative brightness of chairs), or a hierarchy (currency relative rates, chess championships about who will win and by how many games [78], the Superbowl [68] and who will win, presidential elections since 1976 [47]), or a holarchy (percent of increase of GNP and time of recovery of an economy 1992 and 2001 [10, 11]). Even more sophisticated models using networks involving benefits, opportunities, costs and risks to predict the proportion of people to vote for and against digging for oil in Alaska. This more complex approach to decision-making will be the subject of the next part of our presentation. It should further enhance our confidence in the validity of the method and its uses. Such confidence should strengthen our trust in applying it to design strategies for the future and the cause-effect relationship between actions and outcomes.

Chapter 3
Fundamentals of the Analytic Network Process Multiple Networks with Benefits, Opportunities, Costs and Risks

3-1. Introduction

The general theory of the ANP enables one to deal with the benefits, opportunities, costs, and risks (the BOCR merits) of a decision, by introducing the notion of negative priorities for C and R along with the rating (not comparison) of the top priority alternative synthesized for each of the four merits in terms of strategic criteria to enable one to combine the four B, O, C, and R values of each alternative into a single outcome. Strategic criteria are very basic criteria individuals and groups use to assess whether they should make any of the many decisions they face in their daily operations. They do not depend on any particular decision for their priorities but are assessed in terms of the goals and values of the individual or organization. Synthesis is made with two formulas, one multiplicative and one additive subtractive that can give rise to negative overall priorities. This chapter summarizes and illustrates basic complex decisions involving several control criteria under each of the BOCR merits.

In this third chapter on the Analytic Hierarchy and Network Processes (AHP/ANP) approach to decision-making we illustrate with an example made by economists using the ANP, predicting the turn around date of the US economy late in 2001, also expected to occur by other methods of economic forecasting reported on in the news and summarized in the next section. It is again an application with a single control criterion of economic influence as a criterion that controls our assessments as to how influence is distributed. In general, there can be several control criteria or subcriteria, such as economic, social, political that enable us to study all the influences in a complete analysis of a decision problem and some may have different merits: benefits (B), opportunities (O), costs (C) and risks (R). For each control criterion of these B, O, C, and R, one derives priorities for the alternatives of a decision with respect to all the significant influences that cause some alternatives to have higher priority than others. One then combines the weights of the alternatives according to the weights of the control criteria of each of the B, O, C and R assessed in terms of strategic criteria. Strategic criteria are very basic criteria used by individuals and groups to assess whether they should make any of the many decisions they face in their daily operations. Strategic criteria do not depend on any particular decision for their priorities but are assessed in terms of the goals and values of the individual or organization. Finally one rates (not compares) the top ranked alternative for each B, O, C and R and uses the resulting weights to combine the values of each alternatives for the four merits and obtain the final answer in the form of priorities whose relative values are important for choosing the best alternative, for sensitivity analysis and for resource allocation.

Real life problems can involve subtracting absolute numbers from other absolute numbers and the result may be negative numbers as we have done some time ago in making paired comparisons with differences and in scenario construction in planning and with positive and negative priorities as they relate to benefits and costs [56, 62, 64]. Negative priorities can be derived from positive dominance comparisons and from ratings just as positive priorities are, except that the sense in which the question is asked in making the comparisons is opposite to that used to derive positive numbers. For example, to derive a positive scale we ask which of two elements is larger in size or more beautiful in appearance. To derive negative priorities we ask which of two elements is more costly; for example, which of two offenses is a worse violation of the law. In a decision, one may have a criterion in terms of which alternatives are found to contribute to a goal in a way that increases satisfaction, and other alternatives contribute in a way that diminishes satisfaction. Here there is symmetry between positive and negative attributes. Some flowers have a pleasant fragrance and are pleasing whereas other flowers have an unpleasant smell and are irritating; hence a need for negative numbers to distinguish between the two types of contribution. When several criteria are involved, an alternative may have positive priorities for some as in benefits and opportunities and negative priorities for others as in costs and risks.

Because they are opposite in value to positive priorities we need a special way to combine the two. Negative numbers on a Cartesian axis are a result of interpreting negative numbers in an opposite sense to the numbers that fall on the positive side. How we make this interpretation is important. In the AHP we deal with normalized or relative numbers that fall between zero and one. They behave somewhat like probabilities. In practice, probabilities are obtained through counting frequencies of occurrence. In the AHP the numbers are priorities that are obtained by paired comparisons. In passing we note that one can also derive probabilities from paired comparisons in response to the question: "Of a pair of events, which is more likely to occur". Thus it appears that through paired comparisons, the AHP derives more general scales not only dealing with likelihood and probabilities but with preference and importance and possibly others. We now briefly examine the economic benefits of different factors that contributed to the turn around in the US economy experienced late in 2001. This first example involves only positive priorities as in the market share examples of the previous chapter.

3-2. Turn Around Date of the US Economy

Let us consider the problem of the turn around of the US economy and introduce 3, 6, 12, 24 month time periods at the bottom as alternatives [11]. Decomposing the problem hierarchically, the top level consists of the primary factors that represent the forces or major influences driving the economy: "Aggregate Demand" factors, "Aggregate Supply" factors, and "Geopolitical Context." Each of these primary categories was then decomposed into subfactors represented in the second level. Under Aggregate Demand, we identified consumer spending, exports, business capital investment, shifts in consumer and business investment confidence, fiscal policy, monetary policy, and expectations with regard to such questions as the future course of inflation, monetary policy and fiscal policy. (We make a distinction between consumer and business investment confidence shifts and the formation of expectations regarding future economic developments.)

Under Aggregate Supply, we identified labor costs (driven by changes in such underlying factors as labor productivity and real wages), natural resource costs (e.g., energy costs), and expectations regarding such costs in the future. With regard to Geopolitical Context, we identified the likelihood of changes in major international political relationships and major international economic relationships as the principal subfactors. With regard to the subfactors under Aggregate Demand and Aggregate Supply, we recognized that they are, in some instances, interdependent. For example, a lowering of interest rates as the result of a monetary policy decision by the Federal Reserve should induce portfolio rebalancing throughout the economy. In turn, this should reduce the cost of capital to firms and stimulate investment, and simultaneously reduce financial costs to households and increase their disposable incomes. Any resulting increase in disposable income stimulates consumption and, at the margin, has a positive impact on employment and GNP. This assumes that the linkages of the economy are in place and are well understood. This is what the conventional macroeconomic conceptual models are designed to convey.

The third level of the hierarchy consists of the alternate time periods in which the resurgence might occur as of April 7, 2001: within three months, within six months, within twelve months, and within twenty-four months. Because the primary factors and associated subfactors are time-dependent, their relative importance had to be established in terms of each of the four alternative time periods. Thus, instead of establishing a single goal as one does for a conventional hierarchy, we used the bottom level time periods to compare the three factors at the top. This entailed creation of what partly resembles a feedback hierarchy known as a "holarchy" in which the priorities of the elements at the top level are determined in terms of the elements at the bottom level, thus creating an interactive loop. Figure 3-1 provides a schematic representation of the hierarchy we used to forecast the timing of the economic resurgence.

To obtain our forecast, we subsequently multiplied each priority by the midpoint of its corresponding time interval and added the results (as one does when evaluating expected values) in Table 3-1.

We interpret this to mean that the recovery would occur 8.54 months from the time of the forecasting exercise in April 2001. By way of validation, the Wall Street Journal, Friday July 18, 2003, reported that "The National Bureau of Economic Research said the U.S. economic recession that began in March 2001 ended eight months later, not long after the Sept. 11 terrorist attacks. Most economists concluded more than a year ago that the recession ended in late 2001. But yesterday's declaration by the NBER-a private, nonprofit economic research group that is considered the official arbiter of recession timing-came after a lengthy internal debate over whether there can be an economic recovery if the labor market continues to contract. The bureau's answer: a decisive yes."

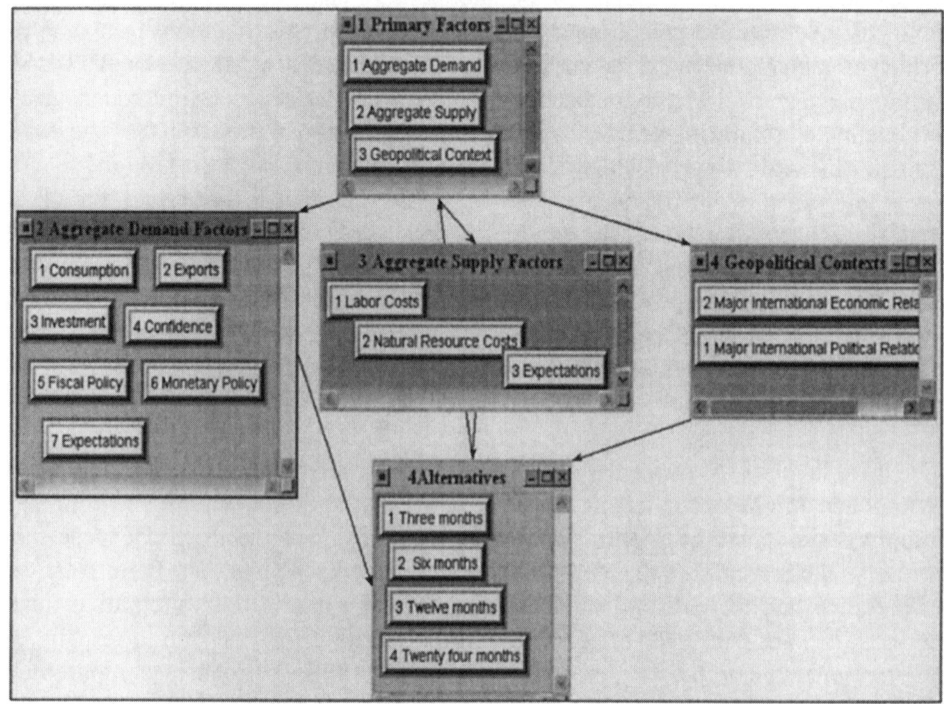

Figure 3-1: Overall View of the "2001" Model

Table 3-1: Converting Time Periods to Priorities

Time Period	Midpoint of Time Period (Expressed in months from present, with the current month as 0.)	Priority of Time Period	Midpoint x Priority
Three months	0 + (3 – 0)/2 = 1.5	0.30581	0.45871
Six months	3 + (6 – 3)/2 = 4.5	0.20583	0.92623
Twelve months	6 + (12 – 6)/2 = 9.0	0.18181	1.63629
Twenty-four months	12 + (24 – 12)/2 = 18.0	0.30656	5.51808
		TOTAL	8.53932

3-3. Benefits, Opportunities, Costs, and Risks – The Ratio and Total Formulas

The synthesized results of the alternatives for each of the four control B, O, C and R merits are combined, along traditional benefit to cost ratio analysis used in economics, to obtain a *ratio outcome* by taking the quotient of the benefits times the opportunities to the costs times the risks for each alternative (BO/CR), then normalizing the results over all the alternatives to determine the best outcome. This formula is only useful when one is certain that the relative measurements are commensurate, that is, of the same order of magnitude. In other words it is meaningless to divide thousands of dollars for benefits, by pennies for costs that is tantamount to dividing by numbers close to zero. There is another more reliable way to combine the B, O, C, and R that gives the total outcome. The top ranked alternative is rated (not compared) for each of the B, O, C and R with respect to strategic criteria that are needed to determine the merits of any decision. From this rating one then obtains normalized respective weights, b, o, c and r and computes the *total outcome bB+oO-cC-rR* for each alternative. Note in evaluating the benefits (opportunities) ones responds to the question of dominance: which alternative contributes the most benefits (opportunities), whereas for costs (risks) one responds to the question which alternative costs (is subject to greater risks) more, which is opposite in sense to the benefits and opportunities and must be subtracted from them. It is known that the ranks obtained from ratio and total syntheses need not coincide.

Note that there is no advantage in using the weights b, o, c and r in the formula (BO/CR) because we would be multiplying the result for each alternative by the same constant bo/cr. Because all values lie between zero and one, we have from the series expansions of the exponential and logarithmic functions the approximation:

$$\frac{bBoO}{cCrR} = \exp(\log bB + \log oO - \log cC - \log rR) \approx 1 + (\log bB + \log oO - \log cC - \log rR) + \ldots \approx$$
$$1 + (bB - 1) + (oO - 1) - (cC - 1) - (rR - 1) = 1 + bB + oO - cC - rR$$

Because the constant one is added to the overall value of each alternative we can eliminate it. The approximate result is that the ratio formula is similar (but not identical, nor particularly numerically close) to the total formula with equal weights assumed for the B, O, C, and R. In sum, the ratio formula should only be used when the measurements involved are of the same order of magnitude.

Note that if one were to use reciprocals like $bB + c(1/C)$, if the benefits are high and the costs are very high $1/C$ would be small and the decision whose costs are very high would be determined by its benefits, contrary to expectations. Thus we no longer use the formula that we used before to avoid negative values: $bB + oO + c(1/C) + r(1/R)$. Also note that the total outcome formula is related to the residual probabilities formula that always gives positive answers: $bB + oO + c(1\text{-}C) + r(1\text{-}R) = bB + oO - cC - rR + c + r$ in which the costs and risks are subtracted from one and in the end it turns out that the same constant $c + r$ is added to the priority of every alternative. However, this last formula may be useful in situations involving BOCR that predict proportionate voting or other type of outcomes measured with positive numbers or statistics.

3-4. Outline of the Steps of the ANP

1. Make sure that you understand the decision problem in detail, including its objectives, criteria and subcriteria, actors and their objectives and the possible outcomes of that decision. Give details of influences that determine how that decision may come out.
2. Determine the control criteria and subcriteria in the four control hierarchies one each for the benefits, opportunities, costs and risks of that decision and obtain their priorities from paired comparison matrices. You may use the same control criteria and perhaps subcriteria for all of the four merits. If a control criterion or subcriterion has a global priority of 3% or less, you may consider carefully eliminating it from further consideration. The software automatically deals only with those criteria or subcriteria that have subnets under them. For benefits and opportunities, ask what gives the most benefits or presents the greatest opportunity to influence fulfillment of that control criterion. For costs and risks, ask what incurs the most cost or faces the greatest risk. Sometimes (very rarely), the comparisons are made simply in terms of

benefits, opportunities, costs, and risks by aggregating all the criteria of each BOCR into their merit.

3. Determine a complete set of network clusters (components) and their elements that are relevant to each and every control criterion. To better organize the development of the model as well as you can, number and arrange the clusters and their elements in a convenient way (perhaps in a column). Use the identical label to represent the same cluster and the same elements for all the control criteria.
4. For each control criterion or subcriterion, determine the appropriate subset of clusters of the comprehensive set with their elements and connect them according to their outer and inner dependence influences. An arrow is drawn from a cluster to any cluster whose elements influence it.
5. Determine the approach you want to follow in the analysis of each cluster or element, influencing (the suggested approach) other clusters and elements with respect to a criterion, or being influenced by other clusters and elements. The sense (being influenced or influencing) must apply to all the criteria for the four control hierarchies for the entire decision.
6. For each control criterion, construct the supermatrix by laying out the clusters in the order they are numbered and all the elements in each cluster both vertically on the left and horizontally at the top. Enter in the appropriate position the priorities derived from the paired comparisons as subcolumns of the corresponding column of the supermatrix.
7. Perform paired comparisons on the elements within the clusters themselves according to their influence on each element in another cluster they are connected to (outer dependence) or on elements in their own cluster (inner dependence). In making comparisons, you must always have a criterion in mind. Comparisons of elements according to which element influences a third element more and how strongly more than another element it is compared with are made with a control criterion or subcriterion of the control hierarchy in mind.
8. Perform paired comparisons on the clusters as they influence each cluster to which they are connected with respect to the given control criterion. The derived weights are used to weight the elements of the corresponding column blocks of the supermatrix. Assign a zero when there is no influence. Thus obtain the weighted column stochastic supermatrix.
9. Compute the limit priorities of the stochastic supermatrix according to whether it is irreducible (primitive or imprimitive [cyclic]) or it is reducible with one being a simple or a multiple root and whether the system is cyclic or not. Two kinds of outcomes are possible. In the first,

all the columns of the matrix are identical and each gives the relative priorities of the elements from which the priorities of the elements in each cluster are normalized to one. In the second, the limit cycles in blocks and the different limits are summed and averaged and again normalized to one for each cluster. Although the priority vectors are entered in the supermatrix in normalized form, the limit priorities are put in idealized form because the control criteria do not depend on the alternatives.

10. Synthesize the limiting priorities by weighting each idealized limit vector by the weight of its control criterion and adding the resulting vectors for each of the four merits: Benefits (B), Opportunities (O), Costs (C) and Risks (R). There are now four vectors, one for each of the four merits. An answer involving ratio values of the merits is obtained by forming the ratio B_iO_i / C_iR_i for alternative i from each of the four vectors. The synthesized ideals for all the control criteria under each merit may result in an ideal whose priority is less than one for that merit. Only an alternative that is ideal for all the control criteria under a merit receives the value one after synthesis for that merit. The alternative with the largest ratio is chosen for some decisions. Companies and individuals with limited resources often prefer this type of synthesis.
11. Determine strategic criteria and their priorities to rate the top ranked (ideal) alternative for each of the four merits one at a time. Normalize the four ratings thus obtained and use them to calculate the overall synthesis of the four vectors. For each alternative, subtract the sum of the weighted costs and risks from the sum of the weighted benefits and opportunities.
12. Perform sensitivity analysis on the final outcome. Sensitivity analysis is concerned with "what if" kind of question to see if the final answer is stable to changes in the inputs, whether judgments or priorities. Of special interest is to see if these changes change the order of the alternatives. How significant the change is can be measured with the Compatibility Index of the original outcome and each new outcome.

Figure 3-2 illustrates the foregoing steps. Although here we treat control criteria as if they are independent, they need not be. In that case one would have a network instead of a hierarchy to represent control criteria and the influences they represent. For this exposition we assume that they are independent, although we have examples where they are treated within the framework of a network.

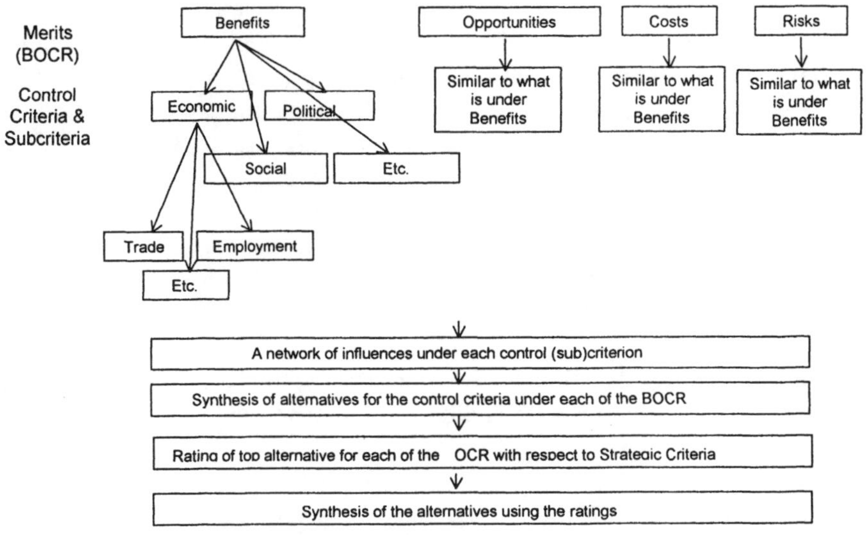

Figure 3-2: General Scheme of ANP

3-5. The Decision by the US Congress on China's Trade Status

This section analyzes the priorities of the options available to the United States in the status of its trade relations with China. The analysis is conducted through four hierarchies: benefits, costs, opportunities, and risks for each of which priorities are developed through the rating approach of the Analytic Hierarchy Process (AHP). In all, 15 criteria are involved in the four hierarchies. Three options were prioritized with respect to the criteria. Sensitivity analysis indicates that granting China the Permanent Normal Trade Relations status is the most desirable [59].

We analyze a decision to select a trade status for China that is in the best interest of the United States before that decision came before Congress for a vote. Since 1986, China had attempted to join the multilateral trade system, the General Agreement on Tariffs and Trade (GATT) and, its successor, the World Trade Organization (WTO). According to the rules of the 135-member nation WTO, a candidate member must reach a trade agreement with any existing member country that wishes to trade with it. By the time this analysis was done, China signed bilateral agreements with 30 countries - including the US (November 1999) - out of 37 members that had requested a trade deal with it.

As part of its negotiation deal with the US, China asked the US to remove its annual review of China's Normal Trade Relations (NTR) status, until 1998 called

Most Favored Nation (MFN) status. In March 2000, President Clinton sent a bill to Congress requesting a Permanent Normal Trade Relations (PNTR) status for China. The analysis was done and copies sent to leaders and some members in both houses of Congress before the House of Representatives voted on the bill, May 24, 2000. The decision by the US Congress on China's trade relations status will have an influence on US interests, in both direct and indirect ways. Direct impacts will include changes in economic, security and political relations between the two countries as the trade deal is actualized. Indirect impacts will occur when China becomes a WTO member and adheres to WTO rules and principles. China has said that it would join the WTO only if the US gives it Permanent Normal Trade Relations status.

It is likely that Congress will consider four options, the least likely being that the US will deny China both PNTR and annual extension of NTR status. The other three options are:

Passage of a clean PNTR bill: Congress grants China Permanent Normal Trade Relations status with no conditions attached. This option would allow implementation of the November 1999 WTO trade deal between China and the Clinton administration. China would also carry out other WTO principles and trade conditions.

Amendment of the current NTR status bill: This option would give China the same trade position as other countries and disassociate trade from other issues. As a supplement, a separate bill may be enacted to address other matters, such as human rights, labor rights, and environmental issues.

Annual Extension of NTR status: Congress extends China's Normal Trade Relations status for one more year, and, thus, maintains the status quo.

There have been many debates as to whether Congress should grant China PNTR status, reflecting the variety of attitudes and feelings toward this subject. Proponents of the China trade bill emphasize only the benefits and opportunities (mostly economic) to be derived from passage of the PNTR bill. Opponents generally argue against the bill because of the costs and risks involved, such as a potential loss of jobs in the US. Moreover, China's PNTR status could eventually increase its expenditures on military modernization and subsequent threats to Taiwan.

The following is a summary of the main criteria in the hierarchies of the benefits, costs, opportunities and risks to the US from acting on this decision.

Benefits to US

A. Increase in US Exports to China

China's PNTR would increase US exports by $3.1 billion per year in the short-term and could increase them by $12.7 billion to $13.9 billion a year by 2005. China promised to lower overall tariffs from an average of 25% to 9%. US firms would have broader accessibility to the Chinese market, particularly in the agriculture, service and financial sectors. For example, there are currently only 25 foreign banks in China that are permitted to take deposits and lend money in China's currency, the renminbi, and there are only seven foreign insurers doing business in China. These foreign companies' operations are restricted to a few cities, such as Shanghai, Shenzen and Guangzhou]. These geographical restrictions would be dropped. However, if China joins the WTO, immense changes would come to the financial markets. Foreign banks would be allowed to do business with Chinese enterprises in renminbi within two years of WTO accession, and with Chinese individuals within five years.

B. Improved Rule of Law

Improved Rule of Law would be guaranteed and could reduce China's infringement on intellectual property rights (IPR), which is a large source of profits. IPR has been a serious cause of trade dispute between the US and China, and has caused large losses in US profits. One of the most important differences between the WTO and its precursor, the GATT, is that the WTO not only deals with trade issues but also covers services and intellectual property rights, according to the Trade-Related Aspects of Intellectual Property rights (TRIPs). All WTO member nations are required to abide by TRIPs. Moreover, China has agreed to US demands that, upon accession to the WTO, it would implement TRIPs without a transition period. Accordingly, China's accession to the WTO should increase the profits of US businesses particularly in software, music recording, and other "high-tech" and cultural industries.

If China joins the WTO, it would obviously have to follow the Rule of Law in accordance with WTO principles. As China becomes more law-abiding, the resulting transparency and predictability in China's actions would likely lead to an improved investment environment in China.

C. China's Promise to Respect US Provisions

China has agreed to adhere to US demands to continue two powerful US provisions designed to protect its domestic industries. Anti-dumping measures for 15 years after China joins the WTO. If the US International Trade Commission and the US Department of Commerce conclude that dumping is occurring, and if the dumping practice by foreign exporters injures domestic industry, the government can impose an anti-dumping duty, which is an import tariff equal to the dumping margin. The US uses antidumping policies much more extensively than do other countries. Section 201 Law of the 1974 Trade Act, also called the escape clause or the safeguard, stipulates that the president can impose severe restrictions of up to five years to reduce imports of a foreign product.

D. Increased Employment

Increased exports can create more jobs, particularly in areas where the US is highly competitive such as in high technology, telecommunication, and farm industries.

E. Benefits to Lower Income Consumers

If the US imposes higher tariffs on Chinese products, as a consequence of any trade dispute between the two countries, US consumers may pay higher prices for consumer goods, such as apparel, toys, and electronic appliances. This would become a burden for lower income households.

Opportunities for US

A. US–Sino Relations

Congress' decision could result in a breakthrough in US-Sino relations in the economic, political, social, cultural, and security arenas. Congress could help draw China, which was isolated until Deng Xiaoping began an extensive economic reform, closer to the rest of the world, and open wider arenas for US-China exchanges.

B. Improve the Environment

China's large population and fast economic growth generate high-energy consumption and exhaust other natural resources, thus causing environmental concerns. There are two reasons why the US might expect better environmental policies in China with PNTR. First, many developing countries, such as China, cannot afford environment-friendly equipment. When China's economy develops further, it is more likely to take measures against environmental degradation. Second, as the US-China Forum on Environment and Development has demonstrated, close relations between China and the US can enhance the US' ability to influence China's behavior regarding environmental protection.

C. Promote Democracy

This category requires no explanation.

D. Improve Human and Labor Rights

The more China is exposed to the rest of the world through the flow of goods, finance, technology and ideas, the more it is likely to become a democratic nation. Labor and human rights are also more likely to be improved through China's exposure to standards adhered to by developed nations.

Costs to US

A. Loss of US Access to China's Market

Competition among nations over China's market is high. If China does not obtain Normal Trade Relations status, it is likely to blame the US. In that case, China would be less inclined to offer US businesses the opportunities given to other competitors in Chinese markets.

B. Possible Job Losses in the US

Labor unions have expressed their concern that jobs would be at risk if Congress passes the bill since some US firms would likely move to China in pursuit of its low-wage labor.

Risks for US

A. Loss of Trade as Leverage over Other Issues

Some believe that the annual review process of China's trade status gives the US an economic leverage over other issues such as human rights, labor rights, and security issues. Consequently, some perceive that granting China Permanent Trade Relation status will sacrifice US leverage over China.

B. US-China Conflict

Denying China PNTR can lead to conflicts between the US and China. Some analysts have suggested that China may become a major rival for the US, replacing the former Soviet Union. Thus, potential friction with China could be a serious cause for concern.

C. China Violating Regional Stability

Failure of engagement with China can yield regional instability, particularly across the Taiwan Strait. Isolating China from the WTO could also lead to a withdrawal of China's commitment to alleviate potential conflict around the Korean Peninsula, and between Pakistan and India

D. China's Reform Retreat

China's leaders, primarily Premier Zhu Rongji, were attempting to reform China's economic system and politics. If the US does not cooperate with this effort, China's reactionary forces, including officials of the Communist Party of China and other privileged groups, might try to pressure the current leaders to diminish their desire to reform China.

Pulling it All Together

The two-sided debate and the imminent decision on China's trade status have motivated us, in this chapter, to use the Analytic Hierarchy Process in order to examine the positives and negatives of the options. This approach will allow us to cull the most promising of the three possible alternatives.

The current analysis brings two strengths to the debate. It is comprehensive in so far as it identifies all issues bearing on the three decision factors: economic, security, and political. It is also an objective examination of the problem based strictly on criteria and priorities that anyone might consider in the decision.

Our analysis involves four steps. First, we prioritize the criteria in the benefits, opportunities, costs, and risks hierarchies. Figures 3-3a and 3-3b show the resulting prioritization of these criteria. The alternatives and their priorities are shown under each criterion. However, the priorities of the alternatives need to be converted to ideal form under each criterion by dividing by the largest priority among them. These ideal priorities of the alternatives are then weighted by the priority of their criterion and the result summed over the criteria to obtain the overall syntheses of the priorities of the alternatives shown beneath each hierarchy. The priorities shown in Figures 3-3a and 3-3b were derived methodically from judgments that compared the elements involved in pairs. The judgment for a given pair expresses the strength of preference for one element over another. This strength of preference can be represented numerically. In order for one to *estimate* our original pairwise judgments (not shown here), one forms the ratio of the corresponding two priorities shown and then takes the closest whole number, or its reciprocal if it is less than 1.0.

It is likely that, in a particular decision, the benefits, costs, opportunities and risks are not equally important, so we must also prioritize them. Thus we need to identify strategic criteria and subcriteria and develop priorities for them using paired comparisons as shown in Figure 3-4. The primary goal of any economic policy is to spur economic development. A trade policy always creates the inequity of "winners" and "losers," and this is why equity needs to be considered. **Economic growth** and **equity** should thus be used as the economic criteria. The security criterion has three subcriteria: **regional security** in Asia, particularly between China and Taiwan, **non-proliferation** efforts to diminish nuclear and conventional military competitions, and the direct **threat to US security.** Two subcriteria are considered under the political criterion: the impact that the decision has on the **American voters** and the spread of **American values** such as democracy, human rights and labor rights.

Next we develop intensities for each of the strategic subcriteria. However in this case all the intensities and their priorities are taken to be identical for all the strategic subcriteria and are shown at the top of Table 3-2. We use them in that table to rate the respective importance of the synthesized ideal alternatives for the benefits, opportunities, costs and risks as shown in Figure 3-3. This rating yields priorities: b, o, c, r for the four ideal alternatives and therefore also for their corresponding merits. For convenience we normalize these priorities as normalization is dividing by a constant that is the sum of the four merit priorities and has no effect on the final overall rankings of the alternatives. Finally, we use these four numbers in Table 3-3 to combine the synthesized priorities of the alternatives in the four hierarchies, to obtain their final rankings, with the two formulas BO/CR and $bB_i + oO_i - cC_i - rR_i$. Note that PNTR is, by far, the preferred outcome.

Stability of the Outcome with Changing Priorities

Our analysis indicates that granting China Permanent Normal Trade Relations (PNTR) status is the best alternative, followed by Amend NTR by normalizing trade relations with China, while enacting a separate bill. The status quo, i.e. annual extension of NTR status with China, is the least favorable option.

Comprehensive sensitivity analysis involves perturbing the priorities of the benefits, opportunities, costs, and risks, while also perturbing priorities of the criteria and the alternatives. We would then note what happens to the rank order of the alternatives to determine if the most preferred one remains the same for all, or at least for a preponderance, of the perturbations. That would be a formidable task, but there are two shortcuts. The first is to assume that the priorities of the alternatives with respect to the criteria are well understood and do not need to be perturbed. That leaves open the perturbations of the two higher-level sets of criteria. Here, we have one possible shortcut and that is to delimit the range of small values up and down in combinations and note the resulting stability of the alternatives' priorities. Even then, stability may not obtain in all cases. One must then decide on a way to justify adopting the leading alternative for the decision. The number of possibilities to try here can be very large. What we have done is to determine the stability of the outcome with respect to changes in the criteria with a fixed priority for the benefits, opportunities, costs, and risks. We then performed sensitivity analyses by fixing the priorities of both the alternatives and criteria at their present values and perturbing priorities of the benefits, opportunities, costs, and risks. This effort led to the following (abridged) conclusions.

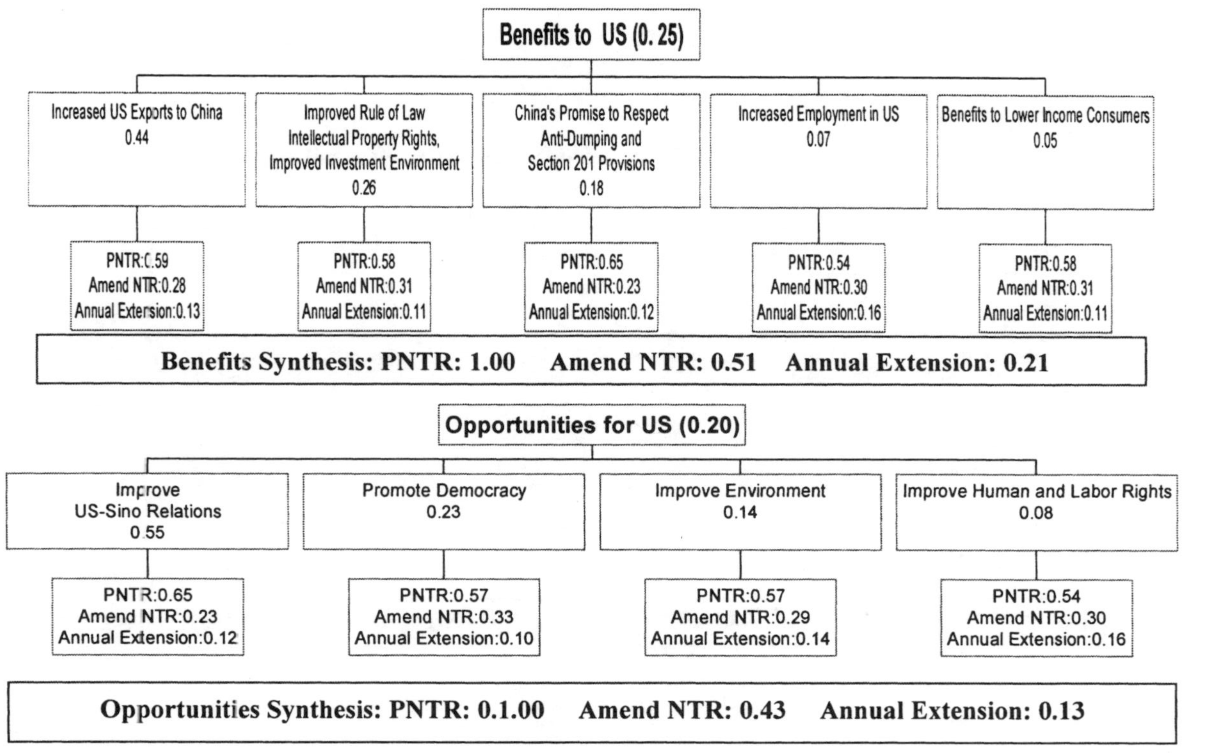

Figure 3-3a: PNTR Decision Hierarchies for Benefits and Opportunities

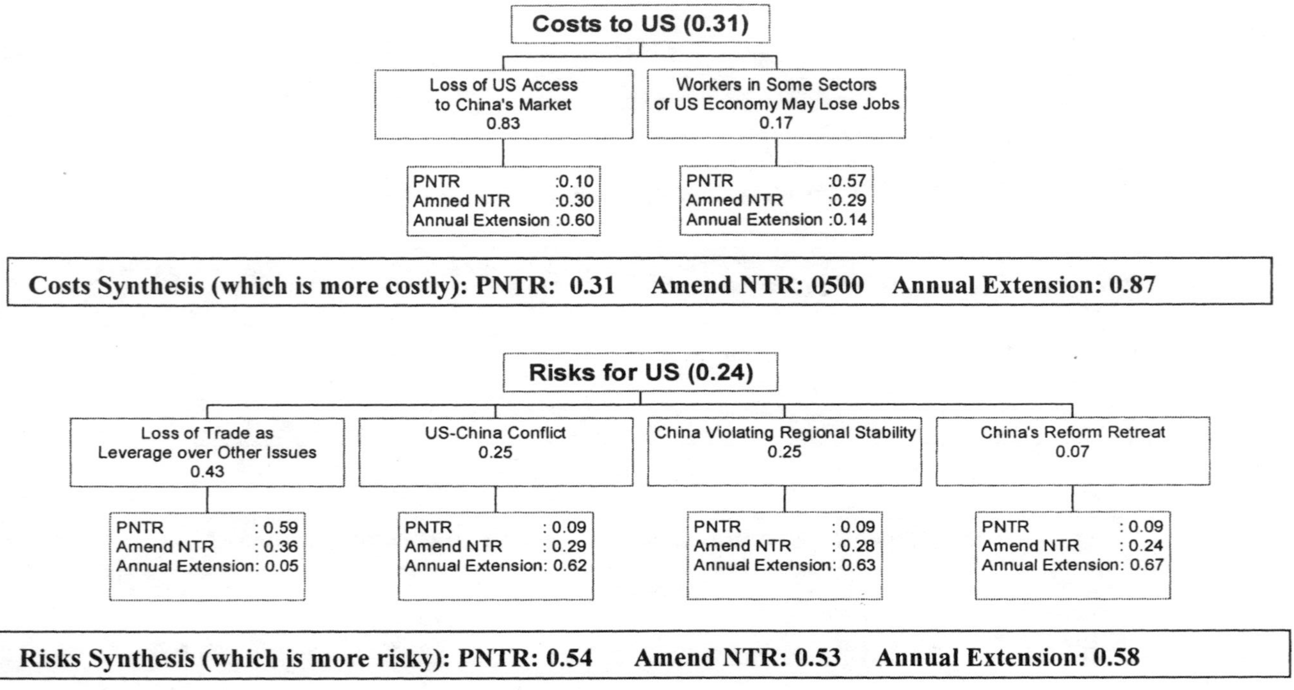

Figure 3-3b: PNTR Decision Hierarchies for Costs and Risks

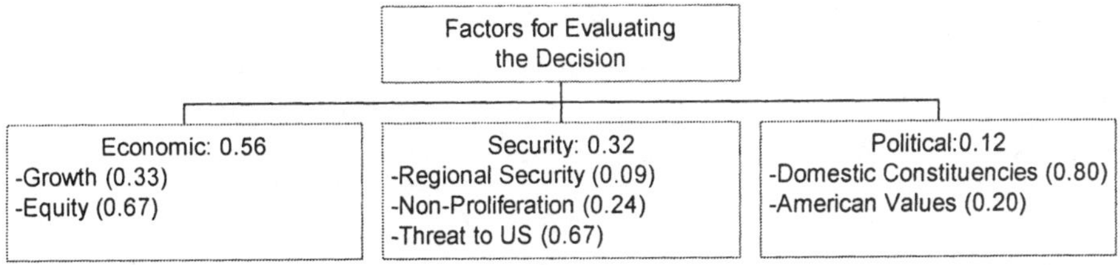

Figure 3-4: Hierarchy for Rating Benefits, Opportunities, Costs and Risks

Table 3-2: Priority Ratings for the Merits: Benefits, Opportunities, Costs, and Risks

Intensities: Very High (0.42), High (0.26), Medium (0.16), Low (0.1), Very Low (0.06)

		Benefits	Opportunities	Costs	Risks
Economic (0.56)	Growth (0.19)	High	Medium	Very Low	Very Low
	Equity (0.37)	Medium	Low	High	Low
Security (0.32)	Regional (0.03)	Low	Medium	Medium	High
	Non-Proliferation (0.08)	Medium	High	Medium	High
	Threat to US (0.21)	High	High	Very High	Very High
Political (0.12)	Constituencies (0.1)	High	Medium	Very High	High
	American Values (0.02)	Very Low	Low	Low	Medium
Priorities		0.25	0.20	0.31	0.24

We are now able to obtain the overall priorities of the three major decision alternatives listed earlier, given as the last two columns in Table 3-3:

Table 3-3: Synthesizing BOCR Using the Ideal Mode

Alternatives	Benefits (0.25)	Opportunities (0.20)	Costs (0.31)	Risks (0.24)	BO/CR	bB + oO - cC - rR
PNTR	1	1	0.31	0.54	5.97	0.22
Amend NTR	0.51	0.43	0.50	0.53	0.83	-0.07
Annual Exten.	0.21	0.13	0.87	0.58	0.05	-0.33

We see that PNTR has the largest outcome priority.

With the original priorities of the benefits, opportunities, costs and risks, or simply BOCR, as given here, sensitivity analysis suggested that the best alternative, PNTR, is insensitive to 13 of the 15 criteria in Figures 3-3a and 3-3b. In only two criteria, "Workers in Some Sectors of US Economy May Lose Jobs," and "Loss of Trade as Leverage over Other Issues," can we change the priorities, individually and together, to make PNTR less desirable. This happens if the importance of the first of the two criteria increases by more than twice its current value, or if the importance of the second increases several times more than its current value. In both these cases, Annual Extension becomes the preferred alternative.

There are numerous combinations of the priorities of the two criteria that could lead to rank reversal. Reversal begins to occur only when the priorities of both criteria are simultaneously increased to twice their current value, which, given circumstances at the time of the decision, was highly unlikely.

When we assumed that the priorities of the alternatives and of those of the criteria were fixed, and then varied the weights of the benefits, costs, opportunities and risks up and down by 5% in all possible combinations, we found that the priorities of the alternatives remained stable in all cases.

Our sensitivity analysis thus indicated that, overall, it is in the best interest of the United States to grant China PNTR status. This analysis was done several months before the congressional vote and the outcome was stable, as the sensitivity analysis showed and the paper was distributed to members of congress several weeks before the vote. The House of Representatives approved legislation establishing PNTR with China on May 24, 2000 by a vote of 237 for and 197 against with one abstention. The Senate passed the bill with 83 for and 15 against on September 19, 2000. President Clinton signed the bill into a law on October 10, 2000. We are hopeful that sharing copies of our analysis with leaders and several members of Congress helped create some value in their deliberations about the best possible outcome.

3-6. A Full BOCR Network Example

We have already seen examples of market share that show how a single network can be used to determine the outcome of influences with respect to a single control criterion, market share. Now we show how the same approach can be generalized to several control criteria that are different for each of the BOCR. Similar to the single criterion example, we use the idealized priorities of the alternatives then synthesized with respect to each of the four merits. This is done after the control criteria are prioritized and their weights are used to weight the priorities of the alternatives. Finally the top ranked alternative with respect to each merit is rated by itself on a set of strategic criteria or subcriteria that are themselves prioritized with respect to their goal. The resulting four ratings are then normalized and used as the priorities of the corresponding B, O, C, and R. The overall results for the alternatives are then obtained by using the two formulas BO/CR and bB+oO-cC-rR, depending on which is the more appropriate one to use for the interpretation of the outcome. This study was done by Juan P. Alberio and Suri Mulani. The Ford Explorer sports utility vehicle (SUV) has been a very popular brand in the US market for a long time. However, 5 years ago several accidents have occurred involving this motor vehicle. This led the industry to review the safety features of the Explorer model, including the special tires for this specific model designed by Firestone. Both companies are not willing to take full responsibility of the accidents leading to a conflict between Ford and Firestone. Conflict aside, the two companies have been trying to determine what will be the best solution to fix this problem.

The analysis in this chapter focuses on determining the optimal decision for the Ford Company regarding the Explorer/Firestone conflict. The Analytic Network Process (ANP) was applied to the problem. There are four possible decision alternatives that Ford Motor Company can make. They are: to discontinue Explorer, to redesign the model, to maintain the current model, and to maintain the current model and change the tire supplier.

On August 9, 2000 the companies Firestone and Ford announced a recall of 6.5 million tires that contained a safety-relate defect. The recall was the result of an abnormal high rate of treads separations that caused catastrophic rollover crashes that maimed and killed drivers and passengers. At that time, the companies jointly had decided that Decatur was the appropriate focus for a recall of Wilderness AT tires, thus excluding millions of identical tires made in Firestone's Wilson, North Carolina and Joilette, Quebec, Canada plants.

The tires had been sold as original equipment on Ford's Explorer SUV, and manufactured according to specifications from Ford.

In May 2001, Ford Motor Company also announced a new recall of 13 million tires from the Ford Explorer models and the termination of the business relationship with Firestone. Ford Motor Company announced in March 2001 that the company would redesign the Explorer model (creating the new Explorer) adding a wider body and incorporating some "rollover" features.

There are several key players in the tire separation tread case. The first is the company that designed and manufactured the tires: Firestone. The second is the company that designed and manufactured the vehicles: Ford Motor Company. The third is the governmental regulation agency: the National Highway Safety Administration (NHTSA).

Under the benefit, cost, and risk models, there are different clusters defined that interact with respect to the control hierarchy established. For benefits and risks, the control hierarchy consists of social and economic factors; while the cost control hierarchy includes social, economic, and political factors. Although the clusters and the specific elements assigned to each network vary due to their interactions, the following general definitions apply to all.

Alternative Decisions

The alternative decisions cluster includes the potential decisions for Ford Motor Company regarding the Ford/Firestone conflict. The potential decisions included are:

Discontinue Explorer production.
Redesign the Explorer model.
Maintain the production of Explorer Model.
Maintain the production of Explorer Model, but change the tire supplier.

Stakeholders

The stakeholders include people or groups that will be impacted by the alternative decisions made by Ford Motor Company. The elements in this cluster are the following:

Customers: current and potential buyers
Community: people who may not be a customer but could be affected by the alternative decisions
Employees: Ford Motor Company employees, including labor and management
Nation's Highway Safety Agency: government agency

Tire Suppliers

This cluster considers current and potential tire suppliers for Ford Motor Company. The elements in this cluster are the following: Firestone, Goodyear, Michelin, and Other Tire Suppliers.

Competition

The competition cluster includes other SUV brands and models owned by Ford Motor Company and other companies. The elements in this cluster are the following:

Ford's other SUV brands (e.g. Escape)
Ford affiliates' SUV brands (e.g. Land Rover)

Other companies' SUV brands (e.g. GM, Honda, Lexus, Dodge, etc)

PUBLIC RELATION

This cluster considers elements that will impact the company's relationships with the stakeholders. The elements in this cluster are the following:

Image: the company's image in public

Trust: reliability in the company's name

Accountability: how the company react to community threats caused by Ford Motor Company's products

Legal Matters: current and potential lawsuits filed against the company

BRAND IMAGE

The Brand Image cluster describes major aspects of the products that will impact the company's image. The elements in this cluster are the following:

Quality, Safety, Prestige, and Service.

COST OF RESOURCES

The cost of resources refers to those costs that Ford Motor Company may have incurred when choosing the alternative decisions. The elements in this cluster are the following:

Layoff costs: the cost that the company would incur in case they decide to reduce the number of employees.

Launching costs: the cost that the company would incur in case they decide to launch a new product.

Write-off costs: the cost that the company would incur in case they decide to reduce the inventory of discontinued products

Production costs: the cost that the company would incur during the production stage

RESOURCES

Resources cluster includes:

Revenues, Production Capacity, and Market Share.

PROCEDURE

In order to rate the Benefits, Costs and Risks in the decision Ford Motor Company would have to make regarding the Ford Explorer Model, we set the goal and 3 criteria: Domestic Issues, International Relations and Human Well-Being. In Domestic Issues, the subcriteria used were: a) Ford Motor Company's reputation, b) Car's Industry reputation and c) US Government's reputation. In the case of International Relations, the subcriteria used were: a) Relationship with customers in other countries, b) Relationship with suppliers in other countries and c) Relationship with other countries' governments. Finally, in the case of Human Well-Being, the subcriteria used were: a) Future Safety Factors, b) Confidence in government agencies and c) Confidence in the Justice system.

The analysis was done using the ANP in the Benefits, Costs and Risks (BCR) model. Each criterion has independent subcriteria, and each sub-criterion contained a detail network. Opportunities were not considered because this was a decision involving corrective action and not opening a new business. The structure of the analysis preceding the strategic criteria is illustrated in Figure 3-5. The subnets are shown in detail Figures 3-6 to 3-12.

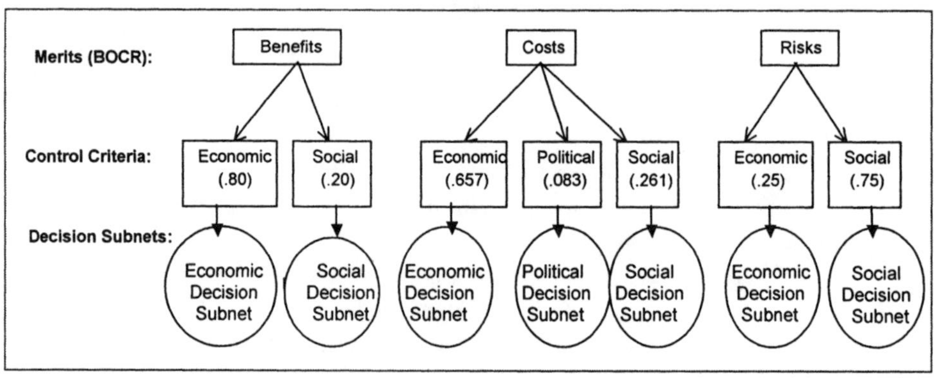

Figure 3-5: The Structure of Merits, Control Criteria and Decision Subnets

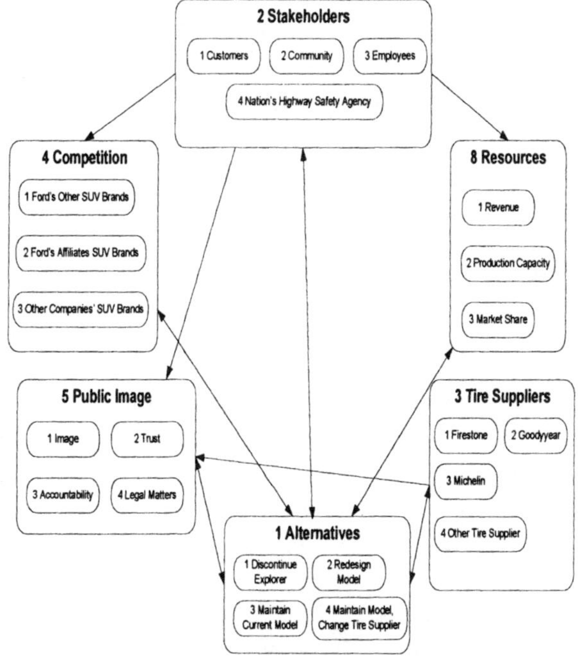

Figure 3-6: Economic Benefits Subnet

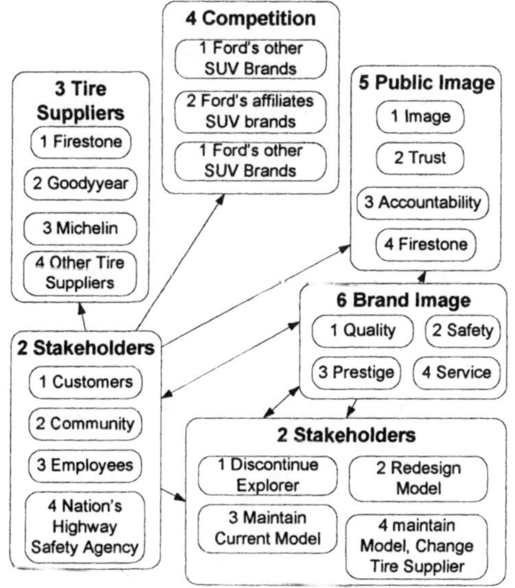

Figure 3-7: Social Benefits Subnet

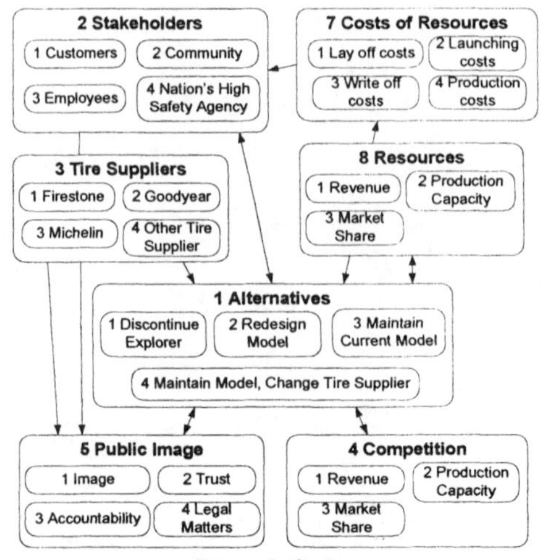

Figure 3-8: Economic Costs Subnet

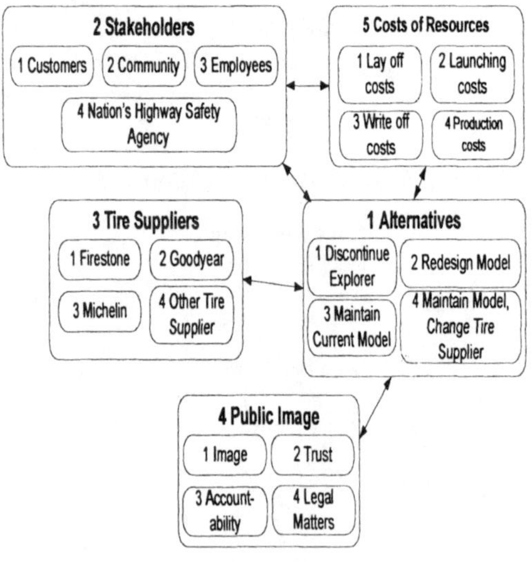

Figure 3-9: Political Costs Subnet

5 Public Image
1 Image
2 Trust
3 Accountability
4 Legal Matters

2 Staholders
1 Customers
2 Community
3 Employees
4 Nation's Highway safety Agency

6 Brand Image
1 Quality
2 Safety
3 Prestige
4 Service

1 Alternatives
1 Discontinue Explorer
2 Redesign Model
3 Maintain Current Model
4 Maintain Model, Change Tire Supplier

Social Costs

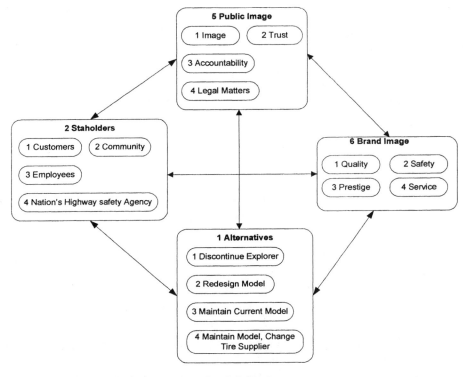

Figure 3-10: Social Costs Subnet

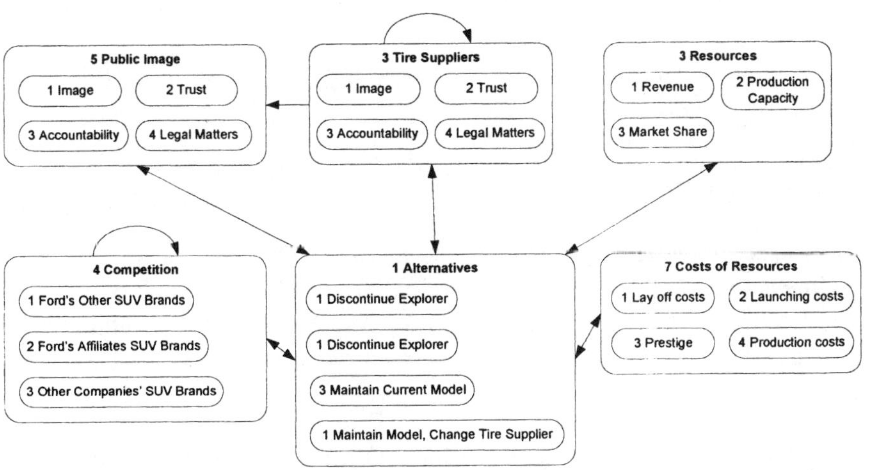

Economic Risks

Figure 3-11: Economic Risks Subnet

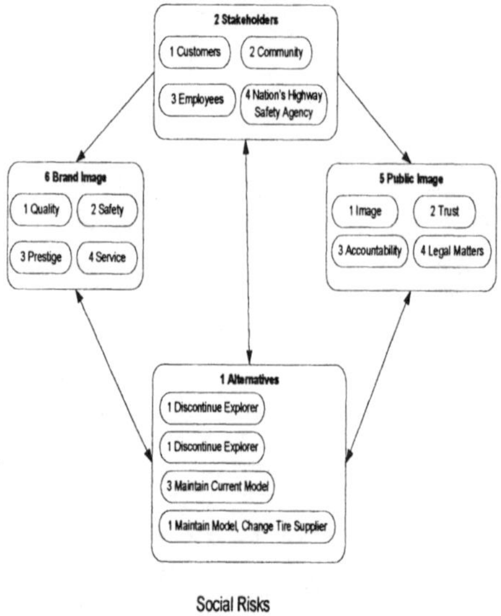

Figure 3-12: Social Risks Subnet

In Table 3-4 we give the final synthesis of the alternatives for each merit. Note that "Discontinue Explorer" is the ideal for benefits and costs but not for risks. Also note that the word ideal does not mean the most preferred, it simply means having the largest priority value.

Table 3-4: Synthesized Alternatives for B, C and R in Ideal Form

Values of Alternatives for B,C and R	Benefits (B)	Costs (C)	Risks (R)
Discontinue Explorer	1	1	.593
Redesign Model	.397	.25	.161
Maintain Current Model	.111	.465	1
Maintain Model, Change Tire Supplier	.542	.554	.308

We now need strategic criteria to rate the merits. Table 3-5 shows the priorities of the intensities in ideal form that is, normalized by dividing each by the largest. These priorities were pairwise compared for preference and the same intensities derived by making pairwise from General Pairwise Comparisons (same for all criteria):

Table 3-5: Intensity Values in Ideal Form for Rating B, C and R

Very High	High	Medium	Low	Very Low
1.000	0.578	0.235	0.118	0.063

Table 3-6 shows the strategic criteria and their subcriteria with their priorities obtained by using paired comparisons. The BCR merits are then rated by taking the ideal alternative for each from Table 3-4 selecting the appropriate intensity for it from table 3-5 for each strategic subcriterion. The overall weighted outcome unnormalized and normalized is shown on the left in Table 3-6. Using these three normalized values for B, C, and R, the final ranking of the alternatives is shown in Table 3-7 computed with two different formulas: the ratio and the total.

Table 3-6: Rating of BCR with Respect to Strategic Subcriteria

			Domestic Issue (.218)			International Relations (.067)			Human Well Being (.714)		
Subcriteria Weights			Ford's Interest	Car Industry Interests	US Gov't Interests	Foreign Customers	Foreign Sup-pliers	Foreign Gov'ts	Safety Factors	Confi-dence in Gov't	Confi-dence in Justice
			0.731	0.081	0.188	0.637	0.105	0.258	0.731	0.188	0.881
Global Weights	Total	Norm-alized	0.160	0.018	0.041	0.043	0.007	0.017	0.522	0.135	0.058
Benefits	0.885	b= 0.485	Very High (1.000)	High (0.578)	Med (0.235)	Med (0.235)	Low (0.118)	Med (0.235)	Very High (1.000)	Very High (1.000)	High (0.578)
Costs	0.730	c= 0.400	Very High (1.000)	Med (0.235)	Low (0.118)	High (0.578)	Very Low (0.063)	Low (0.118)	Very High (1.000)	Very Low (0.063)	Very Low (0.063)
Risks	0.209	r= 0.115	Med (0.235)	Low (0.118)	Very Low (0.063)	Low (0.118)	Med (0.235)	Low (0.118)	Med (0.235)	Med (0.235)	Very Low (0.063)

Table 3-7: Final Ranking of Alternatives All in Normalized Form

	Ratio (B/CR)	Total (bB-cC-rR)
Discontinue Explorer	1.69	.017
Redesign Model	1.55	.074
Maintain Current Model	.239	-.274
Maintain Model, Change Tire Supplier	3.169	.006

We see here that the two formulas give different rankings and we must be guided by the second one because it is a more honest representation using our values as reflected by the strategic criteria. This difference indicates that the approximation is too imprecise and that the general use of BO/CR is not always reliable. It can be blamed in part by dividing by values that are close to zero.

3-7. General Observations

There is an important and delicate distinction to be made in how people who advocate decision-making theories do it in practice and what their mathematics say about it. Let us briefly draw attention to this fact. The criteria of a decision can acquire their importance in two ways. The first is through linking them to experience with alternatives in life. People have learned over time about the priorities of these criteria and when they set weights for them, they cannot do it by isolating themselves from the knowledge they have about the many alternatives known in the past. In this case and strictly speaking the importance of the criteria should be determined in terms of the alternatives by using the ANP. But there is another case where the importance of the criteria is completely independent of the alternatives. Take the example where a doctor determines that a patient has anemia. Anemia is treated for example by eating certain kinds of foods. Strictly speaking, the importance or severity of the anemia (the presence of iron in the blood) is determined by its effects on the health of the patient and does not depend on what foods are eaten. Different foods are then examined according to their iron content to help solve the anemia problem. In this case the criteria are independent of the food alternatives. Thus there are cases where the criteria depend on the alternatives that need the ANP and cases when they do not.

Let us look at the alternatives themselves. Usually, in a decision people identify all the relevant alternatives. Knowing other alternatives would certainly influence what one thinks of any one of them because it is not thought of freely as if it is the only one, but is now conditioned by the quality and number of what other alternatives there are. I claim that in all these cases one cannot treat alternatives as if one knows each one totally on its own merits without knowledge of the other alternatives and proceed to rate them as if they are independent of one another. In addition, by rating them rather than carefully comparing them, the influence of other alternatives on any one of them is captured haphazardly and is not measured carefully. The only possible justification for rating alternatives one at a time is when the alternatives can be introduced without any knowledge or presence of other alternatives, present and past. But that is very difficult to do with our imaginative and intrusive minds. Thus the only justification for any rating method is that it is convenient, not that it honestly reflects independence. Independence is determined not assumed, by comparing the influence of any pair on a third alternative for each criterion as in the ANP. If all comparisons show that no pair of alternatives influences another, the alternatives are assigned zeros for the components of every eigenvector needed for such comparisons and entered in the supermatrix. When alternatives are determined to be independent as to influence on each other, they can be rated one at a time or compared. We said above that how good an alternative on a given criterion is difficult to make because one has in mind all other alternatives and in this sense it still needs to be compared with them pairwise. Even an interrogation process to elicit preferences by asking the decision maker how much he prefers one alternative to another possibly to serve his goals evokes dependence in his mind about other possibilities that makes a given alternative dependent on other alternatives. It has often been said that ratings are useful when there are many alternatives because it is time consuming to make comparisons. But that is not true. *After comparing a few alternatives (or even having one alternative) other alternatives can be compared with it one by one and their overall ranks obtained.* This can be done both in the ideal and in the distributive modes and should take less time than using the ratings approach that needs intensities and scales of measurement. Rating alternatives one at a time is convenient, particularly when there are many, but it is not as precise as paired comparisons because one has to make an educated guess to assign each alternative by itself a number or an intensity for a given criterion. The numbers and intensities used in the model need to be defined carefully so that they are meaningful and effective in separating the alternatives. Obviously, this process itself used in ratings cannot be done without knowledge or presence of alternatives present and past. But alternatives can also be compared with others one at a time or a few at a time, it is not a major difficulty to rank alternatives with paired comparisons by doing them in small groups and linking the groups with pivots and then comparing each new alternative with just one of the alternatives that have already been compared.

The paired comparison process assumes that once alternatives are known, it is inevitable that their evaluation depends on each other no matter how independent they may be in their influences on one another. There are numerous examples to show that this is the case. Paired comparisons are always a more precise way of establishing priorities for alternatives than rating them one at time. The precision is not only because of the requirement for homogeneity in paired comparisons and the linking of inhomogeneous groups with pivots in small stages, but also because they tend to correct the process of estimating relative dominance through redundant judgments. Given the inescapable awareness of much more than a single alternative, to assume that alternatives should be rated one at a time as if they are independent is at best an approximate ranking process whose validity is always in doubt. The only way it can be valid if there is a new field in which a decision has to be made and whose criteria are completely independent of its alternatives as in the medical diagnosis case, whose alternatives are introduced one at a time to the mind of the decision maker without any knowledge of the existence of other alternatives. In that case deciding how good that alternative is would at best be guesswork. In addition, it would be impossible to evaluate that alternative accurately by rating it.

We have on occasion been asked about the role of fuzzy sets in the AHP, because fuzzy sets are the fashion today and some people think they have to use them everywhere. We believe that judgments in the AHP are already fuzzy enough. Despite that, the eigenvector derived from them is very stable to small changes. Our understanding of how people use fuzzy thinking in the AHP is to use the idea of confidence levels in judgments. That itself involves both how a confidence level is elicited and represented and how much faith one has in it and in its validity. Let us assume that a confidence level can in fact be more accurately elicited, the question now is how to introduce it within the framework of the AHP and its eigenvector calculation to make it mathematically tractable to ensure meaningful outcome. The AHP captures the idea of uncertainty in judgments through the principal eigenvalue and the consistency index. It has been suggested by an expert in fuzzy set theory that one consider that the judgments belong to an interval, then think of them as fuzzy and finally use simulation to optimize consistency. Patrick Harker, who used the gradient to determine the best judgment to ask the decision maker to change to improve consistency, writes about this the following: "Beyond the mathematical issues you raise is a fundamental question of human judgment. No one could possibly think of how to change all of the parameters simultaneously; this is simply a mathematical convenience that does not relate at all to human cognition. While one might argue that people could think of changing more than one judgment at a time, changing all $n^2/2$ seems unreasonable. I really believe that the mathematics should point out inconsistencies and guide people, but that people must ultimately make the final call on whether or not the judgments make sense." It would be useful to find conditions under which using fuzzy sets yields more valid answers in problems with high inconsistency than the AHP asking the decision maker to revise his judgments.

What does one do about judgments when alternatives are very close on criteria? If two alternatives are close on one or two criteria, they may not necessarily be close overall. If they are distinct overall, one may want to ignore the small differences and consider them equal on those one or two criteria. If they are very close, one does sensitivity analysis to see if the small differences would change the overall order of the alternatives. If they are sensitive, then concern with how to account for the small differences would be justified, otherwise not. Because there is a threshold of sensitivity, we may not have a precise sense of the differences and thus have to simply use sensible decimal adjustments in the pairwise judgments integer values. Subcriteria on which alternatives are all equal in value cannot be simply dropped without making appropriate and correct renormalization from the top.

Dynamic judgments have been considered in the AHP both within the framework of scenarios to forecast occurrences over different time periods and also analytically as functions of time. All the useful applications made so far, particularly in economic forecasting, have used the scenario approach. Analytically we have shown formally how to represent judgments as they depend on time and worked out examples, but we have not been able to show how with the help of intuition people can be accurate in selecting dynamic functions to represent their judgments. The structures used in the AHP/ANP are amenable to change by introducing new alternatives and criteria and in how their influences are related. New knowledge and better understanding make it essential to remain flexible near the time when a decision must be implemented. The forward-backward approach to planning, an idea first introduced into the field of planning early in the development of the AHP in the 1970's is a useful way to devise plans and test alternatives in the realization of objectives. By its nature a plan is dynamic and iterative allowing for change in structure and in testing the effectiveness of beliefs and values. Planning is controlling and improving change as it happens rather than leaving it to the influence of external forces. Creativity needs to be constantly exercised in the entire decision-making process to make it better serve the needs of the decision maker.

3-8. Conclusions

It is hard to find anything that people do that is more important than decision-making. Decision-making infiltrates everything that we think about or do. It is such an important activity that is done so often, still we cannot do all our decisions as a habit, like eating or sleeping. Decision-making involves the following kinds of concerns: planning, generating a set of alternatives, setting priorities, choosing a best policy after finding a set of alternatives, allocating resources, determining requirements, predicting outcomes, designing systems, measuring performance, insuring the stability of a system with respect to change, optimizing, and resolving conflicts. Solving decision problems has suffered from an overabundance of "patent medicine" techniques without any holistic cure.

We need to learn to do decision-making by structuring our thoughts and by asking the right questions to deepen and broaden our insights so we do it consciously, carefully and clearly. Decision-making requires prioritization. Prioritization is an essential human need to making tradeoffs among the myriad factors we have to consider in most of our decisions. Tradeoff requires measurement of intangibles of which usually there are many in a decision. The AHP/ANP provides the means to do that. One wonders how soon it will be when we will make teaching good decision-making in our schools so that young people grow up knowing the subject and how to do it better than any other subject and practicing it seriously. We can think of at least two ways in which we can increase the use of the AHP/ANP. The first is to help people and organizations that must allocate resources to projects by teaching them to create priorities according to their best understanding. People who work together in a cooperative framework as in a company or hopefully in a government, but do not share the same opinions, need a common framework to structure their decisions and participate cooperatively in providing their judgments. Similarly, organizations that need to plan by exploring together possible futures need the structured approach of the AHP/ANP to forward and backward planning. Resolving conflict problems not only needs prioritization of the needs and grievances of the parties, but a way to mediate the opposing non-cooperative and intangible interests within a framework with which it is possible to tradeoff the gains and losses of the parties to negotiate their differences. The other way to increase the use of the AHP/ANP is to create the means to simplify its use with user friendly software, voting pads to express judgments, good surroundings for pleasant participation, and above all helpful facilitation and leadership to break deadlocks and to move the decision making process forward.

It is fairly evident that decision-making, problem solving and creative thinking are our most fundamental mental activities. Of the three, decision-making is the most important because in problem solving we must first determine the cause of the problem and then make a decision about the best way to remove the cause. Creativity is the handmaiden of decision-making; we need creativity to ensure making better decisions. Knowledge is an integral part of decision-making as it helps identify the relevant factors of a problem and what structure to use, but decision-making without creativity to generate alternative solutions is like gambling, since the best alternative action may not be in the set being evaluated. Yet creativity needs to be introduced early. Creativity without decision-making is aimless because with decision making ideas are converted into practice that we call innovation. Decision-making is so important in shaping our future that we need our creative and intelligence skills to continuously improve our ability to do it by taking advantage of a validated, rigorous and flexible decision making method. I am grateful to my friend Dr. Kirti Peniwati of Jakarta, Indonesia, for her patient help and suggestions to clarify some of the ideas presented in this chapter.

Chapter 4
Applications

4-1. Introduction

In this chapter we provide examples to illustrate the approach we have been using to apply the ANP to complex decisions. For clarity and greater precision, the influence represented in all the derived eigenvectors of priorities entered in a supermatrix must be measured according to a single criterion, such as economic influence. Another supermatrix may represent social influence, and so on. We call such criteria with respect to which influence is represented in individual supermatrices **control criteria**. Because we need to combine all such influences obtained from the limits of the several supermatrices in order to obtain a measure of the priority of **overall influence**, we need to group the control criteria in a structure that allows us to derive priorities for them and use these priorities to weight the corresponding individual supermatrix limits and add. Such a structure of control criteria may itself be elaborate. We have examples where the control structure is itself a network. However, here we confine our attention to hierarchies. For simplicity we call the structure of control criteria a **control hierarchy**.

A cluster or component in the ANP is a collection of elements whose function derives from the synergy of their interaction and hence has a higher-order function not found in any single element. A component is like the audio or visual component of a television set or like an arm or a leg, consisting of muscle and bone, in the human body. A mechanical component has no synergy value but is simply an aggregate of elements and is not what we mean by a component. The components of a network should generally be synergistically different from the elements themselves. Otherwise, they would be a mechanical collection with no intrinsic meaning.

First we identify the four **BOCR merits** and their control criteria and subcriteria and prioritize the importance of criteria for each merit. We then develop a network of influences for each control criterion or subcriterion, always including the alternatives if there are other elements in the network that depend on them. Otherwise, we leave the alternatives out and derive the priorities of the other interdependent elements from the supermatrix and use them as weights in a hierarchy to compare and weight the alternatives. In either case, we put the alternatives in the ideal mode in the final vector for each control criterion. We then weight each resulting vector by the priority of its respective control criterion and add over the criteria for that merit. The overall outcome for a given one of the four merits may not have a top alternative with value one. This is particularly the case when no single alternative is best for all the control criteria of a merit. Next we identify and prioritize strategic criteria and subcriteria and we use them in a rating model. We create intensity levels for each criterion or subcriterion and prioritize these intensities with respect to that criterion. We then rate the overall top ranked overall alternative for each of the four BOCR merits. This yields four ratings priorities, *b, o, c,* and *r* one for each of the corresponding merits. We normalize these four numbers and use them to synthesize the priorities of each alternative *i* for the four merits using the formula $bB_i + oO_i - cC_i - rR_i$ to obtain the final priority of that alternative. There are now many examples that validate this outcome whose numerical answers are close to underlying numbers resulting from some kind of measurement with dollars, number of people or some other number put in relative form. Sometimes it is useful to form B_iO_i / C_iR_i as another measure for each alternative without using the strategic criteria. Note that if we have many alternatives we can put them into homogeneous clusters with a pivot from one to another and use the clusters as alternatives derive priorities for them from the supermatrix or otherwise if the criteria are independent of them and then obtain the priority of each alternative from its cluster as appropriate. The fact that there may be many alternatives does not change the basic approach of the AHP/ANP. However, when there are standards to be complied with rating the alternatives as if they are structurally independent may be regarded as an appropriate and a rough shortcut to prioritizing and ranking them.

An arrow from a cluster to another cluster implies that the elements in the second cluster influence those in the first cluster from which the arrow originates. Second, such an arrow from a cluster to another does not necessarily imply that all the elements in that cluster participate in the influence and thus one needs to identify for each element, using the software, what other elements it interacts with. In developing a supermatrix one needs to compare the influence of all the clusters on any given one of them with respect to the control criterion of that network. This yields a vector of priorities of influence of all the clusters on a given cluster. The comparisons are repeated in several pairwise comparison matrices leading to as many priority vectors for the influence of the clusters as there are clusters themselves. An entry of each such vector is used by the software to automatically weigh every element in a block of the supermatrix that corresponds to the priority of influence of a cluster on another cluster. The resulting supermatrix becomes column stochastic (each column sums to one) and thus can be raised to powers to obtain its limiting priorities. To see why one needs to compare the clusters themselves, we note, for example, that a set of alternatives that is prioritized in two clusters can only get an overall rank in both clusters if the clusters themselves have priorities so one can weigh and combine the priorities of the alternatives in the two cluster.

To summarize the process for a decision in general: we identify the **BOCR** merits and the **control criteria and subcriteria for each merit** and **derive their priorities**; we form a network of influences for each control criterion or subcriterion. A network always contains the alternatives of the decision along with clusters of elements of different kinds of influences and particularly those that influence the alternatives directly. Appropriate lines show influences between clusters **with arrows** from one cluster to another **indicating outer dependence**. Many clusters have **loops** within themselves **indicating inner dependence**. For each network we have an unweighted supermatrix; a weighted supermatrix is obtained by comparing the clusters according to their influence on each other cluster with respect to the control criterion and weighting the blocks of the supermatrix by the corresponding **cluster weights**, so that each of its columns becomes stochastic (adds to one). This matrix is then raised to powers to obtain a limit supermatrix.

By consulting the theory one finds that there are generally two kinds of limits of the supermatrix. One in which all the columns are identical because the network is strongly connected and its supermatrix is irreducible (there is a path between any two of its nodes). Another possible limit has different blocks of the supermatrix with identical columns, an illustration of the case where the values in the limit supermatrix cycle. In this case one takes the average over the length of a cycle to get the overall answer for the priorities.

Ideal synthesis of the priorities of the alternatives is used for each of the four merits, leading to four overall rankings for the alternatives, one for each merit. To combine these four rankings into a single ranking, we identify strategic criteria and derive their priorities and rating intensities. We then rate the top alternative from each of the four merits. Finally, we use the four outcome priorities to synthesize the value of each alternative for the four merits; the sum for the costs and risks is subtracted from the sum for the benefits and opportunities. The outcome may have a negative priority and one often has to choose the best from a set of undesirable (negative priority) outcomes.

The case where there is more than one source cluster, which is a cluster without feedback into it from another cluster in the network, is like a hierarchy with more than one goal. Unless the goals are somehow compared with each other to derive priorities for them, one obtains two different outcome priorities. In a hierarchy, this situation is quickly recognized; in a network it is more difficult. In either case if the different goals have no priorities, the different outcomes are automatically averaged by assuming that the goals have equal priorities. In some situations this may be the best one can do because the different goals or source clusters cannot be compared. Because the alternatives always form the bottom level of a hierarchy, and without feedback from them is a sink cluster of a network, this type of ambiguity should not arise as it may with multiple sources.

In entering judgments in response to the question of influence for the costs and the risks one must ask which is more costly and which is more risky and not less costly and less risky. This is because in paired comparisons the larger element is estimated as a multiple of the smaller one used as the unit and not the other way around.

Sensitivity analysis is useful in helping one to decide on how strongly to intensify pursuing policies that help one achieve a desired outcome. It is a practical tool that gives insight as to whether anything can be done and at what price and effort to make a desired outcome happen.

For whatever it is worth, here is a list of factors and their definitions that are related to what goes into a decision model. Existence is to be or not to be; DNA and information coded in biology; the process of living. Instinct, intuition and tacit (unspoken) knowledge and memory are essential influences on our consciousness. Consciousness and awareness is a process of having perception or knowledge to identify things and attributes of things and relate them to what is already known and stored in memory. One may be conscious but unaware. Sleep is a low level of consciousness and lacks awareness except perhaps in dreaming. Influence is the power of indirectly producing an effect on a person or course of events without the use of force; the power to sway. Power is the ability or capacity to produce an effect; authority. Importance is the degree of effect that we attach to an influence. Importance may be positive or negative as it affects our existence. Priority is precedence by order of importance. Value is worth as measured in usefulness or importance; a principle, standard or quality considered as being worthwhile. Importance and priority precede utility and value because they are needed to define value and therefore are more general for the study of influence. A negative value that involves avoidance can be interpreted as a positive value in what good it can bring about. Anything that has value is important but not all the important things have value. Values define a hierarchy and cannot be all crowded in a network of interdependencies. There are basic values that stand on their own independent of what other values there are. Some people have lost sight of that by advocating a network approach all the time. All knowledge is about things and their influence, and the importance of that influence and its value. Purpose is a result or outcome that is intended or desired. Objective is something worked toward or striven for. Goal is a desired purpose;

objective. Criterion is a standard or test on which judgment is based. An alternative is a course of action. Looking ahead, planning, predicting, taking action, implementing strategies, allocating resources, optimizing the expenditure of resources, negotiation and conflict resolution are things to consider in decision making.

4-2. What Question to Ask and How to Ask It When Making Comparisons

In the ANP, a paired comparison matrix captures the relative dominance of one element over another with respect to a control criterion or of a cluster of elements over another with respect to that control criterion. The study of influence relations requires not only knowledge of the real world but also analytical ability to identify relations and exercise imagination to pursue the analysis. The ANP generically asks questions that a thoughtful person would ask in making decisions. In a hierarchy, we ask the question for making a comparison, which of two elements is more dominant or has more influence (or is influenced more) with respect to a certain element in the level above? In a network we ask, which of two elements is more dominant in influencing a third element with respect to a control criterion? **In both hierarchies and networks the sense of having influence or being influenced must be maintained in the entire analysis**; the two should not be mixed together. To repeat, by convention an arrow in a diagram pointing into a component means that its elements influence the elements in the component from which the arrow emanates.

In fact the real world, to the observing mind, is a set of stimuli that give rise to neural firing. According to neural science today, neural firing is distinguishable in terms of frequency and amplitude. The entire human experience is mapped into these types of signals. It is not surprising then that, at higher levels, brain signals are synthesized in terms of goals. The concrete objects of the real world as well as the strategic concepts of the mind can be decomposed in terms of common attributes, and these, in turn, in terms of finer attributes, and so on. In a sense then, all properties can be reduced to very simple attributes associated with the firing of a single neuron in terms of amplitude and frequency. In particular two apples can be compared with respect to redness as a common property. However, different shades of red may be compared with respect to the relative intensity they stimulate in the brain. In addition redness and greenness may be compared according to the relative intensity they each stimulate in a single neuron or in separate neurons as judged by neurons that do such distinctions at higher levels. There is no prior reason why this process needs to be stopped because someone is unable to accept that such things do take place in the nervous system.

Take an individual with his or her variety of attributes and ask: Is this individual more experienced as a teacher or as a bricklayer and how much better is this individual in doing one activity than the other? It is clear that the mind of the judge has to be trained at recognizing a good teacher or a good bricklayer from a poor teacher or a poor bricklayer. It is the range of experience that enables one to make such fine distinctions, which one must do because an individual may actually be striving to be many things and has achieved different levels of virtuosity in each. Once the major principle of capturing the dominance of any two attributes with respect to a common source is understood, one then needs to exercise care in answering the question of dominance. Given an apple that is mostly red but a little green in one patch, it is clear that this apple is more red than green, and one is seeking a comparison of the total redness to the total greenness in that apple. The diverse examples given in the book show that this can be done. The validity of the results are clearly demonstrated in the predictions that have been made in the area of economics, in sports and other types of competition, and in social and political situations whose outcomes became known later. To the brain, tangibles and intangibles produce similar responses because both cause neurons to fire, thereby enabling us to make distinctions in quality and intensity among them, whether we have measurements for them or not. Both knowledge and experience are matters of social and psychological interpretation. We ask the question: Given an element, which of two elements influences that element more with respect to the control criterion? More specifically for a given criterion, which of two criteria influences that criterion more with respect to the goal or with respect to a higher-order controlling criterion?

The **generic question** to be answered by making pairwise comparisons is: Given a control criterion (subcriterion), a component (element) of the network, and given a pair of components (elements), how much more does a given member of the pair influence that component (element) with respect to the control criterion (subcriterion) than the other member?

In the following sections of this chapter we give different examples of feedback.

4-3. A Simple Prediction Example of Supermatrix - A Single Control Criterion: Turn Around of the US Economy 1992, No Cluster Weights and no BOCR

The object of this exercise was to forecast the most likely date of a turnaround in the US economy in 1992. The top level of this hierarchy consists of the factors representing the forces or major influences driving the economy. These forces are grouped into two categories: "conventional adjustment" and "economic restructuring". Both of these categories are decomposed into sub-factors represented in the second level. For the timing forecast, the third level consists of time periods in which the recovery can occur. Figure 4-1 provides a schematic layout used to forecast the timing of the economic turnaround. This example was done with the economist colleagues A. Blair and R. Nachtmann. One of the significant observations to make here is that paired comparisons can be used to estimate not only priorities for preference and importance but also for likelihood and thus also probability. The AHP/ANP approach has been used since 1976 to forecast presidential elections and other predictive situations many included several years ago in a book on the subject (Prediction, Projection and Forecasting, (with Luis G. Vargas), Kluwer Academic, Boston, 1991) and also illustrated by the exercise applications listed at the end of this chapter.

Because conventional adjustment and restructuring are both time-dependent factors, their relative importance had to be established in terms of each of the four contrasting time periods used to compose the forecast time frame. Thus, instead of establishing a single goal as one does for a conventional hierarchy, we used the bottom-level time periods to compare the two factors at the top. This entailed the creation of a feedback hierarchy known as a "holarchy," encountered in Chapter 2 in which the priorities of the elements at the top level are determined in terms of the elements at the bottom level, thus creating an interactive loop.

With regard to forecasting the strength of the recovery, we used a standard format for the hierarchy, beginning with the primary factors of conventional adjustment and economic restructuring. Their importance for this part of the exercise was established over a six-month period after the turnaround.

Conventional adjustment assumes a status quo with regard to the system of causes and consequences in the economy. The presumption is that the underlying structure of the economy is stationary. Forecasting is possible within acceptable ranges of error. This is achieved by tracing the existing network of stimulus/response patterns initiated by a perturbation in a fundamental parameter of the economy. In our view, conventional adjustment can formally be divided into six macroeconomic subfactors that occupy the second level: consumer spending, investment spending, exports, indicators of confidence in the economy, fiscal policy, and monetary policy. We recognize that these subfactors are in some instances interdependent.

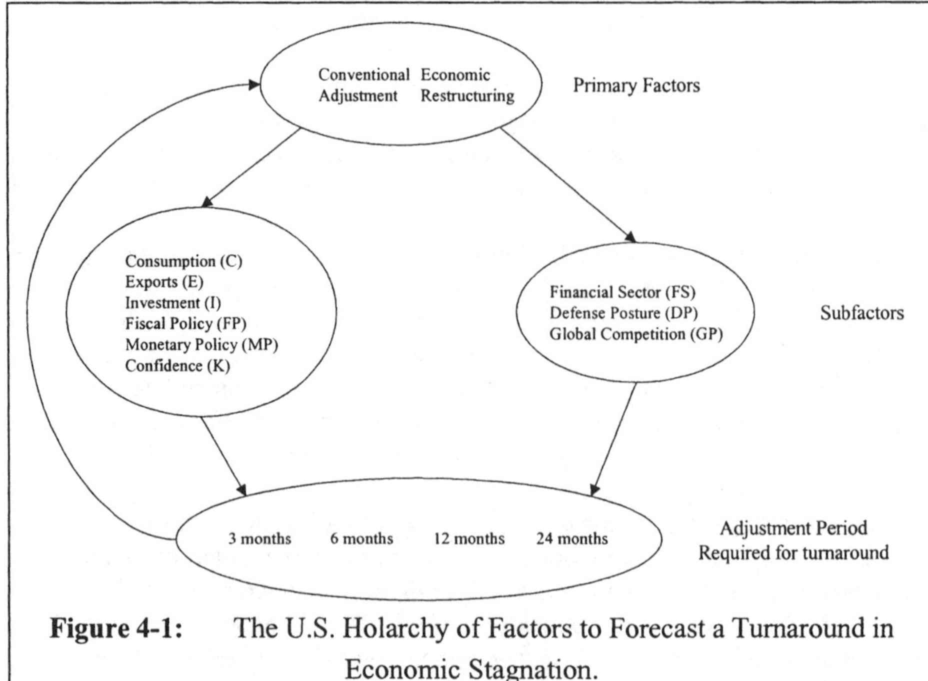

Figure 4-1: The U.S. Holarchy of Factors to Forecast a Turnaround in Economic Stagnation.

Viewed independently, for example, a lowering of interest rates by the Federal Reserve Board should induce portfolio rebalancing throughout the economy. In turn, this should reduce the cost of capital to firms and stimulate investment. Simultaneously, it should reduce financial costs to households and increase their disposable incomes. Any resulting increase in disposable income stimulates consumption and at the margin has a positive impact on employment and GNP. However, all of this assumes that the linkages of the economy are in place and are well understood.

Recent events in the global economy will exert fundamental changes in the way the U.S. economy will operate for the next several years and beyond by inducing an economic restructuring. The Gulf War, the demise of centrally planned economies in Eastern Europe and the former Soviet Union, the integration of Western Europe, the emergence of newly industrialized economies, and the quickening integration of financial sectors throughout the world are all events which suggest an economic structure that is not stationary but is undergoing dramatic change. Prudent recognition of these facts suggests that patience and monitoring of events are appropriate guidelines for public policy.

With regard to the nature of the current economic restructuring, we specifically recognized in this exercise the transformation of the financial sector, the reduction in the defense-based component of the economy, and the changing global competitiveness position of the U.S. economy as additional subfactors in the second level.

Changes in the domestic economic environment induced by these factors affect the economy in ways that are not well understood and are too complex to pursue here. We summarize these effects by estimating the impact of each subfactor on the expected length of time prior to a turnaround, as well as their impact on the relative strength of the ensuing expansion.

With respect to the timing of the turnaround, we considered four possible time periods of adjustment. They are located in the third level as a reasonable breakdown of time in periods long enough to discern change in making the comparisons, but short enough to consider all possible changes over the two-year horizon of the forecast. These periods were: 3 months, 6 months, 1 year, and 2 or more years, dated from late December 1991.

With regard to the strength of the expansion, not shown here because it used a hierarchy instead of a network, our May 1992 exercise employed ranges of average real GNP growth. Specifically, we considered the following possible outcomes: very strong (5.5% to 6.5%), strong (4.5% to 5.5%), moderate (3.0% to 4.5%), and weak (2.0% to 3.0%). These ranges represent annualized measures of percentage change in real gross national product for the first two years of the recovery. While the ranges are somewhat arbitrary, they generally reflect actual experiences during various post World War II cyclical expansions.

The outcomes depend on the quality of judgments. As noted, the first exercise (timing of the turnaround) was conducted during the third week of December 1991 and refined during the first week of January 1992. Estimation of the strength of the recovery was conducted during the second week of May 1992.

Tables 4-1 through 4-4 provide the associated matrices of relative comparisons as well as a limit and completed supermatrix. In providing judgments in answer to questions, the dominant or controlling factor to be held in the mind is the turnaround date of the economy and what influences bringing it about.

Table 4-1: Matrices for Subfactor Importance Relative to Primary Factors Influencing the Timing of Recovery

Panel A: Which subfactor has the greater potential to influence Conventional Adjustment and how strongly?

		C	E	I	K	F	M	Vector Weights
Consumption	(C)	1	7	5	1/5	½	1/5	0.118
Exports	(E)	1/7	1	1/5	1/5	1/5	1/7	0.029
Investment	(I)	1/5	5	1	1/5	1/3	1/5	0.058
Confidence	(K)	5	5	5	1	5	1	0.334
Fiscal Policy	(F)	2	5	3	1/5	1	1/5	0.118
Monetary Policy	(M)	5	7	5	1	5	1	0.343

Panel B: Which subfactor has the greater potential to influence Economic Restructuring and how strongly?

		FS	DP	GC	Vector Weights
Financial Sector	(FS)	1	3	3	0.584
Defense Posture	(DS)	1/3	1	3	0.281
Global Competition	(GC)	1/3	1/3	1	0.135

Table 4-2: Matrices for Relative Influence of Subfactors on Periods of Adjustment (Months) (Conventional Adjustment)

For each panel below, which time period is more likely to indicate a turnaround if the relevant factor is the sole driving force?

Panel A: Relative importance of targeted time periods for consumption to drive a turnaround

	3	6	12	24	Vector Weights
3 months	1	1/5	1/7	1/7	.043
6 months	5	1	1/5	1/5	.113
12 months	7	5	1	1/3	.310
24 months	7	5	3	1	.534

Panel B: Relative importance of targeted time periods for exports to drive a turnaroun

	3	6	12	24	Vector Weights
3 months	1	1	1/5	1/5	.083
6 months	1	1	1/5	1/5	.083
12 months	5	5	1	1	.417
24 months	5	5	1	1	.417

Panel C: Relative importance of targeted time periods for investment to drive a turnaround

	3	6	12	24	Vector Weights
3 months	1	1	1/5	1/5	.078
6 months	1	1	1/5	1/5	.078
12 months	5	5	1	1/3	.305
24 months	5	5	3	1	.538

Panel D: Relative importance of targeted time periods for fiscal policy to drive a turnaround

	3	6	12	24	Vector Weights
3 months	1	1	1/3	1/5	.099
6 months	1	1	1/5	1/5	.087
12 months	3	5	1	1	.382
24 months	5	5	1	1	.432

Panel E: Relative importance of targeted time periods for monetary policy to drive a Turnaround

	3	6	12	24	Vector Weights
3 months	1	5	7	7	.605
6 months	1/5	1	5	7	.262
12 months	1/7	1/5	1	1/5	.042
24 months	1/7	1/7	5	1	.091

Panel F: Expected time for a change of confidence indicators of consumer and investor activity to support a turnaround in the economy

	3	6	12	24	Vector Weights
3 months	1	3	5	5	.517
6 months	1/3	1	5	5	.305
12 months	1/5	1/5	1	5	.124
24 months	1/5	1/5	1/5	1	.054

Table 4-3: Matrices for Relative Influence of Subfactors on Periods of Adjustment (Months) (Economic Restructuring)

For each panel below, which time period is more likely to indicate a turnaround if the relevant factor is the sole driving force?

Panel A: Most likely length of time for restructuring of financial system to support a turnaround

	3	6	12	24	Vector Weights
3 months	1	1/3	1/5	1/7	.049
6 months	3	1	1/5	1/7	.085
12 months	5	5	1	1/5	.236
24 months	7	7	5	1	.630

Panel B: Most likely time required for defense readjustment to affect a turnaround in economy

	3	6	12	24	Vector Weights
3 months	1	1/3	1/5	1/7	.049
6 months	3	1	1/5	1/7	.085
12 months	5	5	1	1/5	.236
24 months	7	7	5	1	.630

Panel C: Most Likely time required for an adjustment to global competition can affect a turnaround in economy

	3	6	12	24	Vector Weights
3 months	1	1	1/3	1/5	.089
6 months	1	1	1/3	1/5	.089
12 months	3	3	1	1/5	.208
24 months	5	5	5	1	.613

Table 4-4: Most Likely Factor to Dominate During a Specified Time Period For each panel below, which factor is more likely to produce a turnaround during the specified time period?

Conventional Adjustment --> CA			
Panel A: 3 Months			
	CA	R	Vector Weights
CA	1	5	.833
R	1/5	1	.167

Restructuring --> R			
Panel B: 6 Months			
	CA	R	Vector Weights
CA	1	5	.833
R	1/5	1	.167

Panel C: 1 Year			
	CA	R	Vector Weights
CA	1	1	.500
R	1	1	.500

Panel D: 2 Years			
	CA	R	Vector Weights
CA	1	1/5	.167
R	5	1	.833

Now we group all the derived vector weights as columns in the appropriate positions of the supermatrix. For example, the first vector we derived from the matrix of subfactors of conventional adjustment is placed in the first column next to the six subfactors and under conventional adjustment. The factors are listed systematically so that the right vectors are listed to indicate the impact of the relevant factors on the left on the factors at the top. The supermatrix, being stochastic (with columns adding to one), is then raised to limiting powers. This is to capture all the interactions and obtain the steady-state outcome (Table 4-5) in which all columns within each block of factors are the same. We are particularly interested in the two identical columns at the bottom left corner of the matrix of Table 4-6a. Either one is given by (0.223, 0.152, 0.201, 0.424).

Synthesis/results. Synthesis, using the SuperDecisions software produced the following results:

A meaningful turnaround in the economy would likely require an additional ten to eleven months, occurring during the fourth quarter of 1992. This forecast was derived from weights generated in the normalized last four entries of the first column of the limit matrix in Table 4-8, coupled with the mid-points of the alternate time periods (so as to provide unbiased estimates):

.223 x 1.5 + .152 x 4.5 + .201 x 9 + .424 x 18 = 10.46 months.[1*]

For completeness we give the limiting forms (Tables 4-6a, 4-6b, 4-6c) of all three phases of the holarchy, which is a cycle with c=3. We display the supermatrix for each phase: Tables 4-6a,b,c, with their sum in Table 4-7. Table 4-8 is derived from Table 4-7 by dividing by 3 to form the average and hence obtain the Cesaro sum.

Table 4-5: The Initial Completed Supermatrix W

	C.A.	E.R.	Con.	Exp.	Inv.	Conf.	F.P.	M.P.	F.S.	D.P.	G.C.	3 mo.	6 mo.	1 yr.	≥2 years
Conven. Adjust	0.0	0.0	0.0	0.0	0.0	0.0	0.0	0.0	0.0	0.0	0.0	0.833	0.833	0.500	0.167
Economic Restruct.	0.0	0.0	0.0	0.0	0.0	0.0	0.0	0.0	0.0	0.0	0.0	0.167	0.167	0.500	0.833
Consumption	0.118	0.0	0.0	0.0	0.0	0.0	0.0	0.0	0.0	0.0	0.0	0.0	0.0	0.0	0.0
Exports	0.029	0.0	0.0	0.0	0.0	0.0	0.0	0.0	0.0	0.0	0.0	0.0	0.0	0.0	0.0
Investment	0.058	0.0	0.0	0.0	0.0	0.0	0.0	0.0	0.0	0.0	0.0	0.0	0.0	0.0	0.0
Confidence	0.334	0.0	0.0	0.0	0.0	0.0	0.0	0.0	0.0	0.0	0.0	0.0	0.0	0.0	0.0
Fiscal Policy	0.118	0.0	0.0	0.0	0.0	0.0	0.0	0.0	0.0	0.0	0.0	0.0	0.0	0.0	0.0
Monetary Policy	0.343	0.0	0.0	0.0	0.0	0.0	0.0	0.0	0.0	0.0	0.0	0.0	0.0	0.0	0.0
Financial Sector	0.0	0.584	0.0	0.0	0.0	0.0	0.0	0.0	0.0	0.0	0.0	0.0	0.0	0.0	0.0
Defense Posture	0.0	0.281	0.0	0.0	0.0	0.0	0.0	0.0	0.0	0.0	0.0	0.0	0.0	0.0	0.0
Global Compet.	0.0	0.135	0.0	0.0	0.0	0.0	0.0	0.0	0.0	0.0	0.0	0.0	0.0	0.0	0.0
3 months	0.0	0.0	0.043	0.083	0.078	0.517	0.099	0.605	0.049	0.049	0.089	0.0	0.0	0.0	0.0
6 months	0.0	0.0	0.113	0.083	0.078	0.305	0.086	0.262	0.085	0.085	0.089	0.0	0.0	0.0	0.0
1 year	0.0	0.0	0.310	0.417	0.305	0.124	0.383	0.042	0.236	0.236	0.209	0.0	0.0	0.0	0.0
≥ 2 years	0.0	0.0	0.534	0.417	0.539	0.054	0.432	0.091	0.630	0.630	0.613	0.0	0.0	0.0	0.0

[1] Number of months after late December 1991 or early January 1992.

Table 4-6a: Limit Supermatrix Phase I

	C.A.	E.R.	Con.	Exp.	Inv.	Con.	F.P.	M.P.	F.S.	D.P.	G.C.	3 mo.	6 mo.	1 yr.	≥ 2 years
Conven. Adjust	0	0	0	0	0	0	0	0	0	0	0	0.484	0.484	0.484	0.484
Econ. Restructure	0	0	0	0	0	0	0	0	0	0	0	0.516	0.516	0.516	0.516
Consumption	0.057	0.057	0	0	0	0	0	0	0	0	0	0	0	0	0
Exports	0.014	0.014	0	0	0	0	0	0	0	0	0	0	0	0	0
Invest.	0.028	0.028	0	0	0	0	0	0	0	0	0	0	0	0	0
Confidence	0.162	0.162	0	0	0	0	0	0	0	0	0	0	0	0	0
Fiscal Policy	0.057	0.057	0	0	0	0	0	0	0	0	0	0	0	0	0
Monetary Policy	0.166	0.166	0	0	0	0	0	0	0	0	0	0	0	0	0
Financ. Sector	0.302	0.302	0	0	0	0	0	0	0	0	0	0	0	0	0
Defense Posture	0.145	0.145	0	0	0	0	0	0	0	0	0	0	0	0	0
Global Compet.	0.070	0.070	0	0	0	0	0	0	0	0	0	0	0	0	0
3 months	0	0	0.223	0.223	0.223	0.223	0.223	0.223	0.223	0.223	0.223	0	0	0	0
6 months	0	0	0.152	0.152	0.152	0.152	0.152	0.152	0.152	0.152	0.152	0	0	0	0
1 year	0	0	0.201	0.201	0.201	0.201	0.201	0.201	0.201	0.201	0.201	0	0	0	0
≥ 2 years	0	0	0.424	0.424	0.424	0.424	0.424	0.424	0.424	0.424	0.424	0	0	0	0

Table 4-6b: Limit Supermatrix - Phase II

	C.A.	E.R.	Con.	Exp.	Inv.	Con.	F.P.	M.P.	F.S.	D.P.	G.C.	3 mo.	6 mo.	1 yr.	≥ 2 years
Conven. Adjust	0	0	0.484	0.484	0.484	0.484	0.484	0.484	0.484	0.484	0.484	0	0	0	0
Econ. Restruct.	0	0	0.516	0.516	0.516	0.516	0.516	0.516	0.516	0.516	0.516	0	0	0	0
Consum.	0	0	0	0	0	0	0	0	0	0	0	0.057	0.057	0.057	0.057
Exports	0	0	0	0	0	0	0	0	0	0	0	0.014	0.014	0.014	0.014
Invest.	0	0	0	0	0	0	0	0	0	0	0	0.028	0.028	0.028	0.028
Confid.	0	0	0	0	0	0	0	0	0	0	0	0.162	0.162	0.162	0.162
Fiscal Policy	0	0	0	0	0	0	0	0	0	0	0	0.057	0.057	0.057	0.057
Monetary Policy	0	0	0	0	0	0	0	0	0	0	0	0.166	0.166	0.166	0.166
Financ. Sector	0	0	0	0	0	0	0	0	0	0	0	0.301	0.301	0.301	0.301
Defense Posture	0	0	0	0	0	0	0	0	0	0	0	0.145	0.145	0.145	0.145
Global Compet.	0	0	0	0	0	0	0	0	0	0	0	0.070	0.070	0.070	0.070
3 months	0.224	0.224	0	0	0	0	0	0	0	0	0	0	0	0	0
6 months	0.151	0.151	0	0	0	0	0	0	0	0	0	0	0	0	0
1 year	0.201	0.201	0	0	0	0	0	0	0	0	0	0	0	0	0
≥ 2 years	0.424	0.424	0	0	0	0	0	0	0	0	0	0	0	0	0

Table 4-6c: Limit Supermatrix - Phase III

	C.A.	E.R.	Con.	Exp.	Inv.	Con.	F.P.	M.P.	F.S.	D.P.	G.C.	3 mo.	6 mo.	1 yr.	≥ 2 yrs
Conven. Adjust	0.484	0.484	0	0	0	0	0	0	0	0	0	0	0	0	0
Econ. Restruct.	0.516	0.516	0	0	0	0	0	0	0	0	0	0	0	0	0
Consumption	0	0	0.057	0.057	0.057	0.057	0.057	0.057	0.057	0.057	0.057	0	0	0	0
Exports	0	0	0.014	0.014	0.014	0.014	0.014	0.014	0.014	0.014	0.014	0	0	0	0
Invest.	0	0	0.028	0.028	0.028	0.028	0.028	0.028	0.028	0.028	0.028	0	0	0	0
Confidence	0	0	0.162	0.162	0.162	0.162	0.162	0.162	0.162	0.162	0.162	0	0	0	0
Fiscal Policy	0	0	0.057	0.057	0.057	0.057	0.057	0.057	0.057	0.057	0.057	0	0	0	0
Monetary Policy	0	0	0.166	0.166	0.166	0.166	0.166	0.166	0.166	0.166	0.166	0	0	0	0
Financ. Sector	0	0	0.302	0.302	0.302	0.302	0.302	0.302	0.302	0.302	0.302	0	0	0	0
Defense Posture	0	0	0.145	0.145	0.145	0.145	0.145	0.145	0.145	0.145	0.145	0	0	0	0
Global Compet.	0	0	0.070	0.070	0.070	0.070	0.070	0.070	0.070	0.070	0.70	0	0	0	0
3 months	0	0	0	0	0	0	0	0	0	0	0	0.223	0.223	0.233	0.233
6 months	0	0	0	0	0	0	0	0	0	0	0	0.152	0.152	0.152	0.152
1 year	0	0	0	0	0	0	0	0	0	0	0	0.201	0.201	0.201	0.201
≥ 2 years	0	0	0	0	0	0	0	0	0	0	0	0.424	0.424	0.424	0.424

Table 4-7: Limit Supermatrix - Sum of Phases I, II and III.

	C.A.	E.R.	Con.	Exp.	Inv.	Con.	F.P.	M.P.	F.S.	D.P.	G.C.	3 mo.	6 mo.	1 yr.	≥ 2 yrs
Conven. Adjust	0.484	0.484	0.484	0.484	0.484	0.484	0.484	0.484	0.484	0.484	0.484	0.484	0.484	0.484	0.484
Econ. Restruct.	0.516	0.516	0.516	0.516	0.516	0.516	0.516	0.516	0.516	0.516	0.516	0.516	0.516	0.516	0.516
Consumption	0.057	0.057	0.057	0.057	0.057	0.057	0.057	0.057	0.057	0.057	0.057	0.057	0.057	0.057	0.057
Exports	0.014	0.014	0.014	0.014	0.014	0.014	0.014	0.014	0.014	0.014	0.014	0.014	0.014	0.014	0.014
Invest.	0.028	0.028	0.028	0.028	0.028	0.028	0.028	0.028	0.028	0.028	0.028	0.028	0.028	0.028	0.028
Confidence	0.162	0.162	0.162	0.162	0.162	0.162	0.162	0.162	0.162	0.162	0.162	0.162	0.162	0.162	0.162
Fiscal Policy	0.057	0.057	0.057	0.057	0.057	0.057	0.057	0.057	0.057	0.057	0.057	0.057	0.057	0.057	0.057
Monetary Policy	0.166	0.166	0.166	0.166	0.166	0.166	0.166	0.166	0.166	0.166	0.166	0.166	0.166	0.166	0.166
Financ. Sector	0.302	0.302	0.302	0.302	0.302	0.302	0.302	0.302	0.302	0.302	0.302	0.302	0.302	0.302	0.302
Defense Posture	0.145	0.145	0.145	0.145	0.145	0.145	0.145	0.145	0.145	0.145	0.145	0.145	0.145	0.145	0.145
Global Compet.	0.070	0.070	0.070	0.070	0.070	0.070	0.070	0.070	0.070	0.070	0.70	0.070	0.070	0.070	0.070
3 months	0.223	0.223	0.223	0.223	0.223	0.223	0.223	0.223	0.223	0.223	0.223	0.223	0.223	0.233	0.233
6 months	0.152	0.152	0.152	0.152	0.152	0.152	0.152	0.152	0.152	0.152	0.152	0.152	0.152	0.152	0.152
1 year	0.201	0.201	0.201	0.201	0.201	0.201	0.201	0.201	0.201	0.201	0.201	0.201	0.201	0.201	0.201
≥ 2 years	0.424	0.424	0.424	0.424	0.424	0.424	0.424	0.424	0.424	0.424	0.424	0.424	0.424	0.424	0.424

Table 4-8: Average Limit Supermatrix - Block Normalized

	C.A.	E.R.	Con.	Exp.	Inv.	Con.	F.P.	M.P.	F.S.	D.P.	G.C.	3 mo.	6 mo.	1 yr.	≥ 2 yrs
Conven. Adjust	0.161	0.161	0.161	0.161	0.161	0.161	0.161	0.161	0.161	0.161	0.161	0.161	0.161	0.161	0.161
Econ. Restruct.	0.172	0.172	0.172	0.172	0.172	0.172	0.172	0.172	0.172	0.172	0.172	0.172	0.172	0.172	0.172
Consumption	0.019	0.019	0.019	0.019	0.019	0.019	0.019	0.019	0.019	0.019	0.019	0.019	0.019	0.019	0.019
Exports	0.005	0.005	0.005	0.005	0.005	0.005	0.005	0.005	0.005	0.005	0.005	0.005	0.005	0.005	0.005
Invest.	0.009	0.028	0.028	0.028	0.028	0.028	0.028	0.028	0.028	0.028	0.028	0.028	0.028	0.028	0.028
Confidence	0.054	0.054	0.054	0.054	0.054	0.054	0.054	0.054	0.054	0.054	0.054	0.054	0.054	0.054	0.054
Fiscal Policy	0.019	0.019	0.019	0.019	0.019	0.019	0.019	0.019	0.019	0.019	0.019	0.019	0.019	0.019	0.019
Monetary Policy	0.055	0.055	0.055	0.055	0.055	0.055	0.055	0.055	0.055	0.055	0.055	0.055	0.055	0.055	0.055
Financ. Sector	0.101	0.101	0.101	0.101	0.101	0.101	0.101	0.101	0.101	0.101	0.101	0.101	0.101	0.101	0.101
Defense Posture	0.048	0.145	0.145	0.145	0.145	0.145	0.145	0.145	0.145	0.145	0.145	0.145	0.145	0.145	0.145
Global Compet.	0.023	0.023	0.023	0.023	0.023	0.023	0.023	0.023	0.023	0.023	0.023	0.023	0.023	0.023	0.023
3 months	0.075	0.075	0.075	0.075	0.075	0.075	0.075	0.075	0.075	0.075	0.075	0.075	0.075	0.075	0.075
6 months	0.051	0.051	0.051	0.051	0.051	0.051	0.051	0.051	0.051	0.051	0.051	0.051	0.051	0.051	0.051
1 year	0.067	0.067	0.067	0.067	0.067	0.067	0.067	0.067	0.067	0.067	0.067	0.067	0.067	0.067	0.067
≥ 2 years	0.141	0.141	0.141	0.141	0.141	0.141	0.141	0.141	0.141	0.141	0.141	0.141	0.141	0.141	0.141

4-4. Outsourcing a Firm's Application Development Group

Outsourcing Information Technology (IT) functions is a growing trend in businesses looking for ways to reduce cost and hasten time-to-market of their customer-facing and internal applications. The strategy of outsourcing functions, tasks, and activities to another company has existed for decades. During periods of recession, corporations cut costs by moving jobs that are of a repetitive nature to lower-cost regions, typically "offshore" or in non-U.S. countries. For example, manufacturing companies have been le veraging offshore resources since the 1950s, while the off-shoring of IT started about 10-15 years ago with the movement of legacy system maintenance tasks to Ireland and Canada. According to Bart Perkins, Computer World, businesses are now looking towards outsourcing for three reasons: budget pressures, a view of IT as a "no win" function, and the existence of specialized service providers. Many firms continue to face budget constraints with budgets remaining flat and most firms looking to reduce costs. In some cases, the IT function is viewed as a utility that can and should be outsourced. With the rapid changes in technology, it is difficult for in-house developers to match the skill sets of outsourcers with specialized, targeted skills, making it more attractive to outsource development activities in order to keep up with improvements in technology. Given these views, many businesses are resurrecting the interest in outsourcing. (This analysis was done in the spring of 2004 by Megan D. Farkasovsky and Anna Greda).

IT outsourcing seems to be easier than ever to accomplish: telecommunications have improved drastically, enabling better productivity of a remote workforce; geographic distances are becoming more acceptable with the use of collaboration tools available today, such as online web meetings and improved video conferencing technology. And who can argue with the obvious personnel and IT asset cost reduction opportunities associated with this strategy? All of this, however, must be tempered with the soft costs and risks inherent in moving a firm's codified business processes to a potentially insecure, unstable environment. The decision model network and judgments discussed below is based upon careful research and involvement in the subject.

The Model:
The objective or goal of this model is to address the question: "How should companies staff their application development function?"

Alternatives:
Outsource all application development work
Outsource the design and programming phases

Do not outsource any application development work

Merits:
The merits and elements used in our model are described below and shown in Table 4-9.

Table 4-9: Clusters in the Decision Networks and Elements in the Clusters

BOCR	Control Criteria	Clusters	Elements in Clusters
Benefits	Economic	Financial	1 IT assets, 2 Personnel, 3 Legal
		Operational	1 Time to finish project / job, 2 Use of project management, 3 Knowledge transfer during requirements def, 4 Control / influence over human resources, 5 Fast time-to-market
	Technological	Technology	1 Leverage solutions from prev. business problems, 2 Newest technology available
		Resources	1 Knowledge of latest technologies, 2 Immediately available
Opportunities	Customer related	Customer base	1 Grow into other countries, 2 Customer retention
		Marketing	1 Agile, quick response to customer requests, 2 New features / functionality
	Economic	Business development	1 Expansion into foreign countries, 2 Expand product line
		Financial	1 Make investments, 2 Reduce debt
		Employees	1 Focus - quality assurance of software, 2 Focus - firm's core capabilities, 3 Focus - software alignment with business, 4 Productivity

Table 4-9: Clusters in the Decision Networks and Elements in the Clusters

BOCR	Control Criteria	Clusters	Elements in Clusters
Costs	Economic	Financial	1 IT assets, 2 Personnel, 3 Legal
		Operational	1 Time to finish project / job, 2 Use of project management, 4 Knowledge transfer during requirements def, 4 Control / influence over human resources, 5 Time-to-market
		Resources	1 Knowledge of latest technologies, 2 Immediately available
	Social	Stakeholders	1 Company shareholders perception, 2 Media criticism, 3 Company executives / managers perception, 4 Company employees perception
		Labor	1 US unemployment, 2 Employee morale, 3 Control / influence over human resources, 4 Productivity
Risks	Economic	Financial	1 Legal costs
		Business processes	1 Business process knowledge, 2 Business continuity, 3 Quality assurance
		Security	1 Physical, 2 Intellectual property, 3 Geopolitical environment - stability
		Communication	1 Geographic distance, 2 Communication tool availability - email voice mail, 3 H-1B and L-1 visa availability, 4 Language differences
	Social	Labor	1 Employee morale, 2 Productivity, 3 US unemployment
		Stakeholders	1 Company shareholders perception, 2 Media criticism, 3 Company executives / managers perception, 4 Company employees perception
All networks	Alternatives		1 Outsource all application development work, 2 Outsource the design and programming phases, 3 Do not outsource any application development work

BENEFITS

Economic and Technological control criteria were identified for the benefits portion of the model shown in Figure 4-2.

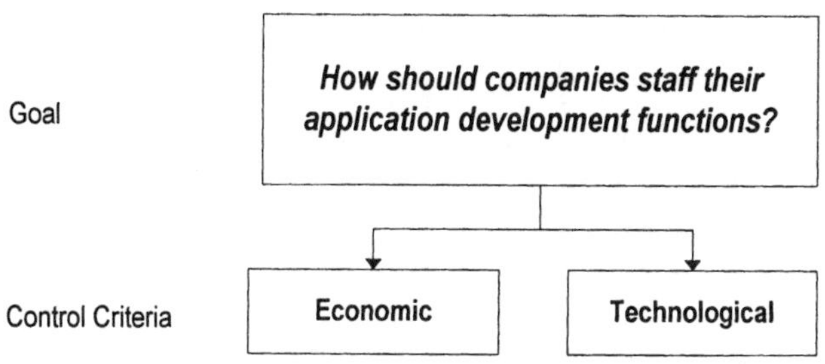

Figure 4-2: Benefits Model

Under Economic benefits, two clusters were identified: Financial and Operational.

> Financial includes nodes: IT assets, Personnel, and Legal. IT Assets refers to the reduction of IT infrastructure costs such as workstations, servers, and licensing; Personnel refers to the reduction of costs for things such as salaries, health insurance, pension benefits; Legal refers to the avoidance of costs associated with contract negotiations.
>
> Operational includes nodes: Time to finish project/job, Use of project management, Knowledge transfer during requirements definition, Control/influence over human resources, and Fast time-to-market. The concepts behind these items are rather self-explanatory; however to expand upon a couple may be necessary. Knowledge transfer during requirements definition is a key item when it comes to documenting system and application requirements and communicating those effectively to the persons programming and testing the application. Fast time-to-market relates to an enterprise's ability to quickly and with agility, meet its customer needs and wants through use of IT solutions.

We shall examine the supermatrices of priorities associated with only one of the decision subnets at the bottom of the model, Economic Benefits shown in Figure 4-3. There are three supermatrices associated with every network, plus the cluster matrix.

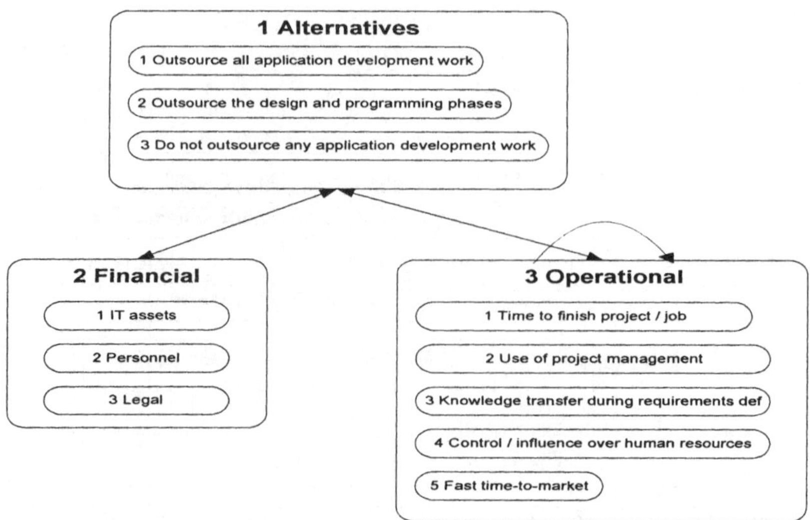

Figure 4-3: Clusters with elements under Economic Benefits

The first supermatrix is the unweighted one, shown in Table 4-10. It has in it all the priorities from all the pairwise comparisons done with respect to Economic Benefits. Table 4-11 shows the priorities obtained by comparing the clusters influence on each one of them with respect to Economic Benefits. These priorities are used to weight the corresponding blocks of unweighted supermatrix in Table 4-10, resulting in the weighted supermatrix in Table 4-12 rendering it stochastic. For example, the (Alternatives, Operational) value of 0.333 above is used to weight all the numbers in the (Alternatives, Operational) component of the unweighted supermatrix. This matrix is then raised to powers to obtain the limit supermatrix shown in Table 4-13.

Table 4-10: The Unweighted Supermatrix

		Alternatives			Financial			Operational				
		Outsource all development	Outsource design & pr'g.	Do not outsource	1 IT assets	2 Personnel	3 Legal	1 Time	2 Project management of personnel	3 Knowledge transfer risk	4 Control over personnel	5 Fast time-to-market
Alternatives	1 Outsource all development	0.000	0.000	0.000	0.754	0.754	0.754	0.627	0.558	0.088	0.091	0.644
	2 Outsource design & pr'gming	0.000	0.000	0.000	0.181	0.181	0.181	0.280	0.320	0.195	0.218	0.271
	3 Do not outsource	0.000	0.000	0.000	0.065	0.065	0.065	0.094	0.122	0.717	0.691	0.085
Financial	1 IT assets	0.458	0.540	0.333	0.000	0.000	0.000	0.000	0.000	0.000	0.000	0.000
	2 Personnel	0.126	0.163	0.333	0.000	0.000	0.000	0.000	0.000	0.000	0.000	0.000
	3 Legal	0.416	0.297	0.333	0.000	0.000	0.000	0.000	0.000	0.000	0.000	0.000
Operational	1 Time to finish project / job	0.185	0.223	0.077	0.000	0.000	0.000	0.000	0.196	0.000	0.000	0.000
	2 Use of project management	0.345	0.116	0.164	0.000	0.000	0.000	0.000	0.000	0.000	0.000	0.000
	3 Knowledge transfer risk	0.113	0.260	0.351	0.000	0.000	0.000	0.000	0.493	0.000	0.000	0.000
	4 Control over personnel	0.060	0.100	0.197	0.000	0.000	0.000	0.000	0.311	0.000	0.000	0.000
	5 Fast time-to-market	0.296	0.301	0.210	0.000	0.000	0.000	0.000	0.000	0.000	0.000	0.000

Table 4-11: The Cluster Priority Matrix

	Alternatives	Financial	Operational
Alternatives	0.000	1.000	0.333
Financial	0.833	0.000	0.000
Operational	0.167	0.000	0.667

Table 4-12: The Weighted Supermatrix

		Alternatives			Financial			Operational				
		Outsource all developmt	Outsource design & pr'g.	Do not outsource	1 IT assets	2 Personnel	3 Legal	1 Time	2 Project management of personnel	3 Knowledge transfer risk	4 Control over personnel	5 Fast time-to-market
Alternatives	1 Outsource all development	0.000	0.000	0.000	0.754	0.754	0.754	0.627	0.186	0.088	0.091	0.644
	2 Outsource design & pr'gming	0.000	0.000	0.000	0.181	0.181	0.181	0.280	0.107	0.195	0.218	0.271
	3 Do not outsource	0.000	0.000	0.000	0.065	0.065	0.065	0.094	0.041	0.717	0.691	0.085
Financial	1 IT assets	0.382	0.450	0.278	0.000	0.000	0.000	0.000	0.000	0.000	0.000	0.000
	2 Personnel	0.105	0.136	0.278	0.000	0.000	0.000	0.000	0.000	0.000	0.000	0.000
	3 Legal	0.347	0.247	0.278	0.000	0.000	0.000	0.000	0.000	0.000	0.000	0.000
Operational	1 Time to finish project / job	0.031	0.037	0.013	0.000	0.000	0.000	0.000	0.131	0.000	0.000	0.000
	2 Use of project management	0.058	0.019	0.027	0.000	0.000	0.000	0.000	0.000	0.000	0.000	0.000
	3 Knowledge transfer risk	0.019	0.043	0.059	0.000	0.000	0.000	0.000	0.329	0.000	0.000	0.000
	4 Control over personnel	0.010	0.017	0.033	0.000	0.000	0.000	0.000	0.207	0.000	0.000	0.000
	5 Fast time-to-market	0.049	0.050	0.035	0.000	0.000	0.000	0.000	0.000	0.000	0.000	0.000

Table 4-13: The Limit Supermatrix

		Alternatives			Financial			Operational				
		Outsource all developmt	Outsource design & pr'g.	Do not outsource	1 IT assets	2 Personnel	3 Legal	1 Time	2 Project management of personnel	3 Knowledge transfer risk	4 Control over personnel	5 Fast time-to-market
Alternatives	1 Outsource all development	0.343	0.343	0.343	0.343	0.343	0.343	0.343	0.343	0.343	0.343	0.343
	2 Outsource design & pr'gming	0.095	0.095	0.095	0.095	0.095	0.095	0.095	0.095	0.095	0.095	0.095
	3 Do not outsource	0.055	0.055	0.055	0.055	0.055	0.055	0.055	0.055	0.055	0.055	0.055
Financial	1 IT assets	0.189	0.189	0.189	0.189	0.189	0.189	0.189	0.189	0.189	0.189	0.189
	2 Personnel	0.064	0.064	0.064	0.064	0.064	0.064	0.064	0.064	0.064	0.064	0.064
	3 Legal	0.158	0.158	0.158	0.158	0.158	0.158	0.158	0.158	0.158	0.158	0.158
Operational	1 Time to finish project / job	0.018	0.018	0.018	0.018	0.018	0.018	0.018	0.018	0.018	0.018	0.018
	2 Use of project management	0.023	0.023	0.023	0.023	0.023	0.023	0.023	0.023	0.023	0.023	0.023
	3 Knowledge transfer risk	0.021	0.021	0.021	0.021	0.021	0.021	0.021	0.021	0.021	0.021	0.021
	4 Control over personnel	0.012	0.012	0.012	0.012	0.012	0.012	0.012	0.012	0.012	0.012	0.012
	5 Fast time-to-market	0.024	0.024	0.024	0.024	0.024	0.024	0.024	0.024	0.024	0.024	0.024

The synthesized results are obtained for the alternatives from the limit matrix. Note that in this case the limit matrix has all columns the same. The column labeled "Raw" in the Synthesized Results table shown in Table 4-14 are the first three numbers in the first column of the limit supermatrix in Table 4-13. The column labeled "Normals" is obtained by normalizing the entries in the raw column by dividing them by their sum. The column labeled "Ideals" is obtained by normalizing the entries in the raw column by dividing by the largest value in that column.

Table 4-14: Synthesized Results from Benefits Economic Decision Subnet

Alternatives	Ideals	Normals	Raw
1 Outsource all application development work	1.000	0.696	0.343
2 Outsource the design and programming phases	0.277	0.193	0.095
3 Do not outsource any application development work	0.160	0.111	0.055

The network associated with Technological benefits as shown in Figure 4-4 has two clusters: Technology and Resources.

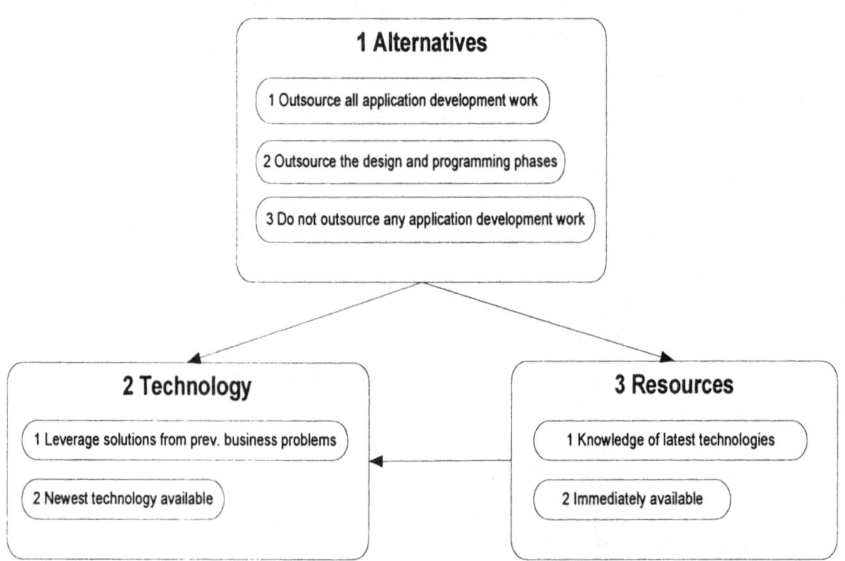

Figure 4-4: Technological Benefits Network

The Technology cluster includes the following nodes: Leverage solutions from previous business problems and newest technologies available. The first item relates to an application development group's ability to take what it has learned from solving similar or other business problems in the past, and leveraging or applying that experience to a current or new problem. The second item relates to an enterprise being able to take advantage of newer technologies without a lot of cost to the firm in terms of ramping up its IT infrastructure.

The Resources cluster includes the following nodes: Knowledge of latest technologies and immediately available. These speak to the human resource aspect of technology benefits in that people are knowledgeable in the newest ways to use technology and these people are readily available to work on a new high priority project.

Table 4-15 gives the synthesized results for Technological Benefits.

Table 4-15: Synthesized Results for the Technological Benefits Network

Alternatives	Ideals	Normals	Raw
1 Outsource all application development work	1.000	0.441	0.219
2 Outsource the design and programming phases	1.000	0.441	0.219
3 Do not outsource any application development work	0.267	0.118	0.058

Table 4-16 gives the combined results for the Economic and Technological nodes in Tables 4-14 and 4-15 after weighting by their respective priorities of 0.833 and 0.167 and adding.

Table 4-16: Overall Results for Benefits

Alternatives	Ideals	Normals	Raw
1 Outsource all application development work	1.000	0.635	1.000
2 Outsource the design and programming phases	0.397	0.252	0.397
3 Do not outsource any application development work	0.178	0.113	0.178

OPPORTUNITIES

Economic and Customer-related control criteria were identified for the opportunities portion of the model shown in Figure 4-5.

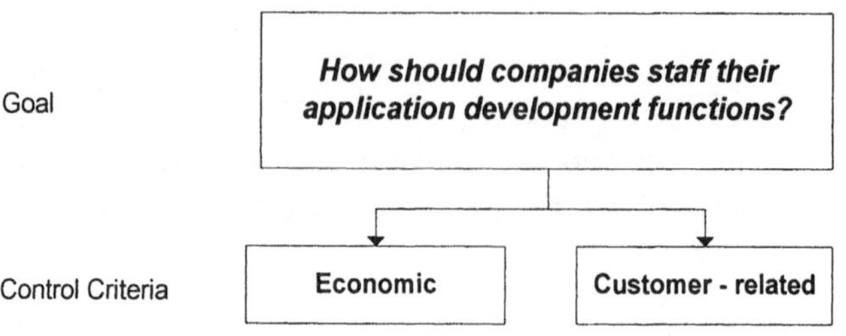

Figure 4-5: Opportunities Model

Under Economic opportunities, there are three clusters: Business development, Financial, and Employees.

Business development includes nodes: Expansion into foreign countries and Expand product line. Expanding into foreign countries is an opportunity when outsourcing with non-U.S. vendors. Expanding product line may be a stretch, but it is identified as an opportunity because the cost reduction provided by outsourcing may enable expansion of a firm's offering.

Financial includes nodes: Make investments and Reduce debt. Opportunities to engage in these financial activities may be present more readily when outsourcing as opposed to not outsourcing (i.e., rather than investing in a firm's own IT assets and personnel, the firm may identify an opportunity to invest money saved through outsourcing.)

Employees include nodes: Focus-quality assurance of software, Focus-firm's core capabilities, Focus-software alignment with business, and Productivity. The three "focus" opportunities identified relate to having IT employees concentrate on these value-added competencies rather than focusing on the rote tasks of programming or coding. An opportunity to increase productivity among employees may also be present when outsourcing.

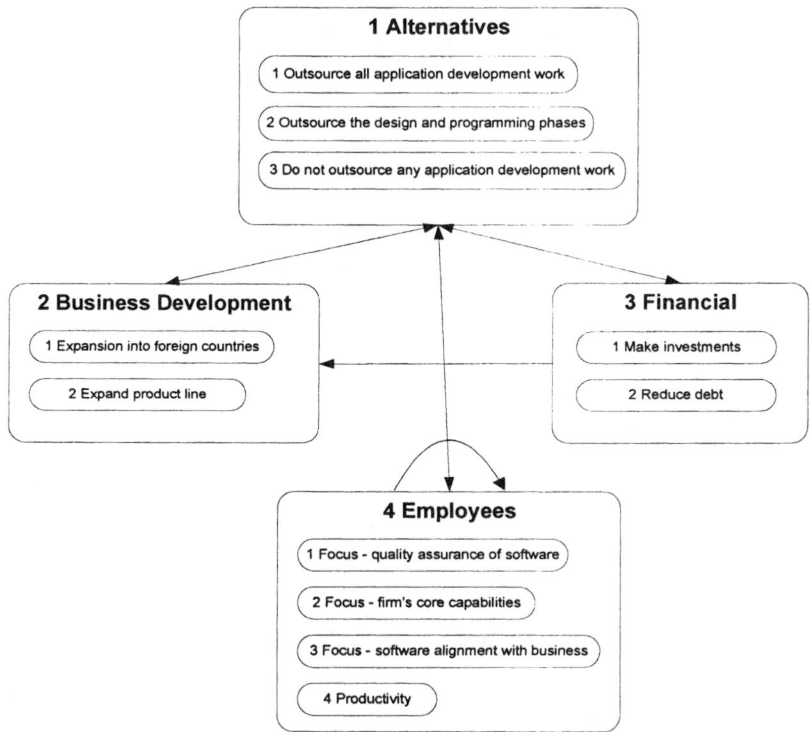

Figure 4-6: Network of Clusters with Elements under Economic Opportunities

Figure 4-6 exhibits the network of influences under the control criterion Economic Opportunities.

Under Customer-related opportunities, two clusters were identified: Customer base and Marketing, see Figure 4-7.

Customer base includes nodes: Grow into other countries and Customer retention. Expansion of customer base by growing into other countries may be an opportunity with respect to the outsourcing alternatives. By meeting (exceeding) customer business needs and requirements through technology, a firm has an opportunity to better retain its existing customers.

Marketing includes nodes: Agile, quick response to customer requirements and New features/functionality. By having an applications development process that is able to quickly address customer requirements, a firm has an opportunity to improve its marketing to new and existing customers. New features/functionality in an application can be marketed and present another customer-based opportunity for the firm.

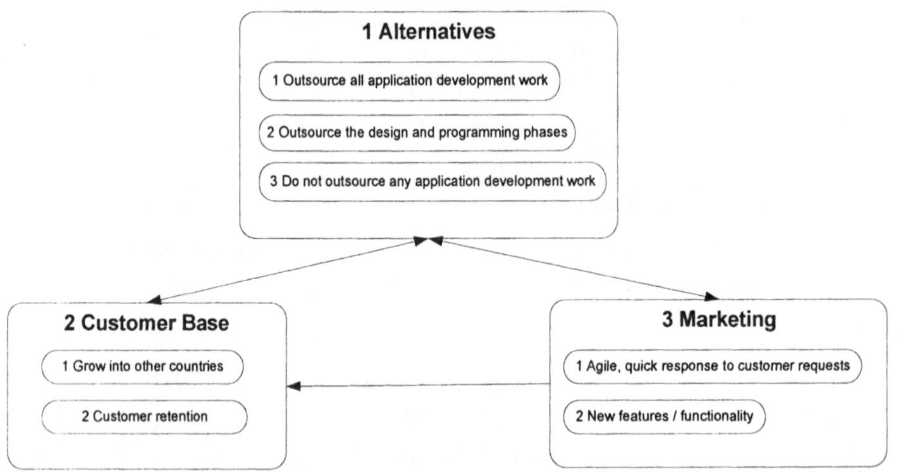

Figure 4-7: Clusters with elements under Customer-related Opportunities

COSTS

Economic and Social costs were identified for this portion of the model as in Figure 4-8.

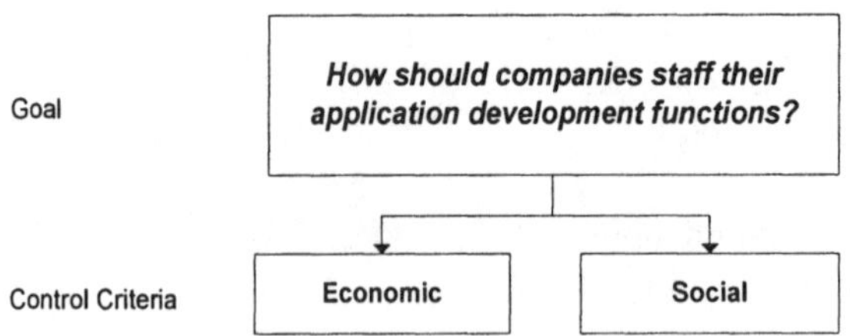

Figure 4-8: Costs Model

Under Economic costs, three clusters were identified: Financial, Operational, and Resources.

Financial includes nodes: IT Assets, Personnel, and Legal. IT Assets refers to the cost of retaining IT infrastructure for things such as workstations, servers, and licensing; Personnel refers to the retention of costs for things such as salaries, health insurance, pension benefits; Legal refers to the accumulation of costs associated with contract negotiations.

Operational includes nodes: Time to finish project/job, Use of project management, Knowledge transfer during requirements definition, Control/influence over human resources, and Fast time-to-market. In terms of cost, the first four items' cost increases with outsourcing. They are interrelated with or without outsourcing. Fast time-to-market relates to an enterprise's ability to quickly and with agility, meets its customer needs and wants through use of IT solutions. Without outsourcing, this becomes a cost.

Resources include nodes: Knowledge of latest technologies and immediately available. Without outsourcing, these two items become costs; resources with knowledge of the latest technologies may not be available quickly.

Figure 4-9 illustrates the influences identified under Economic costs.

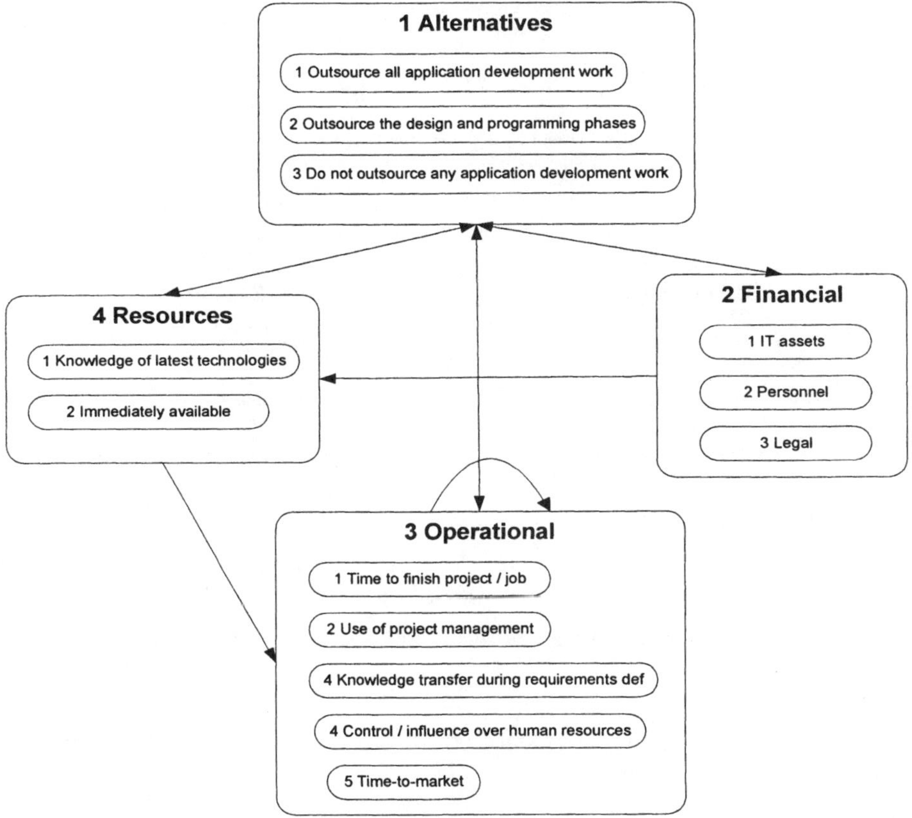

Figure 4-9: Clusters with Elements under Economic Costs

Under Social costs, two clusters were identified: Stakeholders and Labor.

Stakeholders include nodes: Company shareholders' perception, Media criticism, Company executives/managers' perception, Company employees' perception. These four nodes are rather self-explanatory and represent the influence of various perceptions of stakeholders on the decision.

Labor includes nodes: U.S. unemployment, Employee morale, Control/influence over human resources, Productivity. Again, these nodes are rather self-explanatory in terms of costs for the alternatives.

Figure 4-10 shows the interactions under Social Costs.

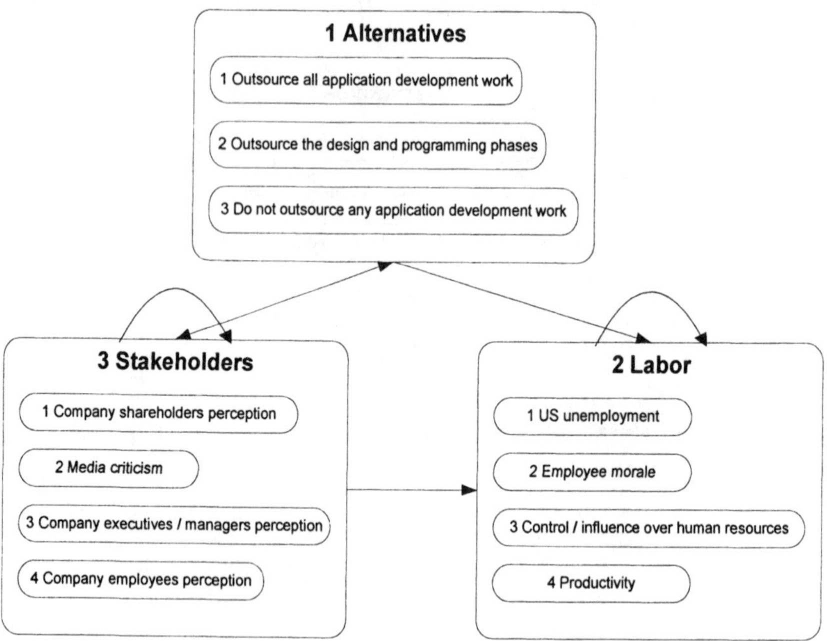

Figure 4-10: Clusters with Elements under Social Costs

RISKS

Economic and Social risks were identified for this portion of the model shown in Figure 4-11.

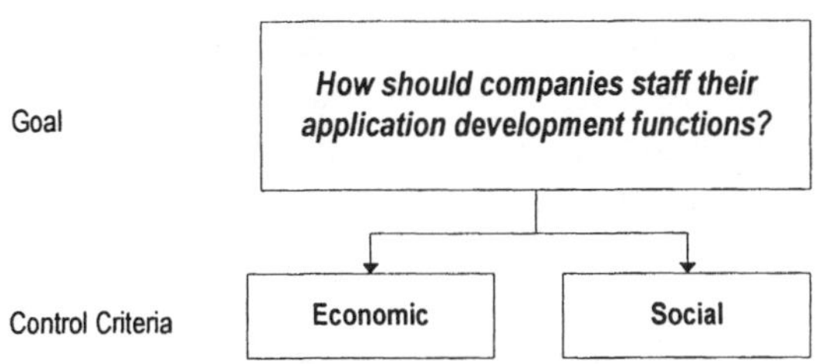

Figure 4-11: Risks Model

Under Economic risks, four clusters were identified: Financial, Security, Communication, Business processes.

Financial includes node: Legal costs. The risk of incurring legal costs is represented here.

Security includes nodes: Physical, Intellectual property, and Geopolitical environment – stability. The risk to the physical security of servers and other IT equipment is represented through the Physical node. The Intellectual property node represents the risk of losing control or ownership of programs and software written for an enterprise. The Geopolitical environment risk pertains to the increased risk of outsourcing a firm's programming function to an area of the world that is or soon may be at war.

Communication includes nodes: Geographic distance, Communication tool availability – email/voice mail, H-1B and L-1 visa availability, Language differences. Distance, communication tool availability, and language differences represent the risks of poor communication as a result of outsourcing. With the risk that H-1B and L-1 visas will be limited, a firm may have a much more difficult time bringing in foreign outsourcers to work closely and communicate with its U.S.-based personnel.

Business processes includes nodes: Business process knowledge, Business continuity, and Quality assurance. By outsourcing the areas represented by these nodes reflect the risk that any of these could suffer.

Under Social risks, we identified two clusters: Labor and Stakeholders.

Labor includes nodes: Employee morale, Productivity, U.S. unemployment. These nodes are rather self-explanatory in terms of risks and influence on the alternatives.

Stakeholders includes nodes: Company shareholders' perception, Media criticism, Company executives/managers' perception, and Company employees' perception. These four nodes are rather self-explanatory and represent the various stakeholders' perceptions' influence on this decision in terms of risk.

Figures 4-12 and 4-13 illustrate the interactions under Economic and Social Risks respectively.

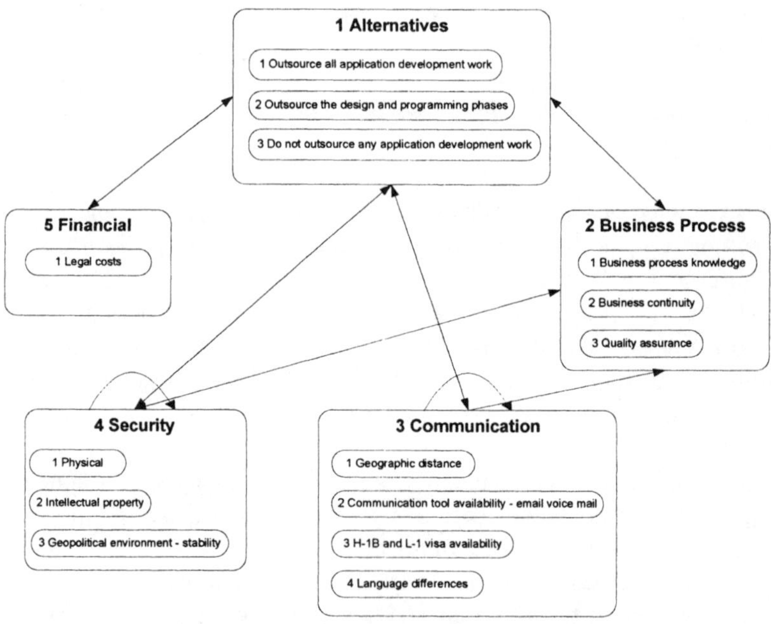

Figure 4-12: Clusters with Elements under Economic Risks

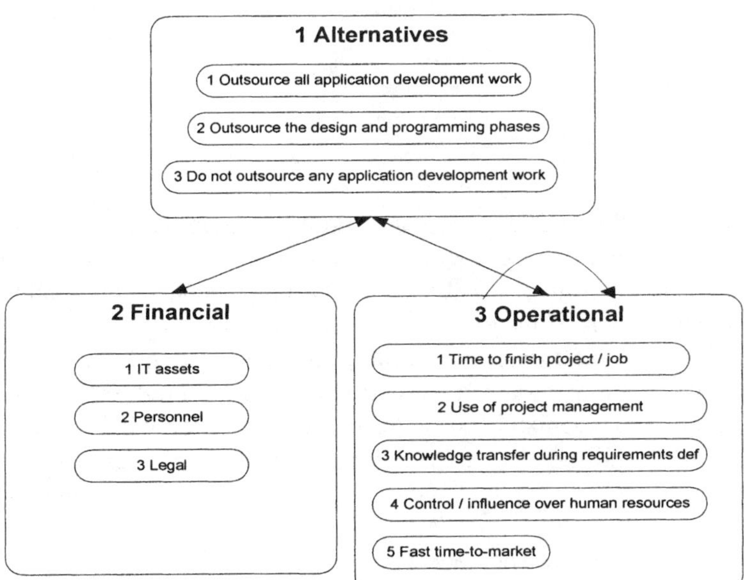

Figure 4-13: Clusters with Elements under Social Risks

BOCR PRIORITIES

The elements under each of the BOCR merits received priorities through pairwise comparisons, as shown in Table 4-17.

Table 4-17: Criteria and Elements with Their Priorities

BOCR	Criteria	Elements	Local priorities	Global priorities
Benefits	Economic	1 IT assets	0.4505	0.1091
		2 Personnel	0.1758	0.0426
		3 Legal	0.3737	0.0905
		1 Time to finish project / job	0.1745	0.0477
		2 Use of project management	0.2296	0.0628
		3 Knowledge transfer during requirements def	0.2274	0.0628
		4 Control / influence over human resources	0.1209	0.0331
		5 Fast time-to-market	0.2475	0.0677
	Technological	1 Knowledge of latest technologies	0.1852	0.0453
		2 Immediately available	0.8148	0.1991
		1 Knowledge of latest technologies	0.8000	0.2136
		2 Immediately available	0.2000	0.0534
Opportunities	Customer - related	1 Grow into other countries	0.2848	0.0949
		2 Customer retention	0.7152	0.2384

BOCR	Criteria	Elements	Local priorities	Global priorities
		1 Agile, quick response to customer requests	0.8333	0.1852
		2 New features / functionality	0.1667	0.0370
	Economic	1 Expansion into foreign countries	0.5000	0.0828
		2 Expand product line	0.5000	0.0828
		1 Make investments	0.6667	0.1104
		2 Reduce debt	0.3333	0.0552
		1 Focus - quality assurance of software	0.3121	0.0619
		2 Focus - firm's core capabilities	0.2291	0.0454
		3 Focus - software alignment with business	0.2639	0.0523
		4 Productivity	0.1948	0.0386
Costs	Economic	1 IT assets	0.2631	0.0398
		2 Personnel	0.5472	0.0827
		3 Legal	0.1897	0.0287
		1 Time to finish project / job	0.2458	0.0601
		2 Use of project management	0.1457	0.0356
		4 Knowledge transfer during requirements def	0.2168	0.0530
		4 Control / influence over human resources	0.0832	0.0203
		5 Time-to-market	0.3084	0.0754
		1 Knowledge of latest technologies	0.2589	0.0391
		2 Immediately available	0.7411	0.1120
	Social	1 Company shareholders perception	0.1486	0.0379
		2 Media criticism	0.2695	0.0687
		3 Company executives / managers perception	0.2261	0.0577
		4 Company employees perception	0.3558	0.0907
		1 US unemployment	0.0621	0.0294
		2 Employee morale	0.2995	0.1415
		3 Control / influence over human resources	0.1204	0.0569
		4 Productivity	0.5180	0.2448
Risks	Economic	1 Legal costs	1.0000	0.1142
		1 Business process knowledge	0.2744	0.0475
		2 Business continuity	0.4423	0.0765
		3 Quality assurance	0.2833	0.0490
		1 Physical,	0.2741	0.0345
		2 Intellectual property	0.4452	0.0561
		3 Geopolitical environment - stability	0.2807	0.0354
		1 Geographic distance	0.0823	0.0107
		2 Communication tool availability - email voice mail	0.3638	0.0473
		3 H-1B and L-1 visa availability	0.2163	0.0281
		4 Language differences	0.3376	0.0439
	Social	1 Employee morale	0.4654	0.1540
		2 Productivity	0.3874	0.1282
		3 US unemployment	0.1472	0.0487
		1 Company shareholders perception	0.1486	0.0369
		2 Media criticism	0.2298	0.0570
		3 Company executives / managers perception	0.3939	0.0977
		4 Company employees perception	0.2276	0.0564

Table 4-18 represents priorities for the Alternatives with respect to each BOCR control criterion. These values are used to establish the overall outcome, shown in Table 4-21. To get there one identifies and prioritizes strategic criteria and subcriteria shown in Figure 4-18. One then develops a ratings model with intensities and their priorities for each strategic criterion or subcriterion as in Table 4-19. One then rates the top overall alternative for each merit with respect to the strategic subcriteria as in Table 4-20 thereby obtaining priorities for the merits. Finally one uses these priorities to synthesize the ideal priorities of each alternative with respect to the four merits and obtain the final outcome in the multiplicative and subtractive forms as in Table 4-21. Figures 4-14 to 4-17 illustrate the sensitivity and stability of the outcomes with respect to each of the four merits to legitimize the synthesis that follows.

Table 4-18: Priorities for Alternatives under each Control Criterion of BOCR

Merit	Control Criterion	1 Outsource all application		2 Outsource the design		3 Do not outsource	
		Normalizing by cluster	Limiting	Normalizing by cluster	Limiting	Normalizing by cluster	Limiting
Benefits	Economic	0.5824	0.2821	0.2166	0.1048	0.2110	0.0974
	Technolog.	0.4437	0.2168	0.4437	0.2168	0.1126	0.0550
Opportunities	Cust. rel.	0.4573	0.2033	0.3748	0.1666	0.1679	0.0746
	Economic	0.4362	0.2053	0.3381	0.1592	0.2257	0.1062
Costs	Economic	0.2882	0.1307	0.2797	0.1268	0.4320	0.1958
	Social	0.3682	0.1003	0.3416	0.0931	0.2902	0.0791
Risks	Economic	0.4332	0.1979	0.4332	0.1979	0.1336	0.0610
	Social	0.3779	0.1591	0.3779	0.1591	0.2442	0.1028

Sensitivity Graphs for BOCR

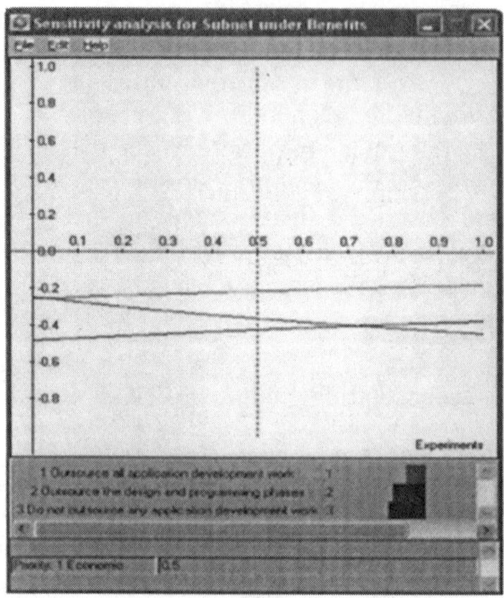

Figure 4-14: Sensitivity Graphs for Benefits

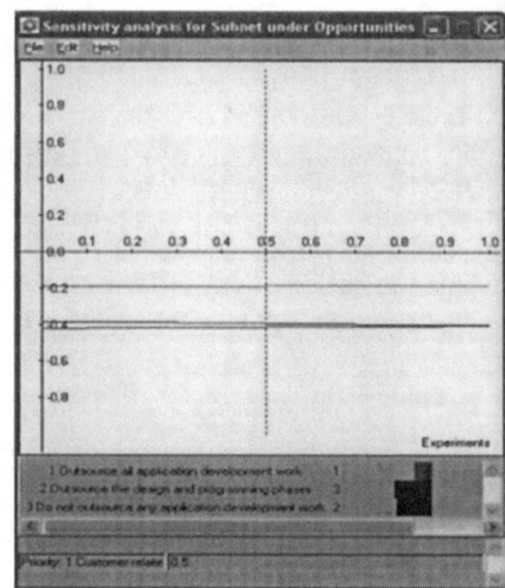

Figure 4-15: Sensitivity Graphs for Opportunities

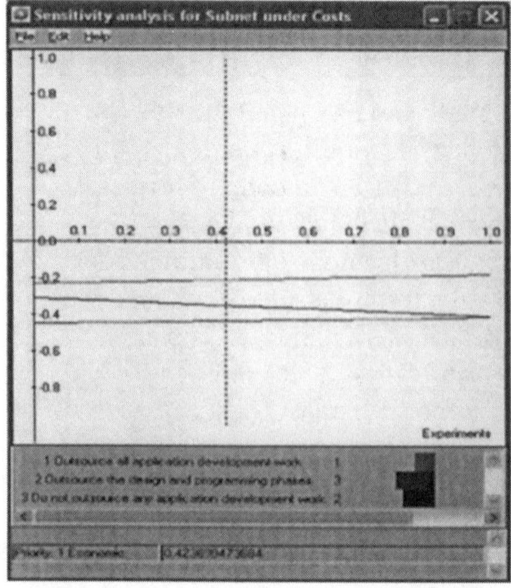

Figure 4-16: Sensitivity Graphs for Costs

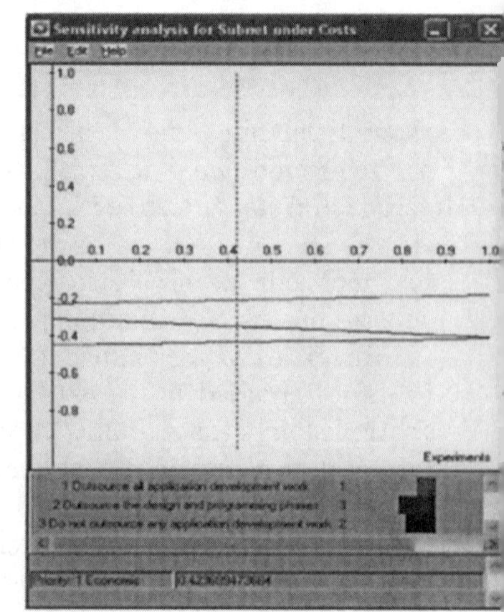

Figure 4-17: Sensitivity Graphs for Risks

Strategic criteria include the following criteria and subcriteria:
Financial
Technology
  Availability of experts
  Flexibility
Time-to-market
Social
  Media perception
  Shareholder & employee perception

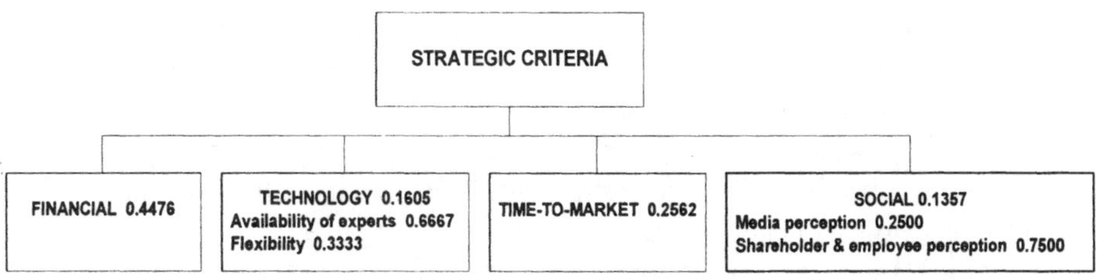

Figure 4-18: Strategic Criteria

The **ratings scale** shown below was used to rate the alternatives with respect to the strategic criteria.

Table 4-19: Strategic Criteria Scale for Ratings

Financial (0.3453)	Availability of experts (0.0826)	Flexibility (0.0413)	Time–to-market (0.1977)	Media perception (0.0262)	Shareholder & employee perception (0.0785)
High possibility to reduce costs (0.5909)	Immediately (0.6267)	Hi (0.6267)	Fast (0.4626)	Very supportive (0.4626)	Very supportive (0.4626)
Moderate possibility to reduce costs (0.2754)	Moderately (0.2797)	Medium (0.2797)	Moderately fast (0.3073)	Moderately supportive (0.3073)	Modcrately supportive (0.3073)
Somewhat unlikely to reduce costs (0.0905)	Delayed (0.0936)	Low (0.0936)	Average (0.1416)	Neutral (0.1416)	Neutral (0.1416)
Unlikely to reduce costs (0.0432)			Moderately slow (0.0584)	Moderately unsupportive (0.0584)	Moderately unsupportive (0.0584)
			Slow (0.0299)	Very unsupportive (0.0299)	Very unsupportive (0.0299)

RATING THE TOP ALTERNATIVES

Table 4-20: Rating Importance of Benefits, Opportunities, Costs and Risks

	Financial	**Availability of experts**	**Flexibility**	**Time–to-market**	**Media perception**	**Shareholder & employee perception**	**Priorities**
Benefits	High possibility to reduce costs	Immediately	Hi	Fast	Moderately unsupportive	Moderately unsupportive	**0.2983**
Opportunities	High possibility to reduce costs	Immediately	Hi	Fast	Moderately supportive	Moderately supportive	**0.1051**
Costs	Somewhat unlikely to reduce costs	Moderately	Med	Average	Moderately unsupportive	Moderately unsupportive	**0.2983**
Risks	High possibility to reduce costs	Immediately	Hi	Fast	Moderately unsupportive	Moderately unsupportive	**0.2983**

After pairwise comparison of the alternatives and rating of the merits, the model shows that Alternative 1: "Outsource all application development work," is the best choice. The main driver of this outcome is the financial benefits. Using background research and personal interviews to describe this model and compare and rate its nodes, one is not surprised by this outcome.

Table 4-21: Overall Outcome

Alternatives	Benefits 0.2983	Opportunities 0.1051	Costs 0.2983	Risks 0.2983	Outcome BO/CR	Outcome bB + oO – cC - rR
1 Outsource all application development work	1.0000	1.0000	0.8313	1.0000	1.2030	-0.1429
2 Outsource the design and programming phases	0.3972	0.8277	0.7468	1.0000	0.4402	-0.3156
3 Do not outsource any application development work	0.1776	0.4908	0.9759	0.3570	0.2502	-0.2930

4-5. Disney Decision: A New Theme Park in Greater China

In order to enhance operations in foreign market, Disney is constantly searching for areas where it can expand into new markets. According to the projected number of foreign visitors, Walt Disney World expects to increase the current level from 20 percent foreign visitors in domestic parks to 50 percent as well as to expand its theme park business outside the U.S. To achieve these projected numbers Disney needs to make an aggressive attempt to expand its presence in foreign markets, especially Greater China. However, considering the diverse social and economic backgrounds within this area, Disney needs to carefully evaluate the possible benefits as well as the costs and potential risks. In this model, we narrow down the alternatives to Hong Kong, Shanghai, Taiwan and no investment in Greater China. In fact, an awakening and growing middle class in these three areas is exactly the prime target audience for a Disney theme park. (This analysis was done in the fall of 2004 by Amber Ling-Hui, Lin SzuLun Peng).

ULTIMATE GOAL FOR DISNEY

Disney's approach is to make a minimal equity investment in any operating entity and generate most of its returns through royalty, licensing, and fee income streams.

MAIN MODEL

BOCR NETWORKS AND CLUSTER DEFINITIONS

Under the benefits, opportunities, costs, and risks (BOCR) models, networks are established for each of the control criteria in their respective control hierarchies. Clusters of elements and their interactions are established with a cluster of alternatives being included in each network. The benefits networks yield the alternatives with the most benefit and the opportunities networks yield the alternatives with the most opportunities, whereas the costs and risks networks yield the alternatives that are the most costly or pose the most risk.

The flow of the decision process is to first build the control criteria hierarchies for each of the BOCR models, then build the subnetworks for the selected control criteria. The selected control criteria should be at least 70% of the priority of all the control criteria in the control hierarchy. One then makes the connections and judgments among the clusters in the subnetworks to evaluate the highest priority alternative for each control criterion. The importance of the BOCR must then be determined by rating them with respect to the strategic criteria of the organization or decision maker. In what follows we have worked backwards from the overall ideal alternatives determined first with respect to each of the four merits in order to obtain the best overall answer after rating them with respect to the strategic criteria as shown in Table 4-22.

CONTROL CRITERIA AND SUBNETS OF THE BOCR

Each of the BOCR has control criteria as in Figure 4-19 whose priorities are established through pairwise comparisons. The control criteria in turn have associated network sub-models that contain the alternatives of the decision and clusters of elements. Thus priorities for the alternatives are determined in each of the subnets. These are weighted by the priority of their respective control criterion, and summed to obtain the overall outcome for each merit and the outcomes then multiplied by the BOCR weights from the rating model and combined to give the final results. The alternatives appear in a cluster in every decision subnet, so they are defined only once here. There are three locations being considered for the first Disney theme park in Greater China plus the alternative of not building at all. They are:

ALTERNATIVES

Don't invest in Greater China at all
Invest in Hong Kong
Invest in Shanghai
Invest in Taiwan

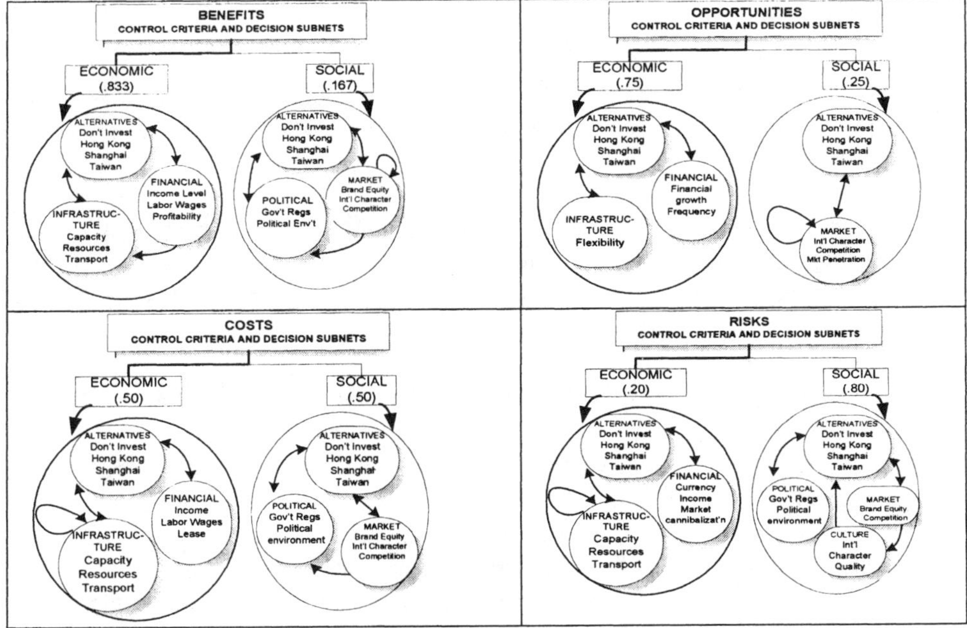

Figure 4-19: Decision Sub-networks with Clusters and Nodes for each of the BOCR

CLUSTERS IN BENEFITS/SOCIAL SUBNET

Alternatives
Market

Brand Equity: For the brand equity, we consider it as an intangible asset to Walt Disney. Brand equity represents Disney's reputation and image in the market. Within this subnet, we will examine how much benefit each alternative can bring to Disney in terms of increasing their brand equity.

International Character: International character refers to having a diversified visitor base. The higher the diversification of the visitor base, the more it benefits Disney.

Market Competition: Market competition refers to the number of competitors having a comparable scale in each market. Within the benefit cluster, we will discuss the level that Disney can benefit from the competition in the market under each alternative.

POLITICAL FACTORS

Government Regulation: We believe that favorable local government regulations on theme park businesses will definitely benefit Disney's operation in that area and vise versa.

Political Environment: We believe a stable political environment will create a promising investment environment. Thus, the benefits will be measured based on the current political stability and potential political instability of each alternative.

INTERACTIONS BETWEEN CLUSTERS IN THE BENEFITS/SOCIAL SUBNET

In this subnet, we can see the interactions among clusters as well as interactions within clusters.

Market Factors: First of all, since the government regulations and political environment will affect the international character and the market competition in a market, we can see an interaction between market cluster and political factors cluster. Besides, different choices that Disney makes will affect the company itself in terms of brand equity, international character and competition in the market. Finally, the competitive ability of the company and the international character of the market may also affect Disney's brand equity at the end. Thus, we can see another interaction within the market cluster itself.

Political Factors: Besides the interaction with the market cluster, the political factors cluster also interacts with the alternatives cluster because the political factors are affected by the alternatives.

Alternatives: While each alternative affects factors in the market and political clusters, those factors also effect Disney's decision among alternatives in return. Thus, there are also backward interactions between the alternatives cluster and the other two clusters.

NODES IN THE BENEFITS/ECONOMIC SUBNET CLUSTERS

Alternatives
Financial Factors

Gross and disposable income level: Under this factor, only the current gross and disposable income level of the area's citizens will be considered. We assume that a higher income level in the local area will bring more business to the Disney facility and further increase Disney's revenue.

Labor Wage: Labor refers to the current level of local labor's wages. A lower labor wage will benefit Disney by reducing operating overheads.

Profitability: Profitability refers to the profits forecast based on the current market situation.

INFRASTRUCTURE

Accommodation Capacity: The current hotel accommodation capacity.

Resources: The current construction quality and efficiency of the area.

Transportation: Transportation here means the current level of development of local railroads, airports, tunnels, etc. If the area is already well developed, Disney can benefit from an instant resource of transportation system for customers.

Tables 4-22 to 4-24 show the details of synthesizing the results for the Benefits merit.

Table 4-22: Benefits/Economic Results

Graphic	Alternatives	Total	Normal	Ideal	Ranking
	Don't invest in Greater China	0.0273	0.0579	0.1242	4
	Hong Kong	0.2201	0.4662	1.0000	1
	Shanghai	0.1379	0.2922	0.6267	2
	Taiwan	0.0867	0.1837	0.3940	3

Table 4-23: Benefits/Social Results

Graphic	Alternatives	Total	Normal	Ideal	Ranking
	Don't invest in Greater China	0.0045	0.0099	0.0219	4
	Hong Kong	0.2059	0.4521	1.0000	1
	Shanghai	0.1556	0.3417	0.7558	2
	Taiwan	0.0894	0.1963	0.4342	3

Combining the outcomes from the social and economic decision subnets for the benefits model produces the results shown below. The normalized values (in bold) show that Hong Kong offers the most benefits, and by a significant amount, at 46.4%.

Table 4-24: Benefits Synthesized Results

Graphic	Alternatives	Total	Normal	Ideal	Ranking
	Don't invest in Greater China	0.107	**0.050**	0.107	4
	Hong Kong	1.0000	**0.464**	1.000	1
	Shanghai	0.648	**0.301**	0.648	2
	Taiwan	0.401	**0.186**	0.401	3

In the opportunities, costs and risks models, the decision subnets are built based on the same logic as that of the benefits subnets. The details of their clusters and nodes are similar to those of benefits and will not be shown here. A general idea of what they are can be seen in Figure 4-19 above showing the decision sub-networks. The results for each of the control criteria for opportunities, costs and risks are given in Tables 4-25 to 4-27.

We show only the final synthesized results for opportunities, costs, and risks.

Table 4-25: Opportunities Synthesized Results

Graphic	Alternatives	Total	Normal	Ideal	Ranking
	Don't invest in Greater China	0.019	0.010	0.019	4
	Hong Kong	0.428	0.224	0.428	3
	Shanghai	1.000	0.524	1.000	1
	Taiwan	0.462	0.242	0.462	2

Table 4-26: Costs Synthesized Results

Graphic	Alternatives	Total	Normal	Ideal	Ranking
	Don't invest in Greater China	0.104	**0.040**	0.105	4
	Hong Kong	0.610	**0.233**	0.617	3
	Shanghai	0.989	**0.378**	1.000	1
	Taiwan	0.912	**0.349**	0.922	2

Table 4-27: Risks Synthesized Results

Graphic	Alternatives	Total	Normal	Ideal	Ranking
	Don't invest in Greater China	0.116	0.051	0.118	4
	Hong Kong	0.425	0.188	0.434	3
	Shanghai	0.981	0.434	1.000	1
	Taiwan	0.736	0.326	0.751	2

DECISION RATING MODEL

The final step in the decision is to determine the strategic criteria that are more or less the same for the organization or individual in making any decision and use them to rate the BOCR with respect to competition, income level, infrastructure, international character and political support as shown in the table below. We thought the five strategic criteria below pretty well captured Disney's main corporate concerns about their theme parks:

STRATEGIC CRITERIA

Competition – Other successful theme parks in the neighborhood of the Disney Facility may be viewed both positively and negatively. Other theme parks already in the areas represent competition for Disney; however, competitors may also bring more people to the area to visit both facilities at the same time.

Income Level– Gross and disposable income levels of the area's citizens may also affect the success of the park. Consider Tokyo Disney Land for example. Approximately 95% of its visitors are local Japanese; thus, the high average income level of Japanese does appear to contribute to the tremendous success of Disney in Japan.

Infrastructure – Infrastructure in the area of the park and the regional support are also important. Visitors should be able to access the park easily. The transportation system should be well established or enhanced while the park is being constructed. A good area should have the infrastructure to support a park efficiently. Besides, the region should also contribute to extending the time visitors are able to spend at the Disney facilities. For example, a stock of hotel rooms to support park visitors is important and rooms at a variety of price levels, from economy all the way to luxury, should be available when the park opens.

International Character – Disney is looking for "international character" for any theme park it builds in Greater China. A diversified visitor base will reduce the risks of problems in one country having an adverse effect on the flow of international visitors.

Political Support – In all Disney's international operations, support from local government is critical to the Disney Company. This support ranges from providing a good location to build the theme park to insuring sufficient capital flow.

The priorities that result from the ratings of the BOCR for this decision show in Table 4-28 that the most important merit is Benefits at 31.9% followed by Opportunities at 26.4%. This means that the priorities of the alternatives under benefits are weighted more heavily. Benefits at 31.9% drive the decision more than the Risks at 19.3%.

Table 4-28: BOCR Ratings and Priorities

Very Strong 1.000, Strong 0.627, Medium 0.382, Moderate 0.232, Weak 0.148

	Competition 0.127	Income Level 0.190	Infrastructure 0.147	International Character 0.323	Political Support 0.214	Priorities
Benefits	Strong	Very Strong	Strong	Very Strong	Very Strong	0.319
Opportunities	Very Strong	Strong	Strong	Very Strong	Medium	0.264
Costs	Very Strong	Medium	Strong	Strong	Strong	0.223
Risks	Very Strong	Strong	Strong	Medium	Medium	0.193

We see from the overall synthesized results in Table 4-29 that Disney's best option is to build their new theme park in Hong Kong.

Table 4-29: BOCR Model: Overall Synthesized Results

Graphic	Alternatives	Total	Normal	Ideal	Ranking
(Red)	Don't invest in Greater China	-0.006	-0.017	-0.030	3
(Blue)	Hong Kong	0.214	0.567	1.000	1
(Blue)	Shanghai	0.061	0.161	0.284	2
(Red)	Taiwan	-0.096	-0.255	-0.449	4

In the bar graph in Table 4-29 blue bars are positive and red bars are negative so Hong Kong is best and Taiwan is worst. Sensitivity analysis is shown in Figure 4-20. When the importance of benefits is greater than 0.05, investing in Hong Kong is the best choice. At a priority of less than about 0.35 for opportunities, Hong Kong is the best choice, but above that the choice shifts to Shanghai. One might interpret this as meaning that there are great opportunities in Shanghai, but it is also risky as can be seen from the risks sensitivity graph. As the priority of costs increases beyond about 0.38, the best choice shifts from investing in Hong Kong to not investing at all. As the importance of risk increases the preferred alternative is to not to invest as all in Greater China, but since the priority is negative, below the x-axis, this is not a particularly good alternative, though it is the least negative. When risk is less than about 0.50, the preferred alternative is to invest in Hong Kong.

CONCLUSION

In the synthesized result, we see that Hong Kong and Shanghai are the top two choices. With a population of more than 1.29 billion people, China is the most heavily populated nation in the world. With the significant purchasing power and promising business environment of the Chinese market, one is not surprised with this conclusion. However, there is an interesting situation within these two options. If we examine the rank under each subnet separately, we find Hong Kong ranks first under benefits and costs while Shanghai ranks first under opportunities and risks. Considering other foreign theme park investment projects of Disney, we see the company has taken a conservative approach. In the Tokyo Disneyland project, Disney contracted with a Japanese company charging them management fees, royalty and license fees, etc., but not sharing in most of the operation and revenue risk and hence the return. In other words, even though Tokyo Disney has launched into the Japanese market with huge success, Disney is constrained by their contractual arrangements and receives a limited amount of benefits. Thus, in the Euro Disney project, the management team of Disney vowed not to repeat the same mistake in Tokyo project and tried to get the largest ownership that they could; however, the inefficient work projects and culture clashes caused unexpected expenses. Therefore, considering Disney as a company that has resumed its risk adverse attitude toward their overseas investment, it is reasonable for them to choose Hong Kong as the first site to get into the Greater Chinese market. Although Hong Kong is the most costly option with a relatively lower potential future market than Shanghai, the high benefit and low risk seem more attractive and promising to Disney. However, if Disney were willing to sustain a higher risk level, the optimal site would be Shanghai (*shown in the sensitivity analysis of opportunities and risks*).

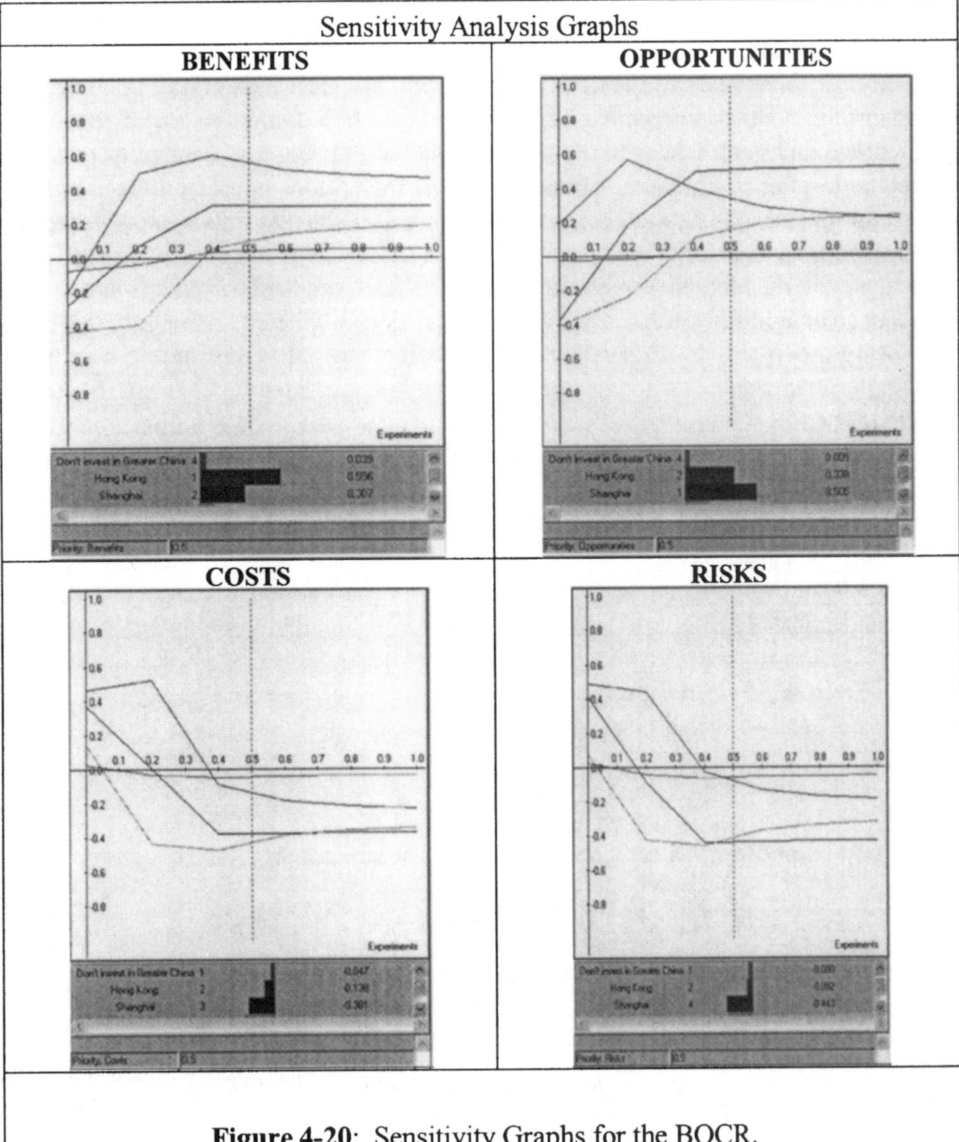

Figure 4-20: Sensitivity Graphs for the BOCR.

4-6. Several Examples of Network Models Summarized in the Encyclicon

TARIFFS ON STEEL IMPORTS BY THE U.S. GOVERNMENT

In accordance with World Trade Organization rules designed to allow for the temporary restructuring of a domestic industry, President Bush announced temporary steel safeguard measures on March 5, 2002, ranging to 30 percent on steel imports under Section 201 of the U.S. trade law. The President imposed the remedy for three years to give the beleaguered U.S. steel industry an opportunity to restructure. Steel companies have to demonstrate action steps they are taking to achieve this goal. Under the law, the President may reduce, change or end the safeguard action if the steel industry fails to make adequate efforts to become more competitive. U.S. trading partners criticized the tariffs imposed in March as a protectionist measures and threatened to retaliate. As stated above, the U.S. Government decided to impose a temporary tariff on steel products up to 30 percent. In addition to the government's decision, two other alternatives imposing tariffs are considered in this analysis. First, what will be the impact if the government decides not to impose a tariff on steel products at all? Second, solve the world-wide overproduction of steel by negotiating a solution to mutual benefit of all parties involved in the World Trade Organization (WTO). In sum, the ANP model includes these two alternatives along with imposing tariffs. (Analysis done by Yong Cheng and Klaus Tenderich in 2002).

ALTERNATIVES: Impose temporary tariff on imported steels, not impose tariff on imported steels, and solve the steel-overproduction issue under WTO.

I. BOCR Weight Development

Figure 4-21 shows the strategic criteria.

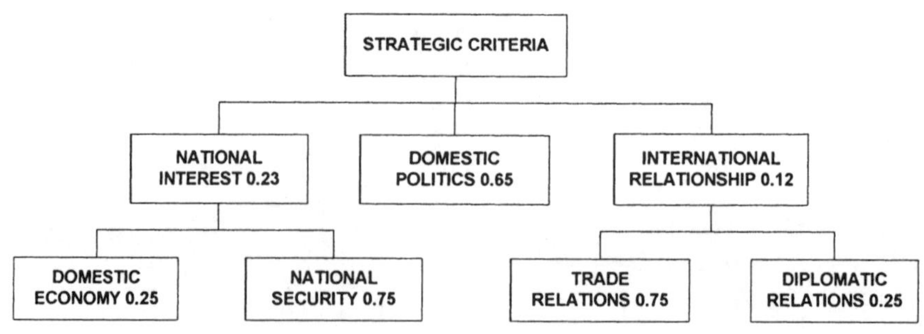

Figure 4-21: Strategic Criteria for BOCR Ratings

The BOCR merits were rated according to five intensities listed in Table 4-30 along with their priorities.

Table 4-30: BOCR Ratings and Priorities
very high (0.47), high (0.27), medium (0.14), low (0.08), very low (0.04)

		Benefits	Opportunities	Costs	Risks
National interest	Domestic economy	medium	low	high	medium
	National security	medium	low	very low	very low
Domestic politics		high	high	low	low
International relationship	Trade relations	low	low	very high	very high
	Diplomatic relations	low	low	very high	high
Priorities		0.3263	0.3029	0.1955	0.1752

II. Synthesis

Table 4-31 shows the overall outcome.

Table 4-31: Overall Outcome

Alternatives	Benefits 0.3263	Opportunities 0.3029	Costs 0.1955	Risks 0.1752	Outcome BO/CR		Outcome bB + oO − cC − rR	
					Ideal	Distrib	Ideal	Distrib
Temporary tariff	1.0000	1.0000	1.0000	1.0000	0.4792	0.2545	0.6553	0.3514
No tariff	0.3873	0.4381	0.4907	0.4103	0.4038	0.2145	0.2096	0.1124
Solve steel overproduction	0.9952	0.7907	0.6504	0.5797	1.0000	0.5311	1.0000	0.5362

The model results clearly support the alternative Solve the steel-overproduction issue under WTO. The result is inconsistent with the government's decision to impose a temporary tariff on steel. There are several factors contributing to the outcome: First, the fact that the U.S. demands free trade from others while practicing protectionism itself heavily weighted against the U.S. decision to impose the steel tariff. Second, the retaliation factor has been highly underestimated in the government's decision. The immediate international response to impose trade tariffs on U.S. goods had a counter impact on the U.S. export industry. Third, the argument that domestic steel production plays an important role for the defense sector seems to be flawed. The U.S. military today uses far less steel than broadly believed. Hence, the Defense Department could easily stockpile as much steel as it will ever need in an emergency. It can also rely on the steel production of its allies, for instance, Canada. Finally, the government's motivation was ill-founded by believing that the imposed steel tariff will "secure" jobs in the damaged steel industry. Studies have shown that the impact on the steel consuming sectors will be disastrous and results in thousands of job losses in the steel consuming industry. The latest steps taken by the U.S. government show more and more exclusions from the imposed steel tariffs. The government realizes that protectionism has a cost which has not been taken adequately into consideration so far. Hence the latest developments support the outcome of the analysis.

III. Sensitivity Analysis

The model is sensitive to changing priorities in the BOCR merits. As the priority of Costs or Risks increases, the alternative of not to impose tariff on imported steels becomes the best option. As the priority of Opportunities increases, the first alternative to impose temporary tariff on imported steels becomes the best option.

IV. Networks and Corresponding Tables

Table 4-32 shows both the local and global priorities of the criteria. The highlighted items in this table became the primary criteria and the subnets shown in Figure 4-22 were developed for each. Table 4-33 shows the clusters of these subnets and the elements in each cluster. By analyzing the subnets the best alternative under each merit is obtained, and this outcome is used to evaluate BOCR merits and then the global priorities are obtained by only using the BOCR priorities as shown in the last column of Table 4-30.

Table 4-32: Clusters in the Decision Networks and Elements in the Clusters

Merit	Criteria	Sub-criteria	Local Priorities	Global Priorities
Benefits 0.326	Economic 0.256	Economic structure	**0.571**	0.048
		Steel industry recovery	0.143	0.012
		Supply & demand	0.286	0.024
	Political 0.671	Domestic political credibility	**0.309**	0.068
		Domestic political stability	**0.582**	0.127
		Military defense	0.109	0.024
	Social 0.073	Employment rate	0.857	0.020
		Environment	0.143	0.003
Opportunities 0.303		Domestic political popularity	**0.630**	0.191
		Globalization	0.058	0.018
		Technology development	0.042	0.013
		WTO dispute resolution	**0.270**	0.082
Costs 0.196	Economic 0.717	Inflation	0.089	0.013
		Steel price	0.100	0.014
		Price of industry-related goods	0.177	0.025
		Retaliation on US exported products	**0.634**	0.089
	Political 0.205	International credibility	**0.750**	0.030
		International support on free-trade	0.250	0.010
	Social 0.078	Crime rate	0.250	0.004
		Social security	0.750	0.011
Risks 0.175		Global credibility	0.059	0.010
		International support on political issues	0.097	0.017
		Leadership in WTO	0.098	0.017
		Domestic industrial infrastructure	**0.746**	0.131

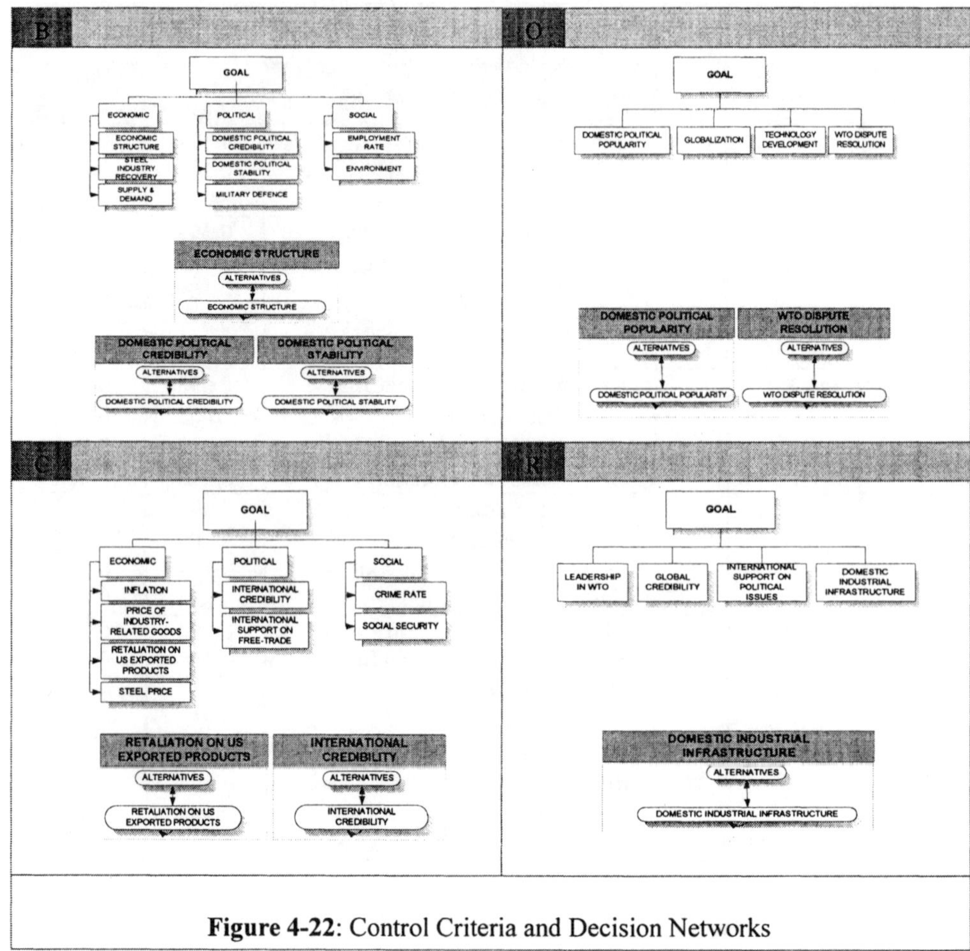

Figure 4-22: Control Criteria and Decision Networks

Table 4-33: Clusters in the Decision Networks and Elements in the Clusters

BOCR	Control Criteria	Clusters	Elements
Benefits	Economic structure	Economic structure	Jobs in steel industry, Jobs in steel-related industry, National industry-reorganization, Technology enhancement
	Domestic political credibility	Domestic political credibility	Voters' confidence in the political party in power, Voters' ongoing support on government decision, Reputation of political party
	Domestic political stability	Domestic political stability	Votes for election, Achievement of political goals, Consistency of domestic policy
Opportunities	Domestic political popularity	Domestic political popularity	Midterm elections, Presidential election in 2004, Future government policy making
	WTO dispute resolution	WTO dispute resolution	Promoting free-trade, Encouraging fair-trade, Leadership role in WTO
Costs	Retaliation on US exported products	Retaliation on US exported products	Us export performance, Labor market, Competitive advantage
	International credibility	International credibility	International reputation, International influence, Support on international issues
Risks	Domestic industrial infrastructure	Domestic industrial infrastructure	Jobs in steel industry, Jobs in steel-related industry, National industry-reorganization, Technology enhancement
All networks		Alternatives	Impose temporary tariff on imported steels, Not impose tariff on imported steels, solve the steel-overproduction issue under WTO

WHAT FORM OF GLOBALIZATION IS BEST FIT FOR COMPANY X?

Many companies face the option of expanding their business and venture into a brand new global market. Deciding on entering another market can be very time-consuming and can end up bankrupting a firm if it does not properly choose and execute the correct globalization strategy. When a company is considering globalization, it must properly weigh many key factors in the decision. Some of these factors are tangible and easily identifiable, while others are intangible and more difficult to quantify. The first decision a company has to make is whether it will be beneficial to globalize at all. If a company decides to globalize, it must choose between three alternatives. (This analysis was done by Doron Farkas, Jennifer Roach, and Rebecca Rothman in 2002).

ALTERNATIVES: Globalization, Globalization via acquisition, Joint globalization, No globalization.

I. BOCR Weight Development

The strategic criteria used in the model are given in Figure 4-23. The intensities used for the strategic criteria are shown in Table 4-34.

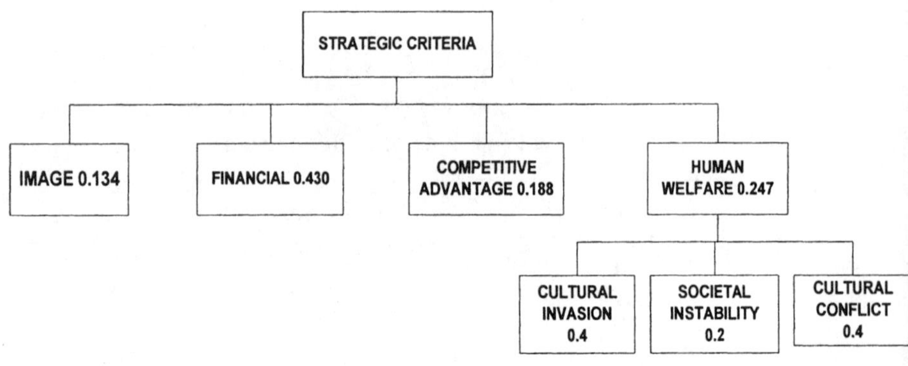

Figure 4-23: Strategic Criteria for BOCR Ratings

Table 4-34: Strategic Criteria and Rating Scale

Image	Financial	Competitive advantage	Cultural invasion	Societal instability	Cultural conflict
high medium low	none low moderate breakeven high extreme	extreme high moderate neutral low detrimental	non-existent slightly medium high	extreme high medium low	very high high moderate low non-existent

II. Synthesis

As shown in Table 4-35, the best alternatives are Globalization via acquisition and Joint globalization. Note that this is a generalized model that can be tailored for the individually unique needs of a firm.

Table 4-35: Overall Outcome

Alternatives	Benefits 0.2803	Opportunities 0.2850	Costs 0.1978	Risks 0.2368	Outcome BO/CR	Outcome bB + oO – cC - rR
Globalization	0.5919	0.3478	0.4920	0.3114	0.6107	0.1765
Globalization via acquisition	1.0000	0.4353	0.6223	0.3593	1.0000	0.4919
Joint globalization	0.9689	1.0000	0.8125	1.0000	0.6124	0.4766
No globalization	0.2834	0.1203	1.0000	0.8172	0.0214	-1.0000

III. Sensitivity Analysis

Sensitivity analysis shows that at any priority level above 0.44 for Costs, or at any priority level above 0.65 for Risks, the optimal result is Globalization.

IV. Networks

Figure 4-24 shows the criteria and the networks.

WHAT SHOULD THE MINIMUM DRINKING AGE BE?

Today, approximately eleven million young American adults under the age of 21 consume alcoholic beverages regularly. Furthermore, underage drinking is a major factor in nearly half of all teenager automobile crashes, the leading cause of death among teenagers. Other consequences of alcohol use result in youth suicides, homicides and fatal injuries. Research has shown that a higher minimum legal drinking age (MLDA) is effective in preventing alcohol-related deaths and injuries among youth. This project aims at determining the ideal minimum legal drinking age. (This analysis was done by Stefanie Kramer, and Sylvia Schulze-Düllo in 2002).

ALTERNATIVES: Lower the drinking age to 18; Lower the drinking age to 18 for beer and wine; Keep the drinking age at 21.

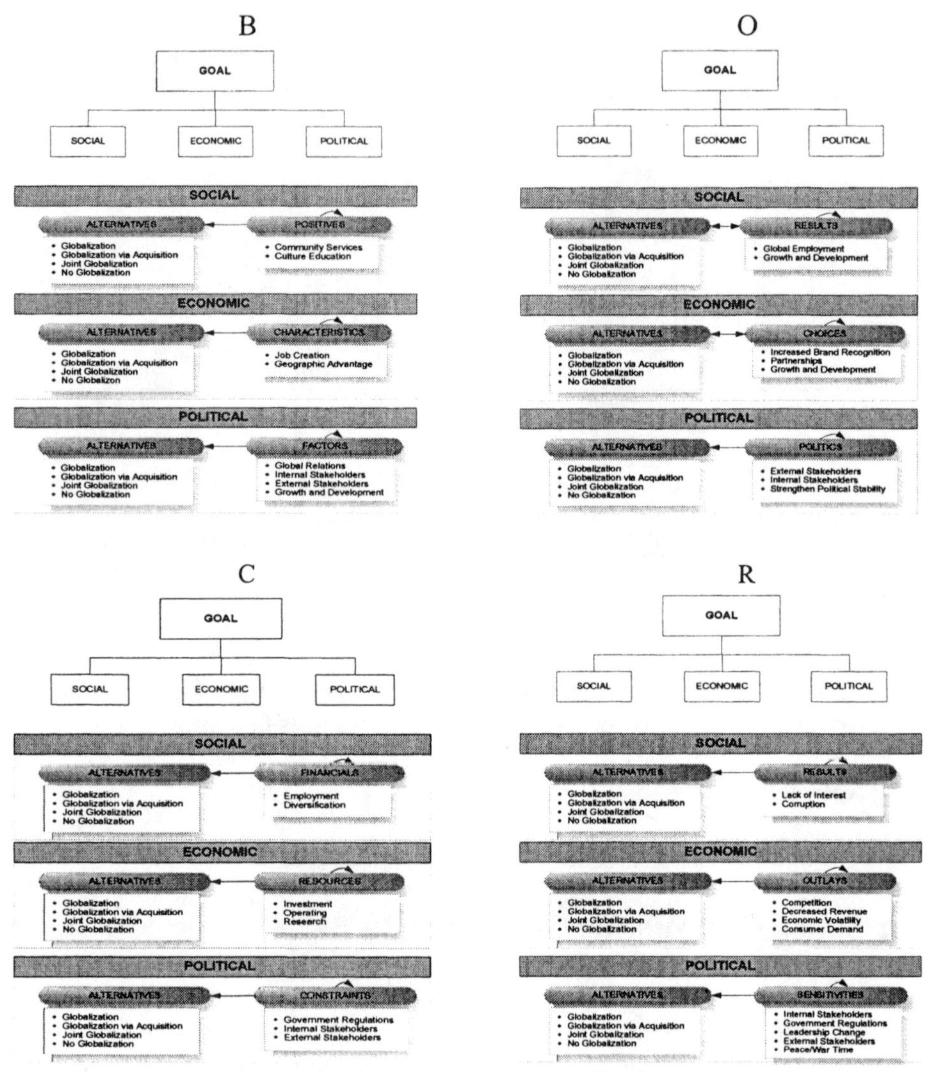

Figure 4-24: Control Criteria and Decision Network

I. BOCR Weight Development

Table 4-36 shows the strategic criteria and their priorities. These priorities are used to obtain the BOCR priorities as shown at the top of Table 4-37.

Table 4-36: Strategic Criteria and Their Priorities

Political (0.122)	Economic (0.230)	Social (0.648)
Tax revenues (0.085)	Micro and Macroeconomic (0.405)	Signaling (0.153)
Global trends/Signaling (0.075)	Education (0.096)	Community (0.069)
Forces of law and order (0.263)	Health costs (0.281)	Consumer (0.046)
Legislative assembly (0.416)	Crime related costs (0.094)	Norms (0.496)
Administration of justice (0.162)	Traffic accidents (0.092)	Dangers / Substitutes (0.236)
	Opportunity costs (0.032)	

II. Synthesis

For this decision, to get the best alternative, one inverts the values of Costs and Risks and then normalizes them to combine (add) the priorities of Costs and Risks with the normalized priorities of Benefits and Opportunities. This gives the overall priorities. Table 4-37 exhibits the overall results.

Table 4-37: Overall Outcome

Alternatives	Benefits 0.1257	Opportunities 0.1672	Costs 0.3065	Risks 0.4006	Outcome BO/CR	Outcome bB + oO – cC - rR
Lower the drinking age to 18	0.4757	0.3026	1.0000	1.0000	0.0199	-1.0000
Lower the drinking age to 18 for beer and wine	0.1865	1.0000	0.2000	0.4122	0.3128	0.0161
Keep the drinking age at 21	1.0000	0.2648	0.0000	0.0073	1.0000	0.4536

The legal drinking age of 21 is the best decision according to this analysis.

III. Sensitivity Analysis

The benefit sensitivity analysis shows that the highest benefits are generated if the MLDA would remain 21. Also if the priority for the opportunities would be larger than 0.842, the preferred option would be to Lower the drinking age to 18 years for beer and wine. Out of the Costs-Sensitivity analysis we see that if the priority for costs were larger than 0.768, the preferred alternative would be a drinking age of 18 years for beer and wine. After having examined all the merit's sensitivity analysis, no surprising results appear. No matter what priority selection for sensitivity is made, the decision to maintain the actual MLDA should be the best alternative.

IV. Networks and Corresponding Tables

Figure 4-25 shows the control criteria and decision networks from which the alternatives were prioritized and synthesized for each of the BOCR merits obtaining their priorities in Table 4-37. Table 4-38 shows the clusters and the elements in each.

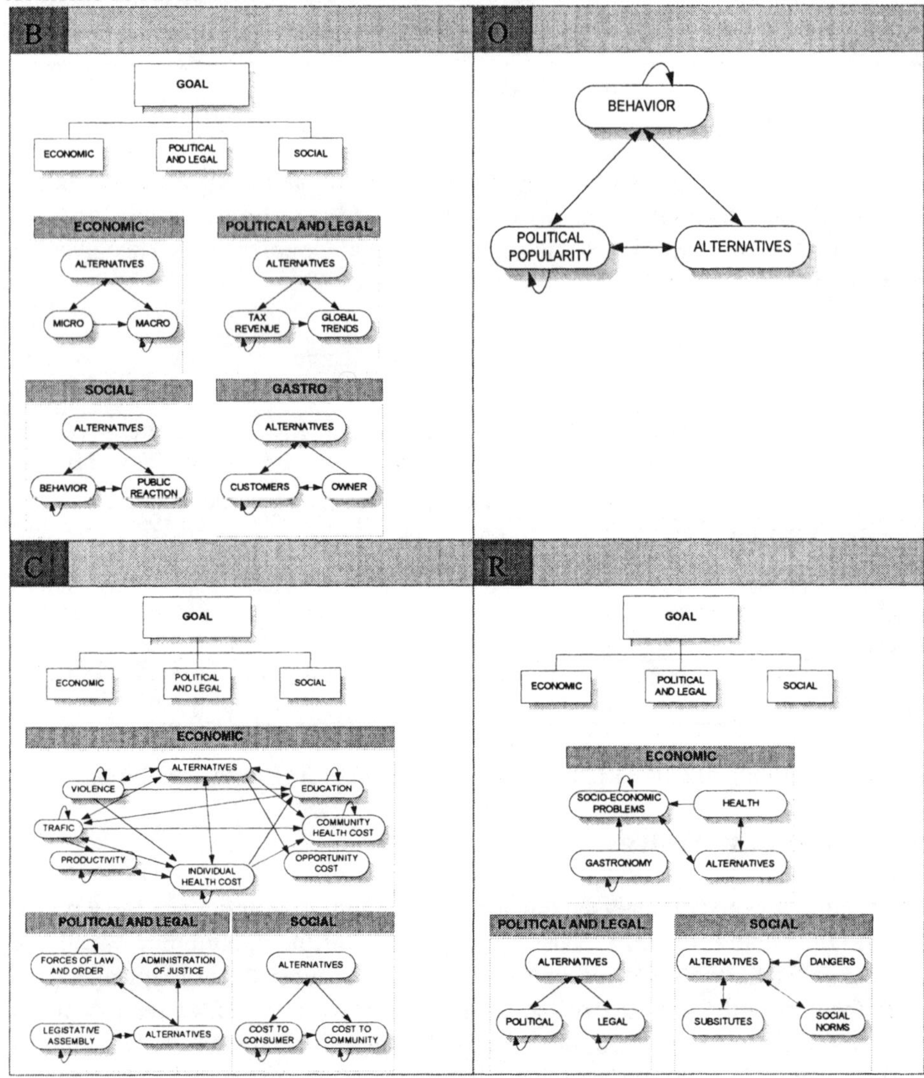

Figure 4-25: Control Criteria and Decision Networks

Table 4-38: Clusters in the Decision Networks and Elements in the Clusters

BOCR	Control Criteria	Clusters	Elements
Benefits	Economic	Micro	Media, Distribution, Production, Gastronomy
		Macro	Tax income, Employment, GDP growth, Exports
	Political and legal	Tax revenues	Funding for education, Infrastructure
		Global trends	Unanimity, Adapting to North American standards, Responsible dealing with alcohol
	Social	Public react.	Extend of hidden drinking, Same rules at college
		Behavior	Learning, Responsibility, Self-discipline
	Gastronomic	Customers	Speed of service, Convenience for young customers, Convenience for older customers
		Owners	New customer base, Higher sales
Opportunities	Political popularity	Political popularity	Less attention towards underage drinking, Involvement younger people in political decision making, Popularity of political parties, Signal
	Behavior	Behavior	Forbidden fruit, Responsibility, Trend for anti-alcoholism
Costs	Economic	Violence	Unscrupulous actions and vandalism, Suicide, Crimes
		Education	Students skip classes, Weaker performance, Reach lower education level
		Community health costs	Hospital charges and costs, Health insurance
		Individual health costs	Addiction, Depression, Injuries, Alcohol poisonings, Deaths
		Opportunity costs	Total consumption
		Productivity	Imprisonment, Stay in hospital, Productivity and work flow, Total loss of labor pool
		Traffic	Crashes and speeding, Carelessness
	Political and legal	Forces of law	Change of law, Legal advice, Controls
		Legist. Ass.	Loss of voters, Disapproval from other parties
		Administration of justice	Number of underage drinking suites, Drinking related violence suits, Creation of new alcohol licenses
		Controls	
	Social	Costs to cons.	Addicts, Young-heavy drinkers, Peer pressure, Substitute drugs
		Costs to community	Medical treatment, Improved infrastructure, Family councils
	Controls	Gastronomy	Door controls, Bar controls
		Communities	Increase police controls, Instructional works
		Education	Parents, Schools and universities, Institutions
Risks	Economic	Socio economic problems	Need for consulting, Family problems, Money problems
		Gastronomy	Loss of senior customers, Convenience for customers, Customer loyalty
		Health	Accidents, Psychotherapy
	Political and legal	Legal	Claim to change drinking age, Enforcement, Funding for enforcement
		Political	Credibility, Signal, Support for election campaign
	Social	Dangers	Hidden drinking, Desire to lower drinking age further, New fringe group, Public drunkenness, Getting off the track
		Social norms	Consumption, Ruthlessness, Influence on community
		Substitutes	Other drugs, Violence
All Networks		Alternatives	Lower the drinking age to 18, Lower the drinking age to 18 for beer and wine, Keep the drinking age at 21

WHAT SHOULD THE RUSSIAN PRESIDENT DO WITH GASPORT?

Gasport (Gazprom) is the world's biggest gas company, which accounts for 94% of Russia's gas production (23% of the world output). It produces about 8% of the country's GDP and contributes about 25% of all tax revenues to the federal budget. More than half-a-million Russians and over 100,000 foreigners are the company's shareholders. About 300,000 people work in the company's enterprises. Gasport is the world's biggest gas exporter. Its deliveries cover about 20% of the natural gas requirements of Western Europe and almost all the needs of Eastern Europe. In the South of Russia, the biggest project there is the Blue Stream project, which provides for the construction of a gas pipeline across the Black Sea to Turkey. Apart from that, a contract has been initiated with India's Ministry of Oil and Natural Gas for prospecting for, the development and operation of a major gas field on the Bay of Bengal shelf. There are many hot issues in the Gasport system nowadays. It needs investment but investors do not want to give their money. One big problem – only Russian residents are allowed to trade Gasport shares on the domestic market while foreigners are only entitled to American Depositary Shares (ADSs), which trade with a huge premium given to local shares. The ring fence has long annoyed foreign investors, led to semi-legal schemes to bypass it, and prevented Gazprom from raising new capital to solve its core problem of falling gas output. Gazprom needs reform, and its development market needs competition. The President of Russia has a chance to be considered as a "true" reformer by taking the necessary actions. Still the temptation is to stay united, at the expense of inner economic effectiveness. Gazprom is a very powerful geopolitical and economical instrument whose costs are also very high. An ANP model is developed to predict the way Russian President will choose in relation to Gazprom. (This analysis was done by Yury Proskurin in 2001).

ALTERNATIVES: De-monopolization, Keep monopoly, Monopoly reorganized under control.

I. BOCR Weight Development

Figure 4-26 shows the strategic criteria with their priorities.

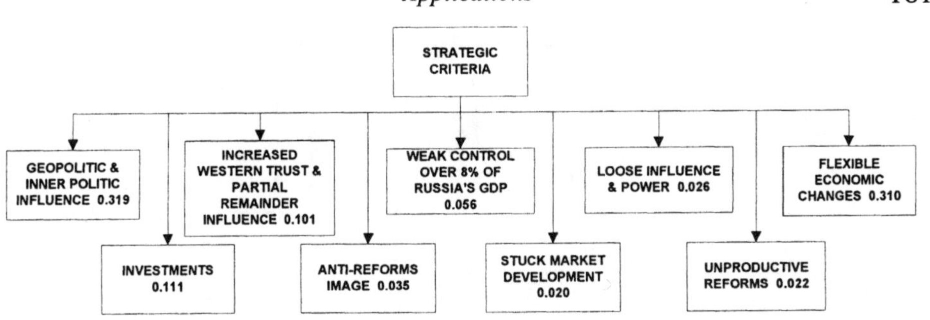

Figure 4-26: Strategic Criteria for BOCR Ratings

II. Synthesis

According to the Table 4-39, the choice, which may be made by Russian President, is Monopoly reorganized under control.

Table 4-39: Overall Outcome

Alternatives	Benefits 0.3493	Opportunities 0.3543	Costs 0.1481	Risks 0.1481	Outcome BO/CR	Outcome bB + oO – cC - rR
De-monopolization	0.5934	0.3978	1.0000	1.0000	0.0553	-1.0000
Keep monopoly	1.0000	0.5818	0.9519	0.6691	0.2139	-0.1080
Monopoly reorganized under control	0.7451	1.0000	0.4376	0.3986	1.0000	0.6605

III. Networks and Corresponding Tables

Table 4-40 shows the clusters and the elements in each network shown in Figure 4-27.

Table 4-40: Clusters in the Decision Networks and Elements in the Clusters

BOCR	Control Criteria	Clusters	Elements
Benefits	Political	Advantages	Geopolitical instrument, Positive image and western support, Inner political instrument, Financial source for top elite, A nation uniting instrument
	Economic	Advantages	25 % tax revenues to Fed budget, Investments, Direct hard currency earnings, A push to develop market, Economic benefits from competition, Inner and outer economic influence, Long-term loan guarantee, Increase of market capitalization
Opportunities	Political	Opportunities	Pro-reforms image, Increased western trust and support , Increased trust and partially remained influence, Increased influence of top elite
	Economic	Opportunities	To draw the investments, To improve corporate governance, To improve and increase influence, To foster reforms, To make economic changes flexibly
Costs	Political	Costs	Weak inner and outer influence, Slow reforms, Anti-reforms image
	Economic	Costs	Small investments, Bad corporate governance, Weak control over currency revenues
Risks	Political	Risks	To lose influence, To build state within the state, Anti-reform image, To lose financial source, To lose nations-tie structure, To increase foreign influence
	Economic	Risks	To lose investment, To maintain low longtime capitalization, To make worse corporate governance, Cash flow, Foreign influence, Weak chance to influence market
All Networks		Alternatives	Demonopolization, Keep monopoly, Monopoly reorganized under control

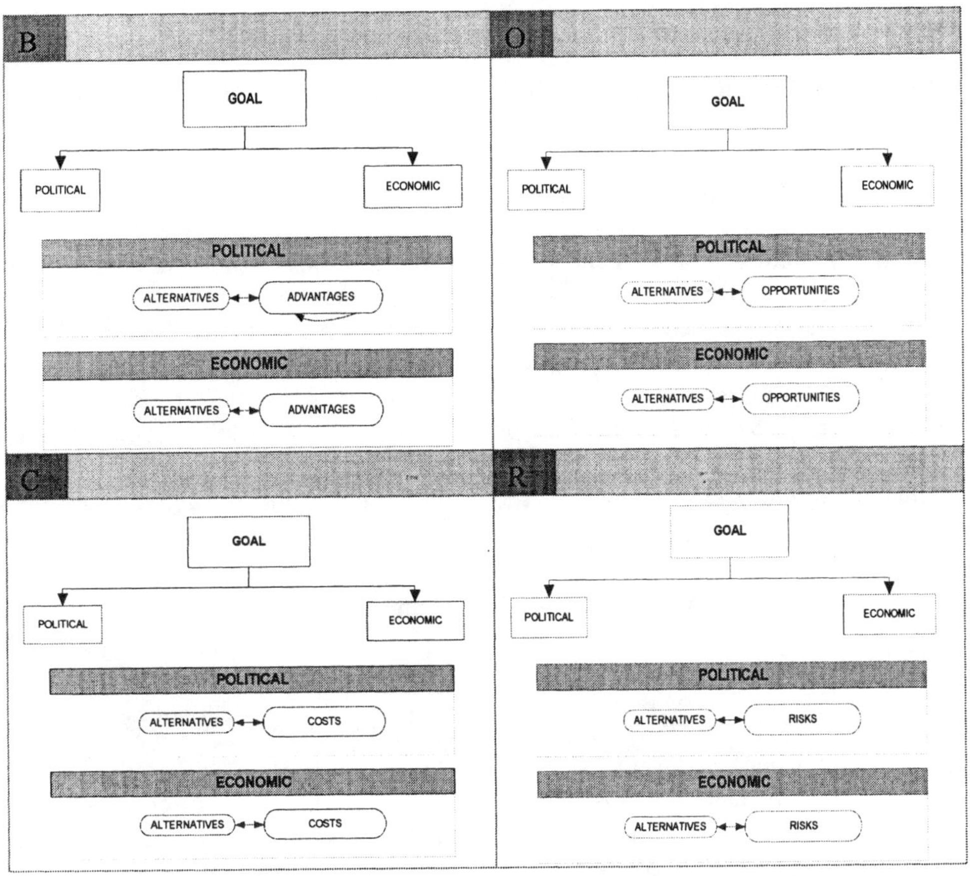

Figure 4-27: Criteria and Decision Networks

STEM CELL RESEARCH FUNDING

Stem Cell research (SCR) has the potential to cure diseases such as Parkinson's, Diabetes, Alzheimer's or any other diseases related to tissue degeneration. Most research occurring in the United States, specifically universities within the United States, is funded by the federal government. Without the use of federal funding, Stem Cell research is almost non-existent. The question arises as to what extent the government should fund the various forms of Stem Cell research. This is not only a political debate but also an ethical debate as well. The ethics lie around the question of whether or not an embryo is a living being. The politicians are battling with possible improvements in health care that could come about using the stem cells as well as the questionable use of government money for research, which has great opposition. (This analysis was done by Lisa Schaefer and Alison Walters in 2002).

ALTERNATIVES: Adult SCR, Do not fund, Leftover embryos, Research only embryos.

I. BOCR Weight Development

A rating system was implemented to compare the BOCR against three strategic criteria: Political, Religious and Social. Political criteria include the federal grant funding that is limited as well as responsible for the future health of the population. Political criteria also include politicians' views and their responsibility to respect the moral of Americans. Religious criteria are the primary ethical considerations of the public. Finally Social criteria encompass the American people as a whole including their overall wellbeing, their ethical beliefs and their safety. Table 4-41 shows the ratings. Table 4-42 gives the final results.

Table 4-41: Strategic Criteria and BOCR Priorities

	Political	Religious	Social	BOCR Priorities
	0.176	0.062	0.762	
Benefits	high	low	high	0.346
Opportunities	high	low	high	0.346
Costs	high	high	medium	0.182
Risks	medium	medium	medium	0.126

II. Synthesis

Overall, leftover embryo SCR is the best funding choice with 1.0000, which also ranked at the top in Benefits, Opportunities, but also created the most Costs. This result demonstrates that the overall Benefits and Opportunities of this type of stem cell research, along with the expected quality of this research are of most importance. Research only embryos follows second at 0.3148, which is consistent with the quality of research that is expected with this type of stem cell research. Funding adult stem research is third at 0.1559 and not funding at 0.0434. This shows that it is better to fund some type of stem cell research, than none at all.

Table 4-42: Overall Outcome

Alternatives	Benefits 0.3467	Opportunities 0.3467	Costs 0.1821	Risks 0.1245	Outcome BO/CR	Outcome bB + oO – cC - rR
Adult SCR	0.2889	0.1670	0.3221	0.7129	0.1559	0.0760
Do not fund	0.3001	0.0940	0.4825	1.0000	0.0434	-0.0933
Leftover embryos	1.0000	1.0000	1.0000	0.7419	1.0000	1.0000
Research only embryos	0.4928	0.5420	0.6788	0.9274	0.3148	0.3402

III. Sensitivity Analysis

No matter how we increase or decrease the weights of Benefits, Leftover embryos alternative remains the highest. As we increase the weight above 0.83, the order of Do not fund and Adult SCR switches.

Using a priority of Costs at 0.5, Adult SCR research is first, followed by Research only embryos. Increasing Costs above 0.55, Do not fund and Leftover embryos switch ranks. When Costs are at 0.43, Leftover embryos becomes the primary funding choice, followed by Adult SCR.

Using a priority of Risks equal to 0.5, Adult SCR is the primary choice, followed by Leftover embryos. Increasing the priority, Adult SCR remains the best alternative. Decreasing Risks to 0.48 and below, Leftover embryos is the best choice, followed by Adult SCR.

IV. Networks and Corresponding Tables

Figure 4-28 gives the decision networks.

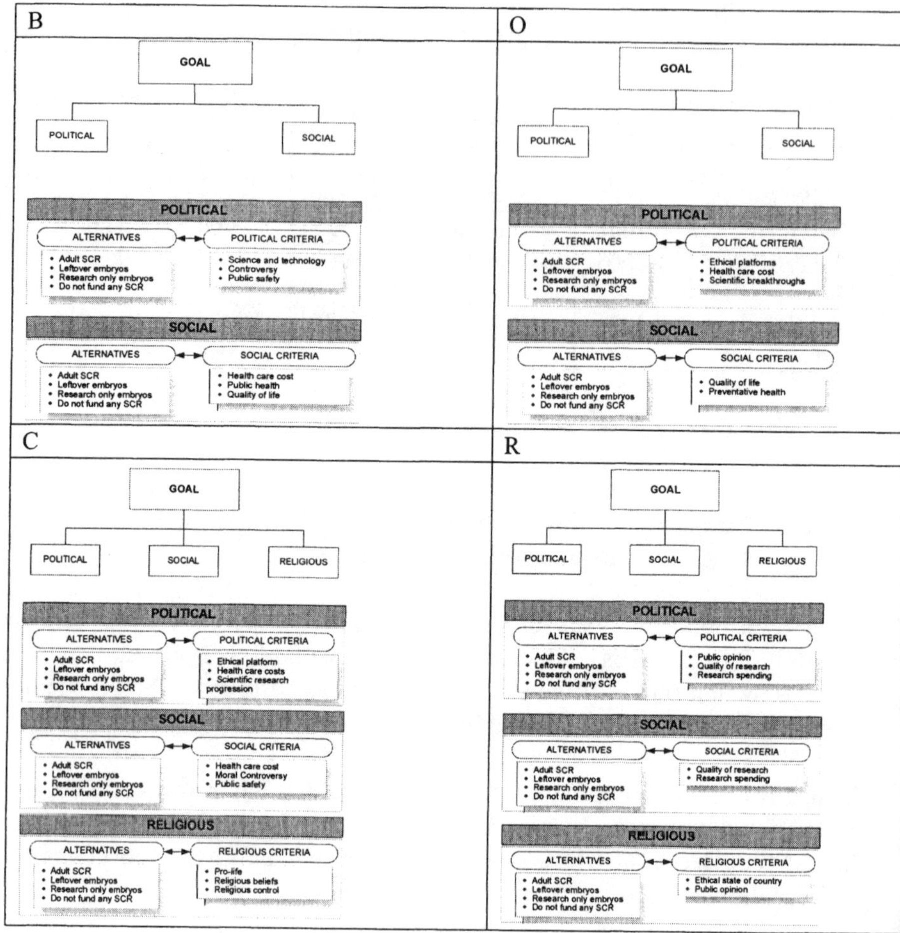

Figure 4-28: Stem Cell Research Control Criteria and Decision Networks

4-7. Projects that have been done using BOCR Analysis

- Action on Arthur Andersen; an ANP Approach
- Actual Job Related Decision about Launching New Diaper Product
- Ad Agency Client – Keep client?

- Ad Agency Client – Keep client?
- Admitting Students
- Affirmative Action: Is It Still Needed?
- Air Marshals
- Allocating Resources to a Department
- American Eagle Growth Strategy
- An ANP Model for Deciding on the Development of the Historic Springfield Schoolhouse in the Strip District
- ANWR Decision: Drill for Oil
- Are No-Kill Animal Shelters the Best Option?
- Ballpark in Philadelphia
- Baseball: Diamond Backs vs. Indians
- Best Alternative for the Use of Genetics
- Best Career Decision
- Best Competitive Strategy for Rite Aid
- Best Smoking Policy
- Bid on Engineering Project
- Build Indoor Car Race Track
- Business Ethics
- Casual Corner Apparel Strategic Business Decision
- Choice of Fiscal Policy to Solve Budget Crisis: New Taxes Best Solution
- Choice of Vendor for New Software
- Choose a Career
- Choosing Best Alternative to Reduce the Effects of Gasoline Price Volatility for Automobiles in the United States
- Choosing Marketing Strategies for an Industrial Product
- Choosing Optimum Career Path after Completing University of Pittsburgh MBA
- Choosing the Best Diet
- Choosing the Best Manufacturing Method for a Plastic Part
- Choosing the Best Office Space for Triangle
- Choosing the Best Part Time MBA Program
- CMU vs. PITT Full-Time vs. Part-time
- Corporate Decision about Locating Data Processing Mainframe
- Credit Card Expansion Strategy
- Cutler-Hammer Case: Product Decision
- D 47 Project in Prague
- Decision Model for Company Downsizing
- Determine the Best Approach for Children with ADD – the Value of Ritalin
- Determining Most Promising Career Opportunity

- Determining the Best Implementation Program among Balanced Scorecard, Lean, and the Integration of Them
- Disney Decision: Where to Put a New Theme Park in China
- Drug Strategy in the US
- Energy Security of the US
- Entrepreneurial Development Decision
- Euthanasia Policy
- Evaluate the Potential Life Span of Humans
- Evaluation of an Entrepreneurial Idea
- Evaluation of Johnson and Johnson
- Focus of US Policy
- Food Model
- Forecasting the Development of the S&P 500
- Funding Pennsylvania Schools
- Furniture Business Decision
- Globalization strategy for company X: Globalization via Acquisition (very slightly better than Joint Globalization)
- Gourmet Pretzel Shop
- Green Bay Packers Best Allocation of Resources under Salary Cap
- Human Tracking System Decision
- Ice Hockey Championship 2003
- Ideal Recovery System in Response to Extreme Events
- Identifying Best Strategy for European Business School
- Information Technology; on Board with the US Navy
- Interest Rate Issue for Brazil
- International Trade USA-China
- Job Hiring Decision
- Legalization of Gambling in Pennsylvania
- Legalization of Marijuana for medicinal purposes
- Location of a Baseball Stadium
- Main Project
- Management Issues Project
- Market Entry Strategy in Asia
- Microsoft X Box Case
- Most Livable City
- Most Undesirable Species
- Navy Assembly Area Ventilation System
- Nursing Home Evaluation
- Office Location
- Optimal Corporate Structure

- Outsourcing IT
- Outsourcing of a Company's Administrative and Financial Services
- Outsourcing the Mellon Trust Fund Accounting Division
- Over-fishing in the U.S.
- Overtime Issue
- Pennsylvania Liquor Store Project
- Picking best MBA Program for Brazil
- Pittsburgh Hockey Arena
- Pittsburgh: 5th & Forbes Re-Development Project
- Plant Closure Decision
- Predict Democratic VP Candidate
- Predicted World Series
- Prediction of the Most Severe HIV Epidemic
- Prescription Drug Importation
- Prescription Drugs for the Elderly: Who Should Pay?
- Presidential Election 2004
- Presidential Election in Taiwan March 2000
- Privatization of Alcohol in PA
- Project Resource Allocation
- Providing Total Asset Visibility in Real Time: Enter alone or Form Alliance?
- Real Estate Model
- Reform the Electoral College?
- Resource Allocation to projects for a Company Based on Business Units
- Roddey vs. Wecht for Allegheny County Executive
- Russian Gazprom Decision
- Same-Sex Domestic Partner Benefits at the University of Pittsburgh
- Select Best Attraction for Pittsburgh
- Select Vendor for Software
- Selecting a Software System to Manage Clinical Trials for Lupus
- Selection of the Host City for the 2000 Summer Olympic Games
- Should Embratel Enter the Call Center Market?
- Should Genetic Engineering in the Embryonic Phase be allowed by Law?
- Should Gradiente Continue its Partnership with Nintendo?
- Should Imported Drugs be Legal?
- Should Israel give West Bank and Gaza Strip to Palestinians?
- Should Minimum Drinking Age be lowered in the US?
- Should Pittsburgh build the Transrapid system?
- Should Pittsburgh have a Living-wage Policy?
- Should Pittsburgh Penguin Hockey Team get Funding for a New Arena?

- Should the Brazilian Government Privatize Telecommunications?
- Should the City of Pittsburgh and Allegheny County, Pennsylvania, Governments Merge?
- Should the Death Penalty be abolished?
- Should the US Influence the IMF and World Bank to provide Debt Relief to HIPC?
- Stabilizing Social Security for the Long Term
- Stem Cell Research Funding
- Steroid Testing for Baseball
- SUV for Porsche?
- Telecom Processes Analysis
- Terminally Ill Pets: best Policy for Handling?
- The best Notification Policy Regarding Individuals Who Test Positive for HIV
- The Country's Most Livable City
- The Death Penalty
- The Ford Explorer Case
- The Relationship between China and Taiwan
- The Steel Industry and Government
- Time off after the MBA
- Travel Decisions in the US
- U.S. Foreign Policy in Iraq: Best to work with UN
- US Policy on Marijuana
- USA Response to North Korean Nuclear Threat
- VA Hospital Decision
- Value of a National Identification System
- Was Moving Pitt Stadium to Steelers a good Idea?
- Was Tariff on Steel Imports best Option?
- Washington Penn Plastic Company, Inc. a Related Diversification Issue
- What should Brazil do about the New Trade Agreement?
- What should Martha Stewart do?
- What to do about Penguins Arena?
- What to Do with Kordell, the Pittsburgh Steelers Quarterback?
- Where to Buy a Season Ski Pass
- Whether and how to Regulate Smoking
- Which City, Pittsburgh, Baltimore, Atlanta, should be a Maglev Site?
- World Series Predicted Winner
- World Trade Center Rebuilding

Chapter 5
Making and Validating Complex Decisions with the AHP/ANP

5-1. Introduction

Several examples that serve to validate the matrices, hierarchies, and networks of the AHP/ANP are given in this chapter. They are then followed by a discussion of the real numbers and how they are generated without the need for an absolute zero, and how they define an absolute scale of measurement that also does not need an absolute zero. In the AHP/ANP the measurement of an alternative depends on what other alternatives it is compared with. The result is that rank can change if alternatives are added or deleted, something that does not occur in one-at-a- time rating of the alternatives by comparing them with an ideal. An example is provided to show that this is natural and need not involve new criteria or change in judgments. A brief discussion of Utility Theory, the other multi-criteria theory, which uses interval scales to measure intangibles and some of its problems and paradoxes, is given. The references at the end include most of the papers that are adverse to the AHP. We make brief comments about several of them in this chapter.

Rational decision-making is the talent we have to be more effective in implementing our ideas in the real world with its risks and resistance to change. Decision-making involves prioritizing our ideas according to the circumstances we face now or might face in the future. A fundamental problem in decision-making is how to measure intangible criteria and how to interpret correctly measurements of tangibles so they can be combined with those of intangibles to yield sensible, not arbitrary numerical results. A crucial test is whether actual measurements can be used precisely as they are when needed.

In this chapter we provide arguments as to why pairwise comparisons are fundamentally a new way, a new paradigm because it creates relative scales from measurements based on an absolute scale of real numbers for making the comparisons. Paired comparisons imply dependence in the measurement of alternatives on the quality and number of other alternatives with which they are compared. Thus due to the dependence of the measurement of each alternative on the other alternatives, the ranking of alternatives could change if new alternatives are added or old ones deleted, contrary to the traditionally held view, basically due to the rating of alternatives one at a time, that rank should not be influenced unless new criteria are added or judgments changed.

As with any enterprise, there has been an effort by different scholars in the academic world to develop methods to improve decision-making. These methods depend on what the latest techniques are in operations research and economic theory both of which use quantitative methods in their analyses. If one accepts the fact that decision making will be here for ever, one must be concerned about the vagaries of inventing techniques and how long they are likely to last. Thus we are forced to look deeper at how people actually make decisions. By doing that we would discover the most appropriate way or ways that would aid lay people in a natural and quick way (not requiring a prolonged graduate level of study and understanding) to make better decisions. One thing is certain. Unlike the complex quantitative methods people invent to use numbers, we should make it possible for people to use numbers directly and independently of complex mathematical formalizations that we invent. That is what the AHP/ANP attempt to do. They organize thinking and elicit judgments in a way that parallels what people do naturally and do not need intrusive coaching and advice to use them correctly.

The AHP/ANP is fundamentally a process of laying out a structure of all the essential factors that influence the outcome of a decision. Numerical pairwise comparison judgments are then elicited to express people's understanding of the importance or likely influence of these elements on the final outcome obtained by synthesizing the priorities obtained from different sets of pairwise comparisons. Sensitivity analysis is also performed to determine the stability of the outcome to wide perturbations in the judgments. The process has been validated in practice in many ways as we show in the next section.

The rest of the chapter is concerned with validation examples, a discussion of absolute scales, a discussion of utility theory as known to this author and as communicated by other knowledgeable scholars as a contrast with the AHP, a discussion of the arbitrariness of always preserving rank and a real life example of rank reversal, why the geometric mean should not be linked to synthesis in the AHP, comments on some of the references that are mostly negative about the AHP, a general discussion and conclusions about the role of the AHP/ANP in mathematical thinking.

5-2. Validation and Validation Examples of Judgment Matrices, Hierarchies and Networks

As in any science, a decision theory needs ways to validate it so that it does not have the appearance of number crunching referred to in popular jargon as, "garbage in garbage out". How does one validate a theory that claims it is normative or prescriptive because it tells people what is good for them to do? What if that turns out not to be the case and a disaster follows the decision? For its success, a decision must look ahead for its consequences. Thus decision-making and prediction are related subjects. It is obvious that decision-making depends on judgments and knowledge, experience and foresight. People often struggle unsuccessfully (e.g., the stock market, the economy, the outcome of conflicts) by using statistical methods on numerical data from the present and past to predict what might happen next. How can we then assume that priorities derived from judgments about intangibles would work any better in prediction? It is a fact that in multi-criteria decisions, the richness of the structure (a hierarchy or a network) of criteria, stakeholders, competitors, environmental influences etc. along with a diversity of alternatives used, that also allows for certain redundancies, provides a better opportunity for capturing more of the influences on the outcome by including both tangibles and intangibles. In other words this type of approach is a richer way to use in prediction than to simply extrapolate on measurements. Sensitivity analysis allows us to examine the effect of varying the influences on the stability of the outcome. To do all that we need a descriptive theory of decision making by not only asking people what they like but also what they think about the durability and satisfaction they would get from their decision when it is influenced and altered by resistance and opposition from many directions.

Using judgments from a variety of experts is generally preferred to that of a single individual for the diversity and breadth that it contributes to producing valid outcomes. In his book Surowiecki 2004, puts forward a paradox: often, the multitude knows better than the wise individual. By examining many cases he concludes that the amalgamated views of a crowd reach a more accurate conclusion than the single expert does. "Under the right circumstances, groups are remarkably intelligent, and are often smarter than the smartest people in them." The two ultimate tests of the wisdom of crowds are the market and democracy. His faith in crowds leads him to argue for decentralized decision-making in companies. "Any major decision should be taken by as large a group of managers as is logistically possible," he argues – admitting that this is a suggestion "so radical as to seem ludicrous". "With most things, the average is mediocrity." "With collective intelligence, it's excellence. You could say it's as if we've been programmed to be collectively smart." A group works better when its members learn on their own independently than from following the crowd. Thomas Jefferson said, "State a moral case to a ploughman and a professor. The former will decide it as well and often better than the latter because he has not been led astray by artificial rules." A crowd of plough persons is thus wiser than a plurality of professors, writes The Economist. In many of our examples, the judgments used were those of more than one person. In some instances a questionnaire was sent out by mail for people to indicate the strengths of their preferences, and they did.

How do we test for the validity of the AHP/ANP? One of the things we can do is to get judgments from many people even those who may not be experts in decision-making but are experts in what they do. Should the answer always match the data available and what if the data themselves are incorrect? What if we don't know enough to create a very complete structure for a decision? We compare its predictions with actual numerical measurements often by using the measurement of compatibility, and also with the outcome of events whose decisions were thought to be good ones according to a preponderance of opinions. Several single matrix examples have already been illustrated for validation of the approach, along with network of economy turn around date, market share examples and China's trade status example. In the remainder of this section we offer one more example of a single matrix, a few examples of hierarchies, one of market share and other examples of networks. Unlike falsification, which proves conclusively that an assertion or an assumption is incorrect by offering a counterexample, validation with examples, no matter how many, can only serve to improve confidence in an idea, but not give it conclusive justification.

The examples are uneven in length because of the different orders of complexity of the applications from which they arise. We hope that the reader will forgive us for this unavoidable situation.

5-3. Single Matrix Validation Example

Very early in the history of the subject, T. Saaty and M. Khouja 1976, did the following exercise on an airplane in 1973. They simply used their common knowledge about the relative influence and standing of these countries in the world (see Table 5-1 below) and without referring to any specific economic data related to GNP values. The two results are close and demonstrate that the general understanding an interested person has about a problem can be used to advantage to make fairly good estimates through paired comparisons.

Table 5-1 gives the judgments using the AHP 1-9 scale and Table 5-2 provides the derived priorities, the actual and relative GNP values.

Table 5-1: Paired Comparisons of the Relative Dominance in Wealth of Seven Nations

	U.S	*U.S.S.R*	*China*	*France*	*U.K*	*Japan*	*W.Germany*
U.S	1	4	9	6	6	5	5
U.S.S.R	1/4	1	7	5	5	3	4
China	1/9	1/7	1	1/5	1/5	1/7	1/5
France	1/6	1/5	5	1	1	1/3	1/3
U.K	1/6	1/5	5	1	1	1/3	1/3
Japan	1/5	1/3	7	3	3	1	2
W.Germany	1/5	1/4	5	3	3	1/2	1

Table 5-2: The Outcome of Estimated Relative Wealth and the Actual and Relative Values

	Normalized Eigenvector	Actual GNP (1972)	Normalized GNP Values
U.S	.427	1,167	.413
U.S.S.R	.23	635	.225
China	.021	120	.043
France	.052	196	.069
U.K	.052	154	.055
Japan	.123	294	.104
W. Germany	.094	257	.091

5-4. Hierarchic Validation Examples

To make good applications one needs expert knowledge of the subject, a structure that represents the pertinent issues, and a little time to do justice to the subject. In this part we give a few hierarchic examples that gave results close to what the values actually were. All the works were published in refereed journals.

WORLD CHESS CHAMPIONSHIP OUTCOME VALIDATION – KARPOV-KORCHNOI MATCH

The following criteria (Table 5-3) and hierarchy (Figure 5-1) were used to predict the outcome of world chess championship matches using judgments of ten grandmasters in the then Soviet Union and the United States who responded to questionnaires they were mailed. The predicted outcomes that included the number of games played, drawn and won by each player either was exactly as they turned out later or adequately close to predict the winner. The outcome of this exercise was officially notarized before the match took place. The notarized statement was mailed to the editor of the *Journal of Behavioral Sciences* along with the paper later (Saaty and Vargas 1991(a).) The prediction was that Karpov would win by 6 to 5 games over Korchnoi, which he did.

Table 5-3: Definitions of Chess Factors

T (1)	Calculation (Q): The ability of a player to evaluate different alternatives or strategies in light of prevailing situations.
B (2)	Ego (E): The image a player has of himself as to his general abilities and qualification and his desire to win.
T (3)	Experience (EX): A composite of the versatility of opponents faced before, the strength of the tournaments participated in, and the time of exposure to a rich variety of chess players.
B (4)	Gamesmanship (G): The capability of a player to influence his opponent's game by destroying his concentration and self-confidence.
T (5)	Good Health (GH): Physical and mental strength to withstand pressure and provide endurance.
B (6)	Good Nerves and Will to Win (GN): The attitude of steadfastness that ensures a player's health perspective while the going gets tough. He keeps in mind that the situation involves two people and that if he holds out the tide may go in his favor.
T (7)	Imagination (IM): Ability to perceive and improvise good tactics and strategies.
T (8)	Intuition (IN): Ability to guess the opponent's intentions.
T (9)	Game Aggressiveness (GA): The ability to exploit the opponent's weaknesses and mistakes to one's advantage. Occasionally referred to as "killer instinct."
T (10)	Long Range Planning (LRP): The ability of a player to foresee the outcome of a certain move, set up desired situations that are more favorable, and work to alter the outcome.
T (11)	Memory (M): Ability to remember previous games.
B (12)	Personality (P): Manners and emotional strength, and their effects on the opponent in playing the game and on the player in keeping his wits.
T (13)	Preparation (PR): Study and review of previous games and ideas.
T (14)	Quickness (Q): The ability of a player to see clearly the heart of a complex problem.
T (15)	Relative Youth (RY): The vigor, aggressiveness, and daring to try new ideas and situations, a quality usually attributed to young age.
T (16)	Seconds (S): The ability of other experts to help one to analyze strategies between games.
B (17)	Stamina (ST): Physical and psychological ability of a player to endure fatigue and pressure.
T (18)	Technique (M): Ability to use and respond to different openings, improvise middle game tactics, and steer the game to a familiar ground to one's advantage.

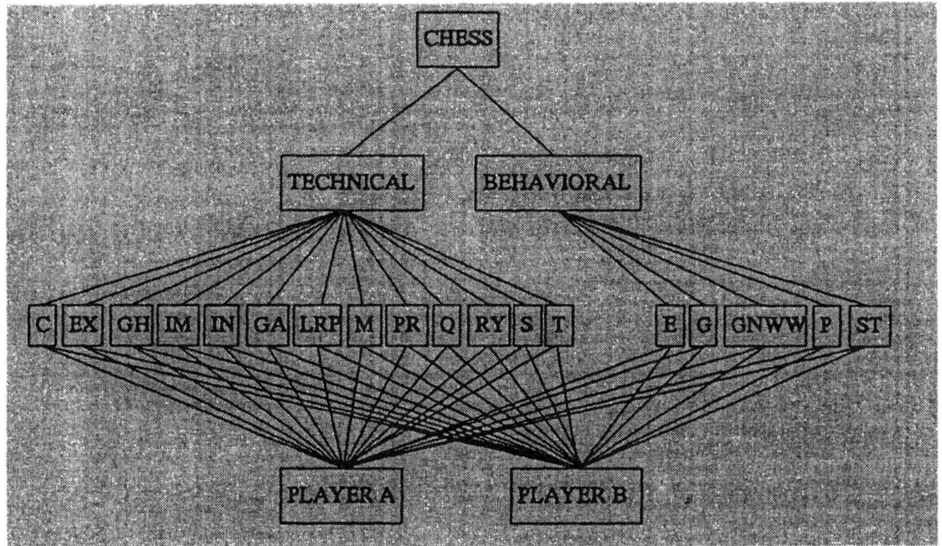

Figure 5-1: Criteria and Players in Chess Competition

MONETARY EXCHANGE RATE – DOLLAR VERSUS THE YEN

In 1987 three economists at the University of Pittsburgh, Professors A. Blair, R. Nachtmann, and J. Olson, worked with T. Saaty on predicting the yen/dollar exchange rate (Figure 5-2). The predicted value was fairly close to the average value for a considerable number of months after that.

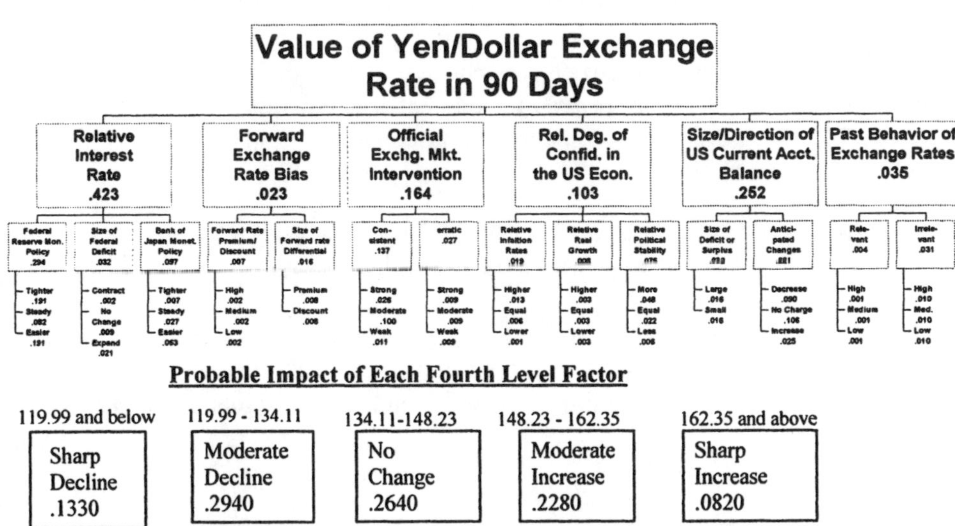

Expected value of 139.90 yen/$ (in late 1980's) computed using midpoints of ranges.

Figure 5-2: The Dollar versus the Yen: Values in the late 1980's

NUMBER OF CHILDREN IN RURAL INDIAN FAMILIES

In a hierarchy whose goal is the optimal family size in India [82] there were four major criteria of Culture (with subcriteria: Religion, Women Status, Manlihood), Economic factors (with subcriteria: Cost of child Rearing, Old Age security, Labor, Economic Improvement, Prestige and Strength), Demographic factors (with subcriteria: Short Life Expectancy, High Infant Mortality) and the Availability and acceptance of contraception (with subcriteria: High Level of Availability and Acceptance of contraception, Medium level of Availability and Acceptance of contraception, low level of Availability and Acceptance of contraception). At the bottom three alternatives were considered: Families with 3 or Less Children, Families with 4 to 7 Children, and Families with 8 or More Children. The outcome of this example for reasons explained in the research paper had two projections of 5.6 and 6.5 children per family (due to regional differences.) The actual value we obtained from the literature after the study was done were 6.8 births per woman in 1972 and 5.6 in 1978.

PREDICTING THE OUTCOME OF THE 1996 SUPERBOWL (SAATY AND TURNER 1995-1996)

My brilliant student David Turner was very interested and knowledgeable about football and he and I worked early in December 1995 at the very start of the playoffs to predict who would go to Superbowl '96 and who would win and who would lose. We used a combination of two hierarchies, one for benefits and one for costs. We predicted that Dallas would win and our own city Pittsburgh would lose which was the correct outcome. On many occasions students tried to make predictions with simplified structures and inevitably ended up making the wrong ones. Of course it is never guaranteed that a prediction of an event that is susceptible to hazards and accidents would come out right as we also mention and give a reference later on.

DECISION BY THE US CONGRESS ON CHINA JOINING THE WORLD TRADE ORGANIZATION (WTO) IN MAY 2000 (SAATY AND CHO, 2001)

This study presented earlier in the book also qualifies as a BOCR hierarchic validation example because it was done long before the decision by Congress was made in favor of China joining the WTO and predicted that outcome.

5-5. Network Validation Examples

TURN AROUND OF THE U.S ECONOMY

This example has already been presented briefly in Chapter 3 of this book, as well as in a Wall Street Journal report about how things came out. The prediction, made more than two years earlier and the surmised actual dates were almost identical.

MARKET SHARES FOR THE CEREAL INDUSTRY (YEAR 2002)

The following is one of numerous validation examples done by my graduate students in business, most of whom work at some company. Many of the examples are done in class in about one hour and without access to data. The answer is only found later on the Internet. The following example was developed by S. Gier and F. John in March 2002. They wrote: To become familiar with the Super Decision software we have chosen to estimate the market shares for the Ready-to Eat breakfast cereal industry. This idea was born after our delicious breakfast with Post's OREO O's. To see how good our assumptions were we compare our calculated results with the market shares of 2001. First we created the model. We identified 6 major competitors in the ready to eat cereal market, Kellogg, General Mills, Post, Quaker, Nabisco and Ralston as our alternatives. There were more companies in this market having an actual cumulative market share of roughly about 6% that it turned out later that we had left out. Since we were only concerned with deriving relative values, the relative shares of other residual companies do not matter.

Major impacts on the companies' market shares are:

- Price of the products offered (named cost for the consumer)
- Advertising / Sales Ratio (how much money is spent for advertising)
- Shelf Space (places where the products are located in the stores)
- Tools (Selling Tools used to increase sales and market shares)
- Distribution / Availability (major distribution channels used to sell the product)

These five major impacts (clusters) are further divided in the following nodes:

Tools: (Coupons, trade dealing, in-pack premiums, vitamin fortifications)
Distribution: (Supermarket Chains, Food Stores, Mass Merchandiser)
Shelf Space: (Premium Space, Normal Space, Bad Space)
Cost: (Expensive, Normal, Cheap)

Advertising: (<15%, <14%, <13%, <12%, <11%, <5%)

Their interactions are depicted in Figure 5-3 below. Second we carried out comparisons and performed calculations to obtain the final result in Table 5-4. Third we compared our calculated market shares with the real market shares for 2001. The table that follows lists estimated market share values and the actual ones taken from the website of the International Data Corporation.

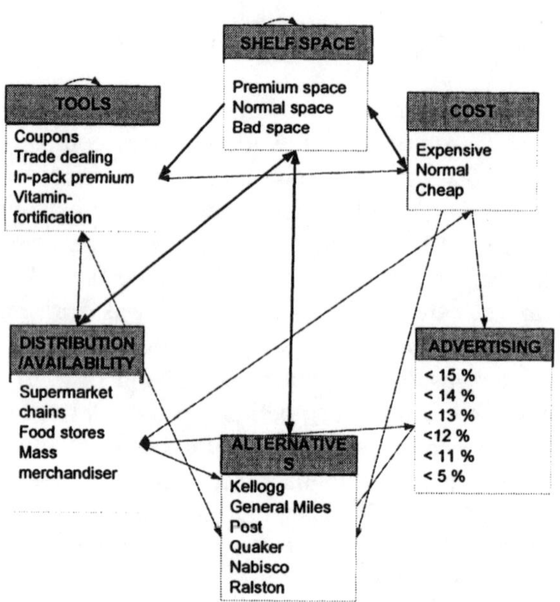

Figure 5-3: Cereal Industry Market Share

Table 5-4: Overall-Results, Estimated and Actual

Alternatives	Kellogg	General Mills	Post	Quaker	Nabisco	Ralston
Estimated	0.324	0.255	0.147	0.116	0.071	0.087
Actual	0.342	0.253	0.154	0.121	0.057	0.073

Compatibility index value: 1.01403 (very good). It is obtained by multiplying element-wise the matrix of ratios of ones set of data, by the transpose of the matrix of ratios of the other set, adding all the resulting entries and dividing by n^2 and requiring that this ratio not be more than 1.1, perhaps even 1.05 or 1.01. as in statistical significance.

5-5. Relationship Between the Supermatrix and the ANP and Input-Output Econometric Analysis

The following proof of the relationship between the supermatrix and Leontieff's Input-Output Model is due to Luis G. Vargas (see also Appendix A on Estimation of Input-Output Technological Coefficients in Saaty and Vargas, 1991 (a).) The figure below depicts interdependence in economic input-output models.

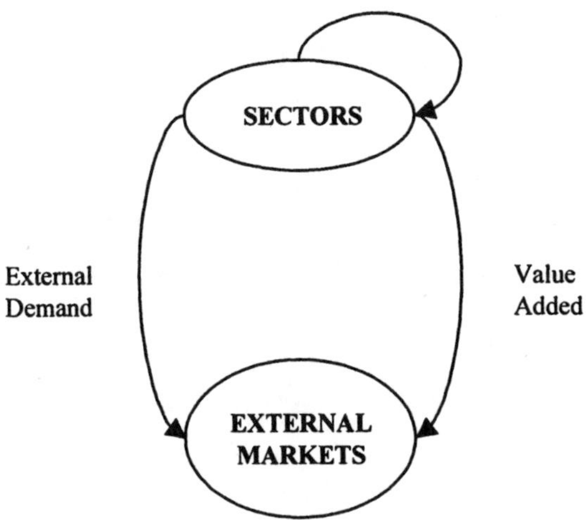

Figure 5-4: Input-Output Network

Let **A** be the matrix of relative input-output coefficients. Let $\boldsymbol{v}$ and $\boldsymbol{d}$ be the relative value added and the relative final demand vectors. Let x_{ij} the amount of resource that sector j receives from sector i. Let v_j be the value added corresponding to sector j and let d_i be the final demand of sector i. The value added of a sector includes wages and salaries, profit-type income, interest, dividends, rents, royalties, capital consumption allowances and taxes. The final demand of a sector includes imports, exports, government purchases, changes in inventory, private investment and sometimes, household purchases. Thus, the input-output matrix is given by:

$$
\begin{array}{cc}
\textit{Sectors} & \begin{array}{cccc} S_1 & S_2 & \cdots & S_n \end{array} \\
\begin{array}{c} S_1 \\ S_2 \\ \vdots \\ S_n \\ \\ \end{array} &
\begin{pmatrix}
x_{11} & x_{12} & \cdots & x_{1n} & d_1 \\
x_{21} & x_{22} & \cdots & x_{2n} & d_2 \\
\vdots & \vdots & \ddots & \vdots & \vdots \\
x_{n1} & x_{n2} & \cdots & x_{nn} & d_n \\
v_1 & v_2 & \cdots & v_n & 0
\end{pmatrix}
\end{array}
$$

Let $I_1, I_2, \ldots, I_n$ be the total input to the sectors and let $O_1, O_2, \ldots, O_n$ be the total output of the sectors, i.e., $\sum_{j=1}^{n} x_{ij} + d_i = O_i$ and $\sum_{i=1}^{n} x_{ij} + v_j = I_j$.

Let the relative input-output coefficients be given by $a_{ij} \equiv \frac{x_{ij}}{I_j}$.

The relative final demand of a sector with respect to the other sectors is given by $a_{i,n+1} \equiv \frac{d_i}{\sum_{h=1}^{n} d_h}$. On the other hand, the relative value added is given by $a_{n+1,1} \equiv \frac{v_j}{I_j}$. Thus, the matrix of interactions represented by the network in Figure 4 is give by:

$$
W = \begin{pmatrix} \mathbf{A} & \bar{a}_{\bullet,n+1} \\ \bar{a}_{n+1,\bullet} & 0 \end{pmatrix} = \left(\begin{array}{cccc|c}
a_{11} & a_{12} & \cdots & a_{1n} & a_{1,n+1} \\
a_{21} & a_{22} & \cdots & a_{2n} & a_{2,n+1} \\
\vdots & \vdots & \ddots & \vdots & \vdots \\
a_{n1} & a_{n2} & \cdots & a_{nn} & a_{n,n+1} \\
a_{n+1,1} & a_{n+1,2} & \cdots & a_{n+1,n} & 0
\end{array}\right)
$$

Because W is a stochastic irreducible matrix, $\lim_{k\to\infty} W^k$ is given by $\bar{w}e^T$ where $\bar{w}$ is a $(n+1)\times 1$ vector that is the principal right eigenvector of W, and $e^T = (1,1,\ldots,1)$ is the $1\times(n+1)$ unit vector. Thus, we have $W\bar{w} = \bar{w}$ or

$$
\sum_{j=1}^{n} a_{ij} w_j + w_{n+1} a_{i,n+1} = w_i, \quad i = 1,2,\ldots,n
$$

$$
\sum_{j=1}^{n} a_{n+1,j} w_j = w_{n+1}
$$

In matrix notation we have:

$$(I - A)\overline{w}_n = w_{n+1}\overline{a}_{\bullet,n+1}$$

$$a_{n+1,\bullet}\overline{w}_n = w_{n+1}$$

where $\overline{w}_n = (w_1,...,w_n)^T$. Thus, we have $\overline{w}_n = w_{n+1}(I - A)^{-1}\overline{a}_{\bullet,n+1}$ and hence, we can write

$$\lim_{k\to\infty} W^k = \begin{pmatrix} w_{n+1}(I-A)^{-1}\overline{a}_{\bullet,n+1} \\ w_{n+1} \end{pmatrix} e^T .$$

Note that $\overline{w}_n = w_{n+1}(I - A)^{-1}\overline{a}_{\bullet,n+1}$ is the relative output of the economy as given by Leontieff's model.

EXAMPLE OF AN INPUT-OUTPUT MATRIX

Consider the following input-output matrix shown in the Table 5-5 below.

Table 5-5: Input-Output Matrix

	Agriculture	Manufacturing	Services	Other	Final Demand	Total Output
Agriculture	10	65	10	5	10	100
Manufacturing	40	25	35	75	25	200
Services	15	5	5	5	90	120
Other	15	10	50	50	100	225
Value Added	20	95	20	90	0	
Total Input	100	200	120	225	225	645

The supermatrix corresponding to this input-output model is given in Table 5-6:

Table 5-6: The Supermatrix for the Input-Output Matrix

	0.1	0.325	0.083333333	0.022222222	0.044444444
	0.4	0.125	0.291666667	0.333333333	0.111111111
W=	0.15	0.025	0.041666667	0.022222222	0.4
	0.15	0.05	0.416666667	0.222222222	0.444444444
	0.2	0.475	0.166666667	0.4	0

and the limiting matrix $\lim_{k\to\infty} W^k$ is given in Table 5-7:

Table 5-7: Limiting Supermatrix of the Input-Output Table

0.114942529	0.114942529	0.114942529	0.114942529	0.114942529
0.229885057	0.229885057	0.229885057	0.229885057	0.229885057
0.137931034	0.137931034	0.137931034	0.137931034	0.137931034
0.25862069	0.25862069	0.25862069	0.25862069	0.25862069
0.25862069	0.25862069	0.25862069	0.25862069	0.25862069

$$\bar{w}_n = \begin{pmatrix} 0.114942529 \\ 0.229885057 \\ 0.137931034 \\ 0.25862069 \end{pmatrix}$$

By normalizing to unity we can see that

$$\bar{w}_n(1 - w_{n+1})^{-1} = \begin{pmatrix} 0.15503876 \\ 0.310077519 \\ 0.186046512 \\ 0.348837209 \end{pmatrix} = \frac{1}{645}\begin{pmatrix} 100 \\ 200 \\ 120 \\ 225 \end{pmatrix}$$

This coincides with the normalized values of the total output of the economy.

T. Saaty and L. Vargas (1979) studied the input-output supermatrix of the Sudan economy (1976) with eigenvector values. Table 5-8 gives the estimates and the actual values in parentheses computed by the now Nobel Laureate Lawrence Klein who participated in the study with his Wharton Forecasting Associates. The results of this fairly complex exercise using paired comparison judgments are generally close to those of the econometric forecasting model.

Table 5-8: Input-Output Table of Sudan Economy (1976) by Wharton Forecasting Associates

	Agriculture	Public Utilities	Manufacturing and Mining	Transportation and Distribution	Construction	Services
Agriculture	.0079 (.00737)	0 (0)	.2331 (.21953)	.0008 (.00042)	.0699 (.06721)	0 (0)
Public Utilities	.0009 (.00024)	0 (0)	.0130 (.01159)	.0075 (.00618)	0 (0)	.0033 (.00283)
Manufacturing and Mining	.0041 (.00393)	0 (0)	0 (0)	.0089 (.00857)	.0379 (.04216)	.0037 (.00322)
Transportation and Distribution	.0691 (.06993)	.1694 (.145360)	.1281 (.12574)	0 (0)	.1115 (.09879)	.0153 (.00641)
Construction	0 (0)	0 (0)	0 (0)	0 (0)	0 (0)	.0546 (.05402)
Services	0 (0)	.0117 (.01030)	.0224 (.02549)	.0224 (.02422)	.0039 (.00520)	.0004 (.000210)

5-6. Desirability of Drilling for Oil in Alaska – the Artic National Wildlife Refuge (ANWR) – ANP Model

A study was done by J. Emanuel and P. Cefalu in 2002 to find out whether drilling for oil should be allowed in the Artic National Wildlife Refuge (ANWR) in northern Alaska. Environmentalists, mostly living in the lower 48 US states had been blocking drilling in the region. In the ANWR study the alternatives were: Drill, Do Not Drill. And the study results were compared against a poll of Alaskan residents asking the question: "Do you think we should drill, or not drill in ANWR?"

ANWR covers 19 million acres on the Northern coast of Alaska north of the Arctic Circle and 1,300 miles south of the North Pole. The consensus of the geologic community is that the Coastal Plain of ANWR represents the highest petroleum potential onshore area yet to be explored in North America. If explored, it is estimated that it will take 15 years or more before oil and gas will reach the market. Legislation was passed in the 1980's that created a majority of the National Parks in Alaska and expanded ANWR to its current size. The Reagan Administration was ready to drill but was derailed by the Exxon Valdez catastrophe. The first Bush Administration likewise wanted to drill, but was unsuccessful. The Clinton Administration designated it as a protected area and it has been that way ever since then. The second Bush Administration, in response to ongoing Middle East violence and the 9/11 terrorist attacks, sees drilling in ANWR as vital not only for economic but national security reasons. Several environmental groups consider ANWR a great American natural treasure and one of the last places on the earth where an intact expanse of arctic and sub-arctic lands remain protected. They feel the habitat, the wildlife, and the culture need to be protected from the exploration of gas and oil. The strategic criteria here are General Public Opinion, International Politics, and Amount of Oil. They are first pairwise compared for importance, then used to rate the importance of the top rated alternative for each of the Benefits, Opportunities, Costs and Risks, called the merits of the decision. The ratings categories themselves are pairwise compared to establish priorities for High, Medium and Low. To select the appropriate rating, keep in mind the highest priority alternative under the merit being evaluated. Do Not Drill is, for example, the highest priority alternative under risk, meaning it is the most risky. The Risk merit under General Public Opinion is evaluated as being low. The results of rating the merits are: Benefits .407, closely followed by Opportunities at .364. In this decision, Costs are found to be unimportant, and Risks are about half as important as the sum of Benefits and Opportunities. These values for the merits nodes are used to weight the values for the alternatives as determined in the subnets they control to give the overall results for the alternatives.

The subnet for Benefits contains a hierarchy of control criteria. Connected to each control criterion node under benefits is a decision network containing the alternatives of the problem. The final results from the subnets are combined in the main network using the formula bB + oO - cC – rR where b, o, c, and r are the values for the decision alternatives from the control subnets, and B, O, C, and R are the priorities of the BOCR as determined by rating them under the strategic criteria. Drill received the value .78 and Do Not Drill the value .22. In a poll (2002) conducted among native Alaskans it turned out that they supported opening ANWR to oil and gas exploration 75% to 19% with 6% undecided. The question asked was "Do you believe oil and gas exploration should or should not be allowed within the ANWR Coastal Plain?" Assigning the 6% undecided equally yields 78% to 22%. The results of the poll are surprisingly close to the results of the model.

There are also examples where predictions based on wrong assumptions gave rise to wrong or unrealistic outcomes. Saaty and Gholmnezhad (1982) gave a wrong estimate of what the price of a barrel of oil would be in subsequent years. That study tended to exaggerate the power and solidarity of OPEC and the ability of other countries to counter high oil prices with various policies. Soon after, it was revised and published by the second author giving much more realistic results by examining the political situation at the time ("Oil Prices," Chapter 8 in Saaty and Vargas 1991(b). See also references at the end of Chapter 8.)

The foregoing validation examples are useful not only by illustrating how some decisions are structured, but also in giving us confidence that judgments have much greater usefulness when applied within a carefully designed structure. If some judgments are biased or if they are uncertain, other judgments can serve to correct or modify them so in the end one obtains a reliable answer. It appears that the process of understanding is not based on one judgment or idea, but on a collection of judgments that support each other in some justified way grounded in the layout of the decision. That is why we believe that having a dictionary of the structures of decisions is a useful undertaking.

5-7. AHP/ANP and the Fundamental Scale of Absolute Numbers

The numbers used in the AHP, both in the fundamental scale used to make paired comparisons and in the derived scales, differ substantially from numbers used from other type of cardinal scales of measurement such as interval and ratio scales used in decision making. The numbers obtained by solving an eigenvalue problem with real number coefficients are also real numbers. Normalizing them is tantamount to dividing an absolute numbers by the sum of absolute numbers that is again an absolute number. The outcome is again an absolute or a real number that is in relative form like probabilities. Let us examine it in the consistent case. Any of the columns of the pairwise comparisons matrix when normalized yields the eigenvector. But any column consists of absolute numbers and normalizing them again yields a vector of relative absolute or real numbers.

The construction of those other cardinal scale numbers requires an arbitrary unit of measurement and all the numbers or measurements are obtained by applying that arbitrary unit linearly as one often does with a variety of coordinate axes, although there are nonlinear axes whose use for measurement in science is very limited. In physics and astronomy one uses mostly ratio scales to develop theories about the real world. One needs to get used to the idea of what the arbitrary unit and different multiples of that unit actually mean in the scheme of human thinking and values in trying to understanding the real world within some context or another.

It is one thing to improvise ways to associate numbers with objects and another to determine the meaning of these numbers. What we read on a scale for weight, length and temperature for example must be interpreted through experience. A temperature reading of 32 degrees Fahrenheit means freezing to a person accustomed to that scale but to a person used to a Celsius scale it means hot weather until that person goes through the operation of translating from one temperature scale to the other. However, when we look for what is important to us and use paired comparisons to articulate importance accurately with an absolute number, that number represents what we actually mean because there are no further numbers to translate it to. It is the ultimate. That is why a discussion of decision-making compels us to examine the measurement of intangibles with which we associate the ideas of importance and of preference and of likelihood as in probabilities. How to measure and refine the scale readings of tangibles is an elementary academic concern with the accuracy of readings and of fitting data that has yet to be interpreted according to meaning. Refining the use of many actual measurements to improve their accuracy and validity would still need a reliable way to make such measurements valuable to our value systems just as it is the case with intangibles.

The numbers used in the pairwise comparisons of the AHP are absolute numbers that are not defined in terms of a unit in order for them to be invariant under the identity transformation. How are they defined? They are real numbers and their derivation depends on how one first defines the positive integers and from there the rational numbers, the positive real numbers the nonnegative real numbers and finally all the real numbers. What is a positive integer?

Bertrand Russell (1948) writes, "The number of a class is the class of all those classes that are similar to it.... "Similar" is a 1-1 relation of which one class is the domain and the other is the range... The act of counting consists in establishing a 1-1 correlation between the set of objects counted and the natural numbers (excluding 0) that are used up in the process." Peano's axioms provide a logical foundation to derive the entire real number system without the need for an absolute zero. Such numbers do not intrinsically need axes with an origin for their representation although the use of axes and geometry facilitates imagining the relative magnitudes of numbers. In the AHP the derived relative scales in the form of the principal right eigenvector of the pairwise comparisons matrix are nonlinear and cannot be simply represented by means of linear axes. We need an appropriate framework for dealing with composite measurements derived with the AHP and the more complex ANP with its infinitely derived composition forms.

Measurement on physical scales with numbers is a very recent discovery. The Julian calendar lost a year by going from the year 1 B.C to the year 1 A.D without having a zero in between because zero was not yet known. People can tell the difference between comfortable, cold, very cold, severely cold and warm, hot, very hot and severely hot. Similarly they can tell about relative brightness and relative sweetness or sourness. They can also tell the difference among degrees of anger and of pleasure and love and so on. The same talent is used to distinguish among different degrees of tact or of persuasion a politician uses or how clear and sharp a teacher's explanation is. One can go on to show that this talent is applied to whatever people deal with and learn about through experience.

Making comparisons is an intrinsic and basic mode of measurement of the mind. It measures not by arbitrarily assigning a number to each object independently of the others, but by identifying the smallest of a pair of objects as the unit (an equivalence class) and estimating the number of times of that unit the larger object is. Comparisons are our way of giving meaning to objects and ideas by relating them to our goals through prioritization, ordering and classification. The AHP/ANP provides us with a scientific way to use comparisons through measurement whether a decision is structured as a hierarchy or more significantly for real life decision as a network with dependence and feedback. Only through heroic oversimplification does one make a decision as a hierarchy of a goal, criteria and alternatives.

Unlike the direct and hard to justify assignment of arbitrary numbers to objects, redundancy in making several comparisons of each object with other objects in a class helps improve the numerical accuracy of the judgments of an informed person expressed in the form of real numbers to estimate the relative dominance of homogeneous objects and derive their priorities in the from of relative numbers that are positive when dealing with criteria that are favorable and negative in the opposite case.

5-8. NORMALIZATION IS BASIC IN RELATIVE MEASUREMENT

To obtain the relative values in the last column of this table, given that the numbers in the two columns under the criteria are represented in form relative to each other, the AHP requires that the criteria be assigned priorities in the following way. One adds the measurement values under each and divides it by the sum of the measurements with respect to all the other criteria measured on the same scale. This gives the priority of that criterion for that unit of measurement. Multiplying the relative values of the alternatives by the relative values of the criteria, and adding gives the final column of Table 5-9. Each of the middle three columns in Table 5-9 gives the value and the value normalized (relative value) in that column.

Table 5-9: Scale Measurement Converted to Relative Measurement

Alternatives	Criterion C_1 Normalized weight = 6/18		Criterion C_2 Normalized weight = 12/18		Sums and Normalized Sums		AHP Synthesized Weighted Relative Values
A_1	1	1/6	3	3/12	4	4/18	4/18 = .222
A_2	2	2/6	4	4/12	6	6/18	6/18 = .333
A_3	3	3/6	5	5/12	8	8/18	8/18 = .444

The outcome in the last column coincides with the last column of ERROR, as it should. More generally, normalization is always needed when the criteria depend on the alternatives as in the Analytic network Process (ANP).

One thing we learn from this example is that if we add new alternatives, the ratios of the priorities of the old alternatives remain the same. Let us prove it for example in the case of two criteria C_1 and C_2. We begin with two alternatives A and B, whose priorities under C_1 and C_2 are respectively, a_i and b_i $i=1,2$ which in relative form are

$$a_i / \sum_{i=1}^{2} a_i \text{ and } b_i / \sum_{i=1}^{2} b_i .$$

The weights of C_1 and C_2 are respectively

$$\sum_{i=1}^{2} a_i /(\sum_{i=1}^{2} a_i + \sum_{i=1}^{2} b_i), \sum_{i=1}^{2} b_i /(\sum_{i=1}^{2} a_i + \sum_{i=1}^{2} b_i).$$

Synthesizing by weighting and adding yields for the overall priorities of A and B respectively

$$(a_1 + b_1)/(\sum_{i=1}^{2} a_i + \sum_{i=1}^{2} b_i), \text{ and } (a_2 + b_2)/(\sum_{i=1}^{2} a_i + \sum_{i=1}^{2} b_i).$$

The ratio of these priorities is $(a_1 + b_1)/(a_2 + b_2)$ which only depends on their values and not on the priorities of the criteria. We note that the sum of the values of the alternatives is used to normalize the value of each alternative by dividing by it. But this value is also the numerator of the priority of that criterion and cancels out in the weighting process leaving the sum of the values of the alternatives under both criteria in the denominator of the final result. This sum in turn cancels in taking the ratio of the priorities of A and B. Now it is clear that if we add a third alternative C, this ratio of the priorities of A and B remains unaffected by the change in the priorities of the criteria due to C. We conclude that in this case where the priorities of the criteria depend on the alternatives, the ratio of the priorities of the alternatives is invariant to adding a new alternative. This invariance should also hold in the stronger case when the criteria are independent of the alternatives, but the alternatives themselves are structurally independent of one another. When proportionality is not maintained because of structural dependence for each criterion, rank can reverse. Thus when the ideal mode is used the ideal must be preserved so that when new alternatives are added, they are compared with the old ideal allowing values to go above one, and thus the ratios among the existing alternatives can be preserved.

One can say that there is a natural law that binds absolute measurement to relative measurement on several criteria and that law is normalization. However, normalization loses information about the original measurements, the original unit of measurement and its associated zero. For example, normalizing measurement in pennies and corresponding values of measurement in dollars yield the same relative values, losing the information that they come from different orders of magnitude and have different units.

5-9. The AHP and Utility Theory – Absolute Scales and Interval Scales

Prior to the AHP, people developed utility functions for the alternatives of a decision with respect to different criteria known as attributes. An attribute is a property of an alternative. However there may be other factors that affect the alternatives that are not intrinsic to them such as environmental, social and political influences that serve as conditions or criteria to be satisfied and hence the more general word criteria instead of attributes is used in the AHP. Utility theory and all other decision-making theories evaluate or rate alternatives one at a time by assuming them to be totally independent of each other. The range of values of the alternatives under them determines the importance of criteria. A criterion is more discriminating (not important) if alternatives are more separated under it. There are different methods for calculating the criteria discrimination "weights" involving lotteries. If the "weights" sum to unity the synthesis is a weighted sum, otherwise a multiplicative principle is used. Because utility functions are based on interval scales and interval scale numbers cannot be added or multiplied, synthesis in utility theory requires that utilities take values in the interval [0, 1].

Despite a long history of science where ideas and theories keep changing, there are still people in the world who have the attitude that if they cannot explain something in their own minds it cannot exist. That is why people steeped in utility theory based on a so called rational thinking find it difficult to understand or believe that the AHP is not only a valid theory but also and much more importantly works in practice even better than what they have convinced themselves cannot be true. All they would have to do is to try a concrete application with open understanding as others have. Let us provide a discussion about why the AHP has intrinsic psychological justification that not many people really know. Tobias Dantzig (1954), by referring to the "opinion of competent observers of animal behavior supported by a weighty mass of evidence" writes on page 1, " Number sense should not be confused with counting, which is probably of a much later vintage, and involves, as we shall see, a rather intricate mental process. Counting ... is an attribute exclusively human, whereas some brute species seem to possess a rudimentary number sense akin to our own." He then goes on to show how birds and wasps have the number sense but his best example is the following. "A squire was determined to shoot a crow which made its nest in the watch-tower of his estate. Repeatedly he tried to surprise the bird, but in vain: at the approach of a man the crow would leave its nest. From a distant tree it would watchfully wait until the man had left the tower and then return to its nest. One day the squire hit upon a ruse: two men entered the tower, one remained within the other came out and went on. But the bird was not deceived: it kept away until the man within came out. The experiment was repeated on the succeeding days with two, three, then four men, yet without success. Finally, five men were sent: as before, all entered the tower, and one remained while the other four came out and went away. Here the crow lost count. Unable to distinguish between four and five it promptly returned to its nest." He emphasizes that not all animals (such as dogs, horses and other domestic animals) have this talent. But insects, birds and humans do. He also says that the human number sense is quite limited. Experiments on primitive people corroborate these observations to a remarkable degree. However, counting has become such a part of our mental workings that psychological tests now have trouble performing tests on our number perception.

The mathematician and cognitive neuropsychologist, Stanislas Dehaene (1997) writes in his book, "Introspection suggests that we can mentally represent the meaning of numbers 1 through 9 with actual acuity. Indeed, these symbols seem equivalent to us. They all seem equally easy to work with, and we feel that we can add or compare any two digits in a small and fixed amount of time like a computer. In summary, the invention of numerical symbols should have freed us from the fuzziness of the quantitative representation of numbers." To a person who does not know anything about numbers as our forebears of the distant past were, they still had the instinct for the different magnitudes 1-9 and used words, grunts and emotions to express them. These are absolute numbers invariant under the identity transformation. This means that they are only invariant on multiplication by the number one, thus they satisfy the relation x=1.x. In paired comparisons the smaller of the two elements being compared has the value of one, and the larger is estimated as a multiple of one, satisfying the requirement of an absolute number. A person who knows nothing about numbers uses the same feelings about intensities to compare what others may call tangibles or intangibles. Not long ago, there were no tangibles whose measurements could be used to check on the accuracy of comparison. However, our validation examples show how these measurements can now help us develop our theories that use judgment intensities so that the derived priorities correspond closely to actual measurements transformed to relative values.

Basic differences between the AHP and Utility Theory are: The AHP is a psychophysical theory that is based on paired comparisons. Utility theory rates alternatives one at a time using utility functions. The AHP also has another rating mode that is entirely based on paired comparisons to create the rating categories. Both modes are needed in making complex decisions. In some decisions the importance of the criteria depends on the alternatives as in the ANP and in other decisions it does not; the scales used when doing pairwise comparisons in the AHP are absolute rather than interval scales; the AHP allows for rank reversal because in paired comparisons how good an alternative is depends on what other alternatives it is compared with, but it also allows for rank preservation by using the concept of an ideal in deriving priorities. The AHP literature includes studies about when to preserve rank and when to allow rank to change. The ANP approach and the absolute scale make it possible to analyze decisions with interdependence and feedback. To the best of our knowledge, utility practitioners resort to Bayesian statistical analysis when there is dependence in decisions. It can be shown that estimating probabilities or likelihoods is a process that can also be done by using paired comparisons and has been applied in numerous prediction problems like the chess validation example and thus Bayesian analysis using actual statistical data is a part of ANP considerations. A study has been made by T. Saaty, and L. Vargas (1998) to show that.

There are seven important areas in which utility theory has been found to have major problems by experts who know the subject and have tried to use its ideas.

1. Utility theory with its axiom about the ordering of alternatives assumes transitivity of preferences: if A is preferred to B and B preferred to C then A must be preferred to C contradicting some happenings in the real world where team A beats team B and team B beats team C but team C beats team A. No such assumption is made in the AHP. My friend, the brilliant John Harsanyi, the well known utility and game theorist who won the Nobel Prize in economics and who coached me about utility theory when I wrote my book on the mathematics of arms control and disarmament, often told me that this intransitivity in the winning of games by teams is an aberration that should be ignored in theory even as it occurs in the real world. The requirement of transitivity is an axiom of utility theory.
2. There are many situations where one cannot develop a utility function. Machina (1987) studied in detail unsolved problems of utility theory.
3. Often, when one develops a utility function, it is incompatible with human understanding and common sense, it is not user friendly, and different methods of constructing utility functions can yield different utilities for the same individual (see McCord, M. and R. de Neufville, 1983.)
4. There is a wide gap between actual data measurements and the estimated values of such data by utility theory.
5. Utility theory has three well-known paradoxes: St. Petersburg's Paradox, Allais' Paradox, and Ellsberg's Paradox (see for example the Internet for what these paradoxes are about). In a mathematical and logical sense one paradox should be sufficient to dismiss a theory as contradictory. In logic a paradox is considered as an antinomy, a contradiction between statements. The presence of a paradox implies incompatibility among the assumptions, some contradiction among the axioms. In so far as truth is naturally regarded as the norm in science, all deviations from the truth, that is falsehood and contradiction, are naturally regarded as paradoxes.

6. Utility measurement is on an interval scale. Readings from an interval scale cannot be added or multiplied. For example, in $(ax_1 + b) + (ax_2 + b) = a(x_1 + x_2) + 2b$ the final outcome of adding on the right does not have the form $ax + b$ of the original scale and is meaningless. However one can take an average reading. Dividing by two above yields an interval scale reading.
7. Utility theory is mainly used for representing preferences in situations involving risk. The construction of utilities requires the use of lotteries. In fact utilities are defined in the space of lotteries. The AHP has been used in both certain risky and uncertain situations with paired comparisons to estimate likelihoods or subjective probabilities. Value theory, predominantly used in multi-criteria theory, is the certainty variant of utility theory.

It has been noted that taking differences in measurements does not give the same idea of dominance. R.K. Sarin (1982) wrote: "The meaning of strength of preference is limited to observations regarding the relative "closeness" or "similarity" of preferences for consequences, rather than to absolute statements that one consequence is twice as good as another." In other words in utility theory, because measurements are on an interval scale, it is not meaningful to make absolute statements about preferences but only about differences. However, paired comparisons are absolute statements about the strength of preference. That is true because in situations where there are ratio scale measurements, the absolute scale values can be taken as the relative values of these measurements which are dimensionless numbers that are absolute. When there are no such scales they are estimates of ratios (absolute numbers) of values of an underlying scale. In sum, in the AHP the derived priorities are absolute numbers that are identical with the relative values of actual measurements on ratio or absolute scales used to represent judgments as ratios. In addition, when the judgments are consistent, the derived priorities have the same ratios, as do the corresponding judgments themselves. Utility theory derives interval scales that by their very nature do not correspond to any measurement scale used in practice except perhaps for temperature, and cannot be used to form ratios of anything unless one goes through a process of taking differences of more than two readings derived prior to carrying out such a forced attempt to convert to ratios. Besides, interval scales cannot be used to derive priorities for criteria and subcriteria, so one has different scales for criteria and for alternatives. Early in its development, authors in utility theory did not think that criteria could be compared to create weights for them.

Early in the development of the AHP a person who works in utility theory and is one of its strong advocates came to visit and stayed at my house. He conveyed to me and other colleagues who work in the AHP that the AHP made people in what they call decision analysis unhappy and made the offer that the utility theory people he represented were willing to use the AHP including the eigenvector approach down to the level of the criteria above the alternatives if we agreed to using utility functions for the alternatives. I pointed out that the AHP was already in the literature and that people would ask why one should not also compare the alternatives. That person went on to create much animosity against the AHP in the United States. This reminds one of Voltaire who said, *"I disapprove of what you say, but I will defend to the death your right to say it."* This person and his colleagues' actions have helped increase interest in the spread of the AHP/ANP by a diversity of people throughout the world through publications and through the International Society on the Analytic Hierarchy Process with its ISAHP meetings held every two years.

5-10. The Interdependence of Alternatives According to Measurement Values – The Arbitrary Preservation of Rank in Ratings

Given a set of alternatives that has been ranked by some procedure, should adding or deleting alternatives change the ranking among the existing set when no criteria are added and no old judgments revised? It is not a law of nature, science or mathematics that this should happen. If alternatives are rated one at a time, it is clear that no alternative old or new has anything to do with this rating process and rank should not change. But is it preserved because of the procedure one selects to use or is it a justifiable process with intrinsic merits. The assumption of independence of alternatives has substantial weaknesses in any rating process that of course does not compare the alternatives. When they are compared their ranks depend on each other in a fundamental way. A poor alternative can look very good when compared with still poorer ones. If that is all one has, the ranks obtained are accurate and real. What does one think of when one rates alternatives? One thinks of the best possible (an ideal) in that class and assigns the present alternative a number that compares with the largest value allowed, a fairly arbitrary and unreliable process. It would be better to perform paired comparisons of an alternative with the ideal than assign it some number from one's mind. One does not know the nature of the number assigned. From comparisons one would know that it is an absolute number even if it is only an estimate. The ideal may not be good enough and the judgments are guesses rather than attempts at measurement. When one alternative has been examined and rated, the mind cannot forget that information which necessarily affects how the next alternative is evaluated. There is no escaping this fact even if different individuals do the evaluation, because awareness of other alternatives influences how any of them is thought of. Thus assuming independence is a poor excuse for not having a better way such as comparisons to do the evaluation. Another problem that cannot be simply ignored by assuming independence is that as the number of alternatives increases to become very large, that number can affect what one thinks of any of the alternatives as some can become less scarce and thus how any alternative is evaluated depends on how scarce or abundant it is. Both these issues are part of the comparisons process but not of rating alternatives one at a time. Rating alternatives one at a time is a convenient but an arbitrary process of number assignment in multicriteria setting. The conclusion is that introducing alternatives or deleting others often can and should have an effect on the ranks of the other alternatives because they cannot be regarded as independent without eventual peril to producing false ranks. When the alternatives depend on each other with respect to measurement the distributive mode of the AHP is used for normalization. When rating alternatives on different criteria by assuming independence one uses the ideal mode of the AHP to preserve rank with respect to these criteria provided that the ideal is not changed. Thus one attempts to preserve rank when performance with respect to an ideal is sought and allow it to change when performance relative to other alternatives is what is desired.

Here are the doubts about preserving rank that Luce and Raiffa (1957) expressed in their book. They give four variations on the axiom about whether rank should or should not be preserved with counterexamples in each case and without concluding that it always should and why.

They write: "Adding new acts to a decision problem under uncertainty, each of which is weakly dominated by or is equivalent to some old act, has no effect on the optimality or non-optimality of an old act."

They elaborate it with: “If an act is non optimal for a decision problem under uncertainty, it cannot be made optimal by adding new acts to the problem.”

They then press it further to: “The addition of new acts does not transform an old, originally non-optimal act into an optimal one, and it can change an old, originally optimal act into a non-optimal one only if at least one of the new acts is optimal.”

They think of the extreme with: “The addition of new acts to a decision problem under uncertainty never changes old, originally non-optimal acts into optimal ones.”

Finally they conclude with: “The all-or-none feature of the last form may seem a bit too stringent ... a severe criticism is that it yields unreasonable results."

5-11. THE 1992 U.S. ELECTIONS AND PHANTOM ALTERNATIVES

A simple example of rank reversal is in the presidential elections of 1992 when the entry of Ross Perot into the election took votes away from Bush. The prediction as to who would win the race prior to Perot's entry is Bush as shown in Figure 5-5. After Perot enters the race, Bush is predicted to lose to Clinton as shown in Figure 5-6, because Perot takes votes from Bush. This is actually what happened and Clinton won. To force rank preservation, start with the situation shown in Figure 5-5 and idealize by dividing by the larger priority of the two candidates, Bush and Clinton, under each criterion. Bush would receive a larger overall priority than Clinton. Then consider Figure 5-6 and idealize by dividing each entry in a column by the largest value in that column thus obtaining Figure 5-7. In Figure 5-7 Bush is still ahead of Clinton and should be the winner, which he was not. In effect, relative comparisons and normalization as in Figure 5-6 take into consideration the relative number of people voting for the candidates by considering each criterion separately, and then weighting and combining the relative numbers. Idealizing gives the wrong answer as rating them one at a time by using intensities under each criterion would.

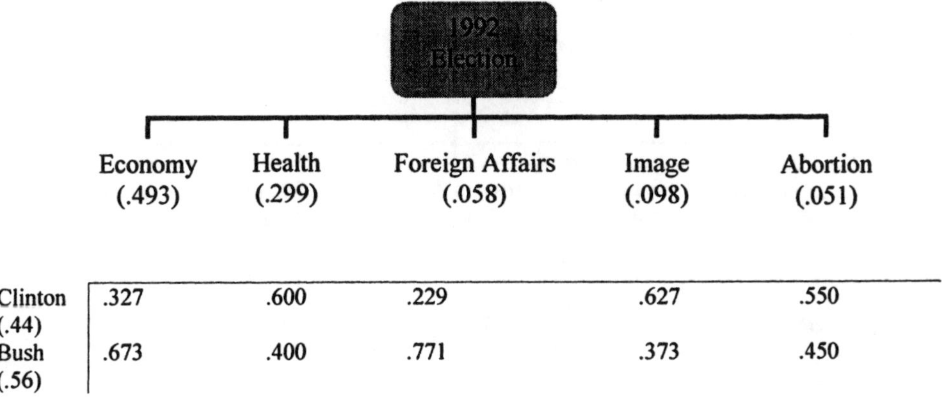

	Economy (.493)	Health (.299)	Foreign Affairs (.058)	Image (.098)	Abortion (.051)
Clinton (.44)	.327	.600	.229	.627	.550
Bush (.56)	.673	.400	.771	.373	.450

Figure 5-5: Presidential Elections with Standings for Bush and Clinton before Perot

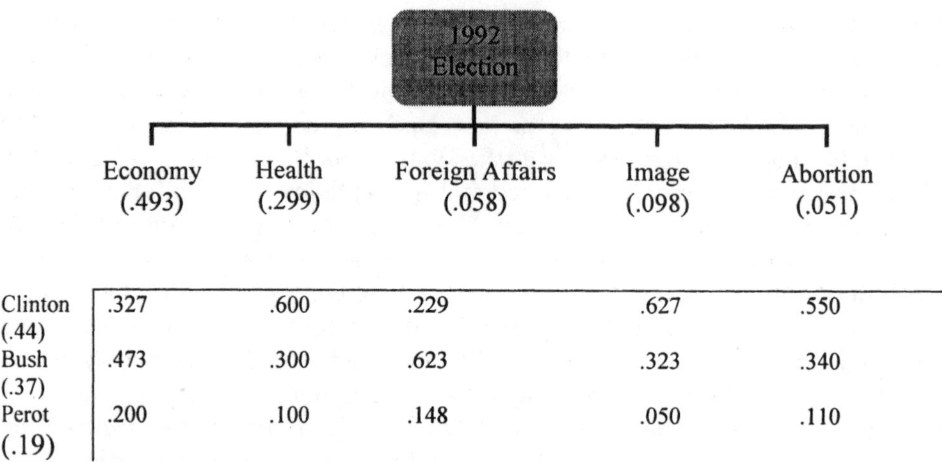

	Economy (.493)	Health (.299)	Foreign Affairs (.058)	Image (.098)	Abortion (.051)
Clinton (.44)	.327	.600	.229	.627	.550
Bush (.37)	.473	.300	.623	.323	.340
Perot (.19)	.200	.100	.148	.050	.110

Figure 5-6: Presidential Race with Three Candidates; Prediction Close to Actual Result

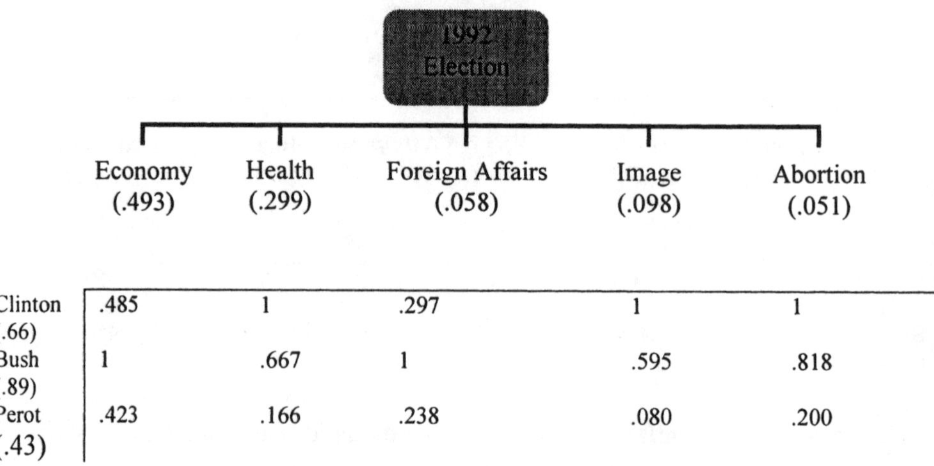

	Economy (.493)	Health (.299)	Foreign Affairs (.058)	Image (.098)	Abortion (.051)
Clinton (.66)	.485	1	.297	1	1
Bush (.89)	1	.667	1	.595	.818
Perot (.43)	.423	.166	.238	.080	.200

Figure 5-7: Forcing Rank Preservation by Idealizing gives Wrong Results

Ruth Corbin and A.A.J. Marley give the following example in the Journal of Mathematical Psychology 11,274-293 (1974). A lady in a small town wishes to buy a hat. She enters the only hat store in town, and finds two hats A and B, that she likes equally well, and so might be considered equally likely to buy. However now suppose that the sales clerk discovers a third hat that is identical to B. Then the lady may well choose hat A (rather than risk the possibility of seeing someone wearing a hat just like hers). But this result contradicts regularity, which says that one cannot increase the probability of a subject's choosing some currently available item by adding further alternatives to the choice set. We note that the criterion "uniqueness" cannot be added to the criteria because then the alternatives would violate what is known as weak independence (which I called structural dependence) that is essential for rating alternatives one at a time.

PHANTOM ALTERNATIVES AS USED IN MARKETING

The following example illustrates an interesting and real occurrence in the world of marketing. A *phantom* alternative A_3 is publicized in the media to deliberately cause rank reversal between A_1 and A_2 with the ideal mode. We begin with A_1 dominating A_2. Introducing A_3 we obtain reversal in the rank of A_2 over A_1 once with A_3 between A_1 and A_2 and once ranking the last of the three. This is the case of a phantom alternative (a car) A_3 that is more expensive and thus less desirable but has the best quality in terms of efficiency. People bought A_1 because it is cheaper, but A_2 is a much better car because of its efficiency. Knowing that a (considerably) more expensive car A_3 will be on the market that also has only slightly better efficiency than A_2 makes people shift their preference to A_2 over A_1, without anything happening that causes them to change the relative importance of the criteria: efficiency and cost. Car A_3 is called a phantom because it is never made, it is proposed in advertising in a way to induce people to change their overall choice, although their preferences remain the same as before. Note that we already showed that with consistent judgments that preserve proportionality among the old alternatives, rank reversal could take place with no change in the weights of the criteria. With inconsistency proportionality is no longer preserved and rank reversal is even more natural. We recall that when dealing with intangibles, judgments are rarely consistent no matter how hard one tries unless they are forced to be consistent afterwards through number crunching.

The following example shows that one can preserve the old judgments, but if the new alternatives have slightly different judgments, the rank will change with the ideal mode when the alternative that is ideal is changed. In Part A of the example, on introducing A_3, the ideal changed from A_2 to A_3 under the second criterion and A_3 has the value .2 under the first criterion. In Part B of the example, the only difference is that A_3 has the value .3 under the first criterion. The upshot is A_2 is the best choice in both after introducing the phantom, but in the first case $A_2 > A_3 > A_1$ while in the second case $A_2 > A_1 > A_3$. As the phantom A_3 becomes more costly (Example – Part B) it becomes the least desirable. Note that because of idealization as A_3 assumes values closer to those of A_2, A_1 would remain the more desired of the two alternatives A_1 and A_2.

Example - Part A

$$\text{Cost}\quad \begin{array}{c} \\ A_1 \\ A_2 \end{array} \begin{array}{c} A_1 \quad A_2 \\ \begin{pmatrix} 1 & 2.5 \\ 1/2.5 & 1 \end{pmatrix} \end{array} \qquad \text{Efficiency}\quad \begin{array}{c} \\ A_1 \\ A_2 \end{array} \begin{array}{c} A_1 \quad A_2 \\ \begin{pmatrix} 1 & 1/9 \\ 9 & 1 \end{pmatrix} \end{array}$$

$$\text{Cost}\quad \begin{array}{c} \\ A_1 \\ A_2 \\ A_3 \end{array} \begin{array}{c} A_1 \quad A_2 \quad A_3 \\ \begin{pmatrix} 1 & 2.5 & 3\frac{1}{3} \\ \frac{1}{2.5} & 1 & 1\frac{1}{3} \\ \frac{1}{3\frac{1}{3}} & \frac{1}{1\frac{1}{3}} & 1 \end{pmatrix} \end{array} \qquad \text{Efficiency}\quad \begin{array}{c} \\ A_1 \\ A_2 \\ A_3 \end{array} \begin{array}{c} A_1 \quad A_2 \quad A_3 \\ \begin{pmatrix} 1 & 1/9 & \frac{1}{9.4737} \\ 9 & 1 & \frac{1}{1.0526} \\ 9.4737 & 1.0526 & 1 \end{pmatrix} \end{array}$$

	Cost	Efficiency			
Alternatives	0.55	0.45	Composition	Normalized Weights	
A1	1	0.111111	0.6	0.8955224	A1>A2
A2	0.4	1	0.67	0.1044776	
			1.27		

Alternatives	0.55	0.45	Composition	Normalized Weights	
A1	1	0.105556	0.5975	0.3212366	
A2	0.4	0.95	0.6475	0.3481183	A2>A3>A1
A3	0.3	1	0.615	0.3306452	
			1.86		

Example – Part B

$$\text{Cost}\quad \begin{array}{c} \\ A_1 \\ A_2 \end{array} \begin{array}{c} A_1 \quad A_2 \\ \begin{pmatrix} 1 & 2.5 \\ 1/2.5 & 1 \end{pmatrix} \end{array} \qquad \text{Efficiency}\quad \begin{array}{c} \\ A_1 \\ A_2 \end{array} \begin{array}{c} A_1 \quad A_2 \\ \begin{pmatrix} 1 & 1/9 \\ 9 & 1 \end{pmatrix} \end{array}$$

$$\text{Cost}\quad \begin{array}{c} \\ A_1 \\ A_2 \\ A_3 \end{array} \begin{array}{c} \begin{array}{ccc} A_1 & A_2 & A_3 \end{array} \\ \begin{pmatrix} 1 & 2.5 & 5 \\ \frac{1}{2.5} & 1 & 2 \\ \frac{1}{5} & \frac{1}{2} & 1 \end{pmatrix} \end{array} \qquad \text{Efficiency}\quad \begin{array}{c} \\ A_1 \\ A_2 \\ A_3 \end{array} \begin{array}{c} \begin{array}{ccc} A_1 & A_2 & A_3 \end{array} \\ \begin{pmatrix} 1 & 1/9 & \frac{1}{9.4737} \\ 9 & 1 & \frac{1}{1.0526} \\ 9.4737 & 1.0526 & 1 \end{pmatrix} \end{array}$$

	Cost	Efficiency			
Alternatives	0.55	0.45	Composition	Normalized Weights	
A1	1	0.111111	0.6	0.8955224	A1>A2
A2	0.4	1	0.67	0.1044776	
			1.27		

Alternatives	0.55	0.45	Composition	Normalized Weights	
A1	1	0.105556	0.5975	0.3310249	
A2	0.4	0.95	0.6475	0.3587258	A2>A1>A3
A3	0.2	1	0.56	0.3102493	
			1.805		

A SECOND EXAMPLE

We begin with two alternatives *A* and *B*. We have pairwise compared them in Table 5-10 with respect to the criteria Efficiency and Cost whose priorities are .5 each:

Table 5-10: Example of Rank Reversal with Change in Ideal

Efficiency (.5)					Cost (.5)						Composite Ideal	
	A	B	Norm	Ideal		A	B	Norm	Ideal	Comp Dist	Comp	Renorm.
A	1	3	0.75	1	A	1	0.5	0.33	0.5	0.542	0.75	0.5294
B	0.333	1	0.25	0.333	B	2	1	0.67	1	0.458	0.6667	0.4706
										1	1.6458	1

The question above is whether to normalize by dividing the weights of the alternatives by their sum (distributive mode) or idealize by dividing by the weight of the largest alternative (ideal mode). The distributive mode gives *A* = .54 and *B* = .46 while the normalized ideal mode gives *A* = .53 and *B* = .47. Now, if we add C that is a relevant alternative under efficiency, because it dominates both A and B we obtain as in Table 5-11:

Table 5-11: Example of Rank Reversal with Change in Ideal

	Efficiency (.5)						Cost (.5)						Composite Ideal	
	A	B	C	Norm	Ideal		A	B	C	Norm	Ideal	Comp Dist	Comp	Renorm.
A	1	3	0.5	0.3	0.5	A	1	0.5	4	0.308	0.5	0.3038	0.500	0.304
B	0.333	1	0.167	0.1	0.17	B	2	1	8	0.615	1	0.3577	0.583	0.354
C	2	6	1	0.6	1	C	0.25	0.13	1	0.077	0.125	0.3385	0.563	0.342
							3.25	1.63	13			1	1.6458	1

Now, the distributive mode gives $A = .30$, $B = .36$ and $C = .34$ with rank reversal between A and B, and the normalized ideal mode gives $A = .30$, $B = .35$ and $C = .34$ again with rank reversal. There is rank reversal with both the distributive and ideal modes because C is dominant with respect to efficiency. Now the old ranks of A and B can be preserved if we maintain the original ideals under each criterion and for each criterion we compare the new alternatives only with the ideal, allowing its value to go above its value of one if necessary. One can even compare it with several of the old alternatives, preserving their relative values but improving any inconsistency only with respect to these values and in view of that adopting a final scale value for the new alternative. In that case we have for the above example the following (Table 5-12):

Table 5-12: Preserving Rank in the Second Example with no Change in Ideal

	Efficiency (.5)						Cost (.5)						Composite Ideal	
	A	B	C	Norm	Old Ideal		A	B	C	Norm	Ideal	Comp Dist	Comp	Renorm.
A	1	3	0.5	0.3	1	A	1	0.5	4	0.308	0.5	0.304	0.75	0.302
B	0.333	1	0.167	0.1	0.333	B	2	1	8	0.615	1	0.358	0.667	0.269
C	2	6	1	0.6	2	C	0.25	0.125	1	0.077	0.125	0.338	1.063	0.429
							3.25	1.63	13			1	2.480	1

Here there is no rank reversal. In this case we have idealized only once by using the initial set of alternatives but never after so that rank would be preserved from then on unless the ideal alternative is deleted in which case we idealize again. Which is the situation in real life? Not that it should but that it turns out that way. How would we know if it is right or not? We know it by experiencing regret. Do we eliminate the regret if we idealize once or many times, most likely not. We would feel that we did not choose correctly. But that would always be the case because process theory teaches us that change is always happening and we can at best always suboptimize in the face of new alternatives (not just new criteria).

Let us summarize. All prioritization uses some kind of comparison. Generally, there are two ways widely recognized for making comparisons. The first is the technically familiar traditional way used by all methods of ranking where one compares or evaluates an alternative with respect to a standard or ideal often represented on a numerical scale and assigns it a value relative to the top value of the scale representing the very best that any alternative (called the ideal) can get. One can have serious difficulty assigning numbers to alternatives because of how it is done and what kind of number is obtained. The other way is to compare each alternative with other alternatives. In the first case one measures absolute performance in relation to an ideal (when it is possible to identify one) defined through long experience. In the second case one measures relative performance in relation to other alternatives. One of these alternatives may in fact be the ideal itself. An alternative can look very good relative to other alternatives but very poor when compared with the ideal. We need both ways. The first (idealistic) way is an incentive to see where we stand, and the second (pragmatic) way is to continue trying to improve. In an interview by Wolf Blitzer on CNN in 2003, the very intelligent and likeable president of Afghanistan, Hamid Karzai who was told that he was criticized by the Congress for not making much progress replied with something like this, "We should not compare ourselves with a standard established according to the ideals of the US Congress. We should look at where we are now relative to where we were a year ago in Afghanistan." One man wrote in his final will and testament to his children: "Do not look to those who are richer than you (the ideal?) lets you become envious, but look to those who are lowlier than you (other alternatives?) to fill your hearts with thanks. A man walked bare foot and complained but when he saw a cripple, he repented and thanked God that he could walk."

5-13. Non-additive Synthesis -Why the Geometric Mean Does not Work

In the AHP, for the priorities $w = (w_1, \ldots, w_n)$ derived from a matrix, we assume that if one uses w to weight the judgments in each row of the matrix $A = (a_{ij})$ and take the sum, one should recover them back proportionately so that one has $Aw = cw$ for some positive constant c otherwise new priorities are obtained. If these are used in turn in the same way as before still new priorities are obtained. This amounts to multiplying by A successively to get $\lim_{k \to \infty} A^k w = cw$ and the only solution of this problem is obtained when $c = \lambda_{\max}$ the principal eigenvalue of A in conformity with the necessary condition that powers of A capture transitivity of all order.

Lack of understanding the rank reversal issue has caused some scholars who like pairwise comparisons and the AHP to look for other ways of synthesis in order to always preserve rank. One much advocated way is to use the geometric mean, minimize $\sum_{i=1}^{n}\sum_{j=1}^{n}(\log a_{ij} - \log\frac{w_i}{w_j})^2$ not the principal eigenvector for deriving priorities even when the judgments are inconsistent (and thus the eigenvector is a necessary condition), thus ignoring the question of the transitivity of dominance in making the comparisons. The geometric mean has the solution $w_i = (\prod_{j=1}^{n} a_{ij})^{1/n} / \sum_{i=1}^{n}(\prod_{j=1}^{n} a_{ij})^{1/n}, i=1,\ldots,n$ that involves the (normalized) products of the judgments in each row of the paired comparisons matrix.

In addition, instead of weighting and adding, to force rank preservation, it was proposed to raise the priorities of the alternatives to the power of the criteria and again take the geometric mean of the outcome for all the criteria thus obtaining the final priority for each alternative. But this multiplicative approach has an inherent weakness. Assume that an alternative has a priority 0.2 with respect to each of two criteria whose respective priorities are 0.3 and 0.5. It is logical to assume that this alternative should have a higher priority with respect to the more important criterion, the one with the value of 0.5, after the weighting is performed. But $0.2^{0.5} < 0.2^{0.3}$ and alas it does not, it has a smaller priority. Let us try this multiplicative approach on a simple problem involving dollars under two criteria. The dollar values of three alternatives under them are 200, 300, 500, and 150, 50, 100, respectively. Summing and normalizing the dollar values for each alternative we get .269, .269, .462. Now let us normalize the values of the alternatives under each criterion. In order to get the total relative outcome we must use the weights of the criteria which in this case depend on the total values of the alternatives under them. The alternatives under the first criterion have the relative weights 200/100, 300/1000, 500/1000, and under the second 150/300, 50/300, 100/300. Thus the criteria have the respective weights 1000/1300 and 300/1300. The additive AHP approach gives the foregoing relative values. The multiplicative approach by raising the relative values of the alternatives to the power of the criteria weights and multiplying, gives .256, .272, .472, not the right outcome. One would think that the procedure of ranking in this way would have been abandoned at first knowledge of this observation. The additive way is justified by a more fundamental way of reasoning about dominance in the context of transitions in graphs and networks using matrix algebra. It also coincides with how electrical engineers think about circuits and the flow of current.

Some people have suggested using different methods of composition because they have found particular instances where their method directly produces an answer that matches what we have developed using arithmetic thinking. But we have examples of nonlinear outcomes that can be obtained by making comparisons like the inverse square optics problem. The areas comparison exercise compares nonlinear, two-dimensional objects of various shapes with each other and gives a good estimate of their relative values. There are other such examples whose answers are obtained by comparing things of higher dimensions with each other. The problem of dimensionality so far appears to be solvable by comparing things, although no one has made a complete scientific study of it. The fact that the area of a rectangle can be defined as the product of two single dimension linear factors obtained by multiplying them does not even touch on the two dimensional surface problem. Very few areas in two dimensions can be defined in this way as a product. In addition and fundamentally, there is no theorem until today that says that there is only one way to approximate to any 2 dimensional surface by breaking it down into many rectangles or any other figure whose area is so simply computed. So the solution of the surface problem using judgment is not solved by logically tying it to one kind of figure through which one can generalize. We admit that the additive approach cannot come up with the same results as any mathematical formula one can contrive. We have not pursued obtaining such results as a multicriteria problem. Putting it differently, a rectangle to a person who never went to school to learn dimensions is simply an area, not a composite. Nor is it guaranteed that area has to always be obtained the way we do it from our schooling. Thus we need to talk about how the mind of an unschooled person naturally synthesizes things for all the eons of time, not about the different ways (normative ways) that it can be forced to do. Its method has to be uniform across everything it does or it would be confused when and how to study and synthesize things quickly in different ways and get a near consistent overall outcome. I think that it is important to understand this. Our minds are presented with structure and intensities from the outside but must do their own computation. The structure is not in them, but how to deal with the structure (the arithmetic of combining signals) is in them. Dimension is not an intrinsic property of the mind. It is related to our analysis of what we see. We cannot change the intrinsic ways our minds work to give us data in a fundamental way.

In mathematics we use linear dimensions to study problems but curvilinear coordinates are also used and other kinds also. There may be a way to lay out the perceived structure of any problem so that its properties can be identified and aggregated in such a way that their relative influences can be captured by making comparisons. That appears to be a more promising approach than taking on different methods of composition for different structures. The danger of customizing the composition for each different structure, is that we would have a fragmentary approach to the world and would still need a customized way to put together the fragments and philosophers have not found such a way yet. Dimensionality is one way to simplify structures in physics, but psychological attributes do not seem to be amenable to such a simplified approach and they are often involved in problems. If we do not have uniqueness in approach on both factors, composition which is measurement, and structure, we really have nothing to tell people when to use this and when to use that. Now it appears that our method of composition is fixed but the structures we apply it to are not fixed.

In contrast with mathematics which is generally a way of analysis, through the AHP/ANP which is a method of synthesis, we are learning to organize structures to obtain valid answers for problems in the real world. Measure theory is a branch of mathematics that is a generalization of the concepts of length, area and volume to arbitrary sets of points that are not intervals or rectangles or boxes. A measure is any rule for associating a non-negative and additive number with a set. The measure of a finite set of rectangles can be defined to be the sum of their areas. For other sets like curved regions with missing point, one needs to define the concepts of outer and inner measure similar to upper and lower sums in integration. If the outer and inner measures of a set are equal, the set is called measurable. The AHP/ANP in their general continuous form provide us with a way involving paired comparisons to give a general meaning to measurement and to the synthesis of different kinds of measurements. The connection to and use of such thinking in measure theory have not been examined.

We conclude by observing that the AHP already has a way to preserve rank indiscriminately by always using ratings with the ideal mode provided that the ideal does not change. In addition, by deriving priorities from paired comparisons, rank can always be preserved if one idealizes only the first time, and then compares each alternative with the ideal, allowing the value to exceed one when that is the case. We note that idealizing each time a new alternative is introduced, only preserves rank from irrelevant alternatives.

5-14. Several Published Comments by People on the AHP

It is useful to include here references about what various people have said about the AHP with comments on some of them. Some of these references and comments are now obsolete by the admission of their authors. We did not feel it is necessary to comment on everyone but nevertheless included it for relative completeness. If one were to take what people who voiced criticisms of the AHP agree with and what they object to and put their opinions together, one would find that the total of what they don't object to would allow the AHP to be exactly as it is now. A brief summary and observations on what some of the references seem to be mainly concerned about, when appropriate, is given. Although the references are fairly exhaustive, we do not believe that it is necessary to comment on everyone. Our comments are made according to the author's alphabetic position.

Barzilai (1998a) writes that hierarchic composition is linear and that it generates nonequivalent value functions from equivalent decompositions. In fact many examples show that hierarchic composition is nonlinear. About other inaccuracies in this paper and false assumptions made by this author in many unrefereed publications criticizing the AHP and all other methods of decision making without offering a creative alternative way; see the paper by Rozann W. Saaty. His fundamental assumption is that for paired comparisons to be valid the underlying scale must be a ratio scale totally ignoring the fact that paired comparisons are given on an absolute scale. For attributes/properties for which a scale has not yet been developed he assumes that there is no information about the type of scale in which it can be measured and hence paired comparisons are invalid. It is clear that absolute comparisons are not only possible but are done all the time by all people. The validity of this process is demonstrated every time people make comparisons. In "On MAUT, AHP, PFM" that appeared in the Proceedings of the ISAHP meeting in Kobe in 1999 he writes that "Basic concepts such as scale type and meaningfulness are not fully understood... they will be fully resolved in a forthcoming paper." That was promised six years ago and we are still waiting. The many works reveal a profound lack of understanding by a non-mathematician of the mathematics of the real numbers that define an absolute scale of measurement. A unit, which is one, does not need an absolute zero to define it as in a ratio scale so it can be used as a standard for the rest of the readings. It is defined as an equivalence class. One man does not need zero to know that there is a single person. Zero was introduced much later in the history of numbers. Relative numbers like probabilities and priorities are simply a set of real numbers divided by a constant. That does not make them dependent on zero for their meaning. In 1998b the same individual proposed a measure of inconsistency for a matrix and for a hierarchy and discussed the revision of judgments.

In 1997, Barzilai and Lootsma argued that if one were to use multiplicative composition, rank would not reverse. But multiplicative composition has been shown to be faulty because, for example, an alternative with the same value under two criteria receives a smaller value for the more important criterion: $.2^{.5} < .2^{.3}$. Always preserving rank is not a good idea as we have seen with our examples. What does one then do to allow for rank reversal due to structural dependencies?

Belton and Gear (1983) wrote that with normalization, rank reversal occurs when the matrices are consistent and copies of alternatives are added and suggest using the ideal mode when the largest entry is the same for the alternatives for every criterion. At the international MCDM meeting in August 2004 at Whistler, Canada, V. Belton explained to a wide audience that her understanding of the AHP 25 years ago as a student was very different than what it is now. She made one to understand that she regrets how people have used that work as a convenient way to attack the AHP without understanding it well. In 1985 they replied to an answer by Saaty and Vargas (1983, 1984) suggesting that one should idealize no matter what the maximum value of the alternatives may be, but adjusting the weights of the criteria in proportion to the values of the largest values of the alternatives under them.

Costa and Vansnick (2001) claim by using two examples and no general proof, that the eigenvector does not preserve the preference relations represented in the pairwise comparisons matrix when that matrix is inconsistent. However, the eigenvector has been shown to be necessary and even small perturbations can be reflected by change of order in the eigenvector that captures all transitivities as it is obtained by raising the matrix to infinite powers according to the well-known theorem of Perron for positive matrices. Dyer (1990) strongly argued that the AHP results are arbitrary, but that the results of Utility Theory that assigns numbers to alternatives one at a time are not. He extends Belton and Gear's example to adding alternatives that are not copies to show that rank reversal can occur, ignoring the fact that the values the alternatives receive depend on what other alternatives they are compared with, showing that rank reversal can occur. His arguments show lack of understanding of the dependence in AHP when one performs pairwise comparisons. Dyer was willing to allow pairwise comparison to derive priorities for the criteria, but not for the alternatives, even though each alternative is a bundle of criteria. Each alternative exhibits an intensity of a criterion that can be compared with that exhibited by another criterion. To always preserve rank is an erroneous and artificial concept when paired comparisons are used which is nearly always when no ideal is known or available to force rankings of alternatives one by one in terms of that ideal.

Finan and Hurley (2002) assumed that a criterion under which all alternatives are indifferent (have equal value) should not have an impact on the final ranking. It turns out that their observation involved incorrect renormalization as has been shown in a paper by Saaty and Vargas (2005). Hurley (2002) pointed to the rank reversal question with critical comments without having looked at the subject in depth about how alternatives depend on each other when they are compared in pairs, an inescapable and more accurate way of doing things. Holder (1990) criticized the optics experiment example used to validate the eigenvector method.

The experiment was repeated by the author with judgments from an expert and got the same original answers. Holder also suggested using a multiplicative (power) scale by now shown to be an invalid approach. Kamenetzky (1982) noted that hierarchic composition is only valid when the criteria are independent among themselves, a correct observation. Lootsma (1993) proposed using a fundamental scale that is a geometric progression and points to the use of the geometric mean for hierarchic composition as a justification for it. The geometric mean as a way of synthesis has major difficulties now widely known including the forcing of rank preservation in every case. Examples have been given which show that a geometric progression is too strong to express judgments on homogeneous objects accurately.

Millet and Wedley (2002) give examples to show that benefits divided by costs times risks does not capture the true effect of risk in every case. We agree that although the quotient formula for the benefits and opportunities over the costs times the risks is sometimes useful, the formula for the synthesis of BOCR involving weighting with respect to strategic criteria, adding the benefits and opportunities and subtracting from it the sum of the costs and the risks is more reliable for obtaining the final ranks of the alternatives. Perez, J., J.L. Jimeno and E. Mokotoff (2004) write a paper that is a rehash of Finan and Hurley's wash criteria paper answered in the literature and addressed above.

Saaty, R.W., (2004) wrote an excellent paper with relevant arguments and many validation examples and applications of AHP/ANP and particularly showed a glaring error and profound misunderstanding of the AHP in a marketing example given by Barzilai to show that the AHP is not to his liking. Salo and Hamalainen (1997) suggested redefining the fundamental scale of the AHP, and proposed using ratios of differences for the judgments from measurements derived from a value function. They also criticized the use of the feedback approach of the Analytic Network Process. Saaty (1997) gave examples and arguments in replying to their proposals.

Schenkerman (1994) criticized hierarchic composition because it does not reproduce a nonlinear geometric mathematical example (the area of a rectangle) that he constructs for the purpose. In fact there are literally thousands of geometric objects associated with mathematical formulas whose dimensions (e.g., areas and volumes and so on) cannot be reproduced by using a hierarchy and hierarchic composition. Schenkerman (1997) also criticized both the ideal and distributive modes of the AHP and used his geometric example to argue his case that they do not give him what he is looking for. He uses measurements under each criterion and does not weigh the criteria by these measurements as one does for example with money under several criteria in order to obtain the correct relative outcome, but assigns them weights conveniently.

Schoner, Wedley, and Choo (1993) argued that there is a relationship between the normalization and weighting processes. They generalized the ideal mode to a linking pin mode where any alternative under a criterion can serve as the normalization referent and thus as the linking element for establishing weights for the covering criteria. Stam and Duarte Silva (2003) gave examples and observed that rank reversal can be avoided with multiplicative synthesis. Again the fact that in performing paired comparisons there is dependence of the measurement of one element on the quality of what it is compared with is overlooked. Enforcing rank preservation all the time is a mistake when paired comparisons are involved. Again Triantaphyllou (2001) used multiplicative composition in an effort to always preserve rank.

Watson and Freeling (1982) maintained (very early in the history of the AHP) that the question asked in making paired comparisons is meaningless, and thus the question cannot be answered because a unit of measurement is needed to answer it. They apparently did not know that the AHP uses absolute scales in making paired comparisons and not ordinal scales. Again in 1983 they reemphasized that the question asked is meaningless in reply to the Saaty, Vargas, and Wendell (1983). More than twenty years after, these concerns sound antiquated.

Wedley, Choo, and Schoner (2001) criticized by means of a monetary validation example the process of just taking the ratio of composite benefit and cost priorities because there is no guarantee that the two sources of priorities are in commensurate units. This subject of commensurability of benefits and costs (dividing dollars by pennies) is important and users are always cautioned in using it. The other formula that involves weighting the BOCR with respect to strategic criteria assigns benefits and costs weights making them commensurate after weighting and does not need to use division.

5-15. Complexity and the AHP/ANP and Conclusions

The AHP/ANP is a simple and transparent decision making theory that is accessible to the layman who makes decisions all the time and would not like to learn complicated mathematical manipulations that are beyond his abilities, experience and understanding. The approach essentially maps or represents what a person does, were that person to lay out the factors of a decision and express his/her judgments about the relations among these factors. Basically the AHP/ANP is an empirical process more concerned with the success of applications and using information from a decision maker in its simplest and most natural form without the use of lottery gambles or similar ways of getting at the information that accommodates the theory at such a high level of sophistication that it is usable only by a trained academic mind. The tools people are trained to use at a university are designed not to be so simple as to put the university out of business in that field. They must be complex enough to create sufficient mystique and puzzlement in the mind so the university professors and students accept the hard work needed to apply them successfully. They would need to publish or perish in writing about them as well.

The mathematics of decision-making is closely linked to how the brain works to make decisions. The workings of the brain are dependent on the decision of neurons to fire or not to fire. That in turn is related in some way to stimulus response theory. The question is whether it is possible to generalize the subject so that stimulus response relates to the laws of physics for example so that what we perceive or are able to perceive coincides with what physics tells us about the laws of nature. But the laws of nature to humans are precisely what they are able to detect with their minds and bodies and then interpret and connect these perceptions. It would seem that all the things we know about are a consequence of what our neurons are capable of registering and synthesizing.

So much of modern applied mathematics is tied to the calculus and its generalizations so that the use of coordinate systems is thought to be mandatory and the only way to analyze problems. In the calculus one deals with relative change with respect to an independent variable that is assumed to change linearly. Is there a way to deal with the idea of rate of change as in the calculus that is based on infinitesimals? We do not have infinitesimals in paired comparisons. Let us assume that the priorities of a set of alternatives have been derived and ordered in increasing fashion. What we can do is to take differences in priorities in successive order and divide them by other differences and speak of the ratio or relative change in the values. We have ratios of pairs of differences in values that is analogous to finding out how much more a derivative changes at one point of a function as compared with its change at another point. This is likely to be a useful concept in decision-making.

The ideas of the AHP/ANP are captured through the Hierarchon, a dictionary of AHP models, and the Encyclicon, a dictionary of ANP models, as a dictionary does sounds and meanings of words. Studying these books is a good way to expand one's knowledge about such decision-making structures.

Negative numbers have been around for several hundred years. It took this writer a long time to find a way to combine negative priority numbers with positive ones, by rating benefits, opportunities, costs and risks (BOCR) and not by comparing alternatives. See the discussion of BOCR in Chapter 3 of this book. The problem was not so much to develop knowledge about how to create priorities for negative or adverse concepts. One simply prioritizes them as to how undesirable they are and multiplies the resulting priorities by minus one. It was how to combine positive and negative priorities. There are several examples in the literature long ago where we had used negative numbers in the past to indicate priorities but did not combine them with positive ones. Since early in 1999 we discovered the way to do that.

There is a popular saying that the proof of the pudding is in the eating. We have to make decisions, we need ways to help us cope with complexity, and today there is a rush by academic people to fill the gap with different methods based on the techniques they have developed and know well. These methods have to be tried and their users will eventually look for the most sound, understandable and communicable way to apply them. Users must eventually justify to themselves and to others why they do what they do from every standpoint. The common sense one uses in decision-making is recorded at least as much in instinct as it is in intellect, and methods that can draw on this would seem to be valuable.

Speaking of justifying manipulations, using fuzzy sets on numerous marketing examples where the ANP produces surprisingly close results (in some less than 1%) should improve them further or else fuzzy thinking is not an answer to improving on the validity of the outcome of the AHP where judgments are already fuzzy. If introducing fuzziness can add anything it must improve the validity of the AHP outcome when compared with actual data.

There are different philosophies about scientific theories and their applications. They make fine distinctions between different aspects of a theory and its applications and where the emphasis should be placed to arrive at truth and validity. The rationalist sees coherence and scope as the crucial requirements. The empiricist regards prediction and validation as the crucial step, making new predictions using the theory then comparing those predictions with the facts to confirm that it worked or is false. The constructivist says that the best test of a theory in science is the consistent and coherent, though diverse, framework it provides to deal with wide ranging situations. But all methods of decision-making must be justified on two bases: the validity of their assumptions and their long-term successful application in practice.

The modern philosopher Paul Feyerabend objects to any single prescriptive scientific method on the grounds that any such method would limit the activities of scientists, and hence restrict scientific progress. He argues that the only approach that does not inhibit progress whatever it may be is "anything goes, which is the terrified exclamation of a rationalist who takes a closer look at history."

The AHP/ANP include basic aspects of the four philosophies of science mentioned above. There is a fairly comprehensive mathematical foundation for the AHP/ANP and it has been used to address a vast breadth of problems and concerns of people regarding the benefits, opportunities, costs and risks of a decision and how to combine them. There have been many and varied applications involving predictions and validations, and other kinds of decision making such as planning and the resolution of conflicts. The AHP and ANP so far appear to be free of paradoxes and do not require strong assumptions. This makes them amenable to wide-ranging uses.

In the intense effort to develop ways to do multi-criteria decision making, one also needs to consider the more general problem of ordering and choosing from among many decisions. We call this subject Multi Decision Decision-Making (MDDM). Unlike multi-criteria decision making, time and sequencing and scheduling must be part of our considerations in MDDM. We are not aware of detailed analyses of this problem. The subject we have in mind is having a multiplicity of decisions each of which has been worked out and the best alternative identified, but now these decisions need to be ordered and implemented in series and in parallel to satisfy certain criteria. Such decisions may influence each other and have dependencies that are related to the criteria chosen. They may in turn have their own benefits, opportunities, costs and risks and one would need to examine them in a broader context than the one used to determine the best outcome for a single decision. This problem touches on the more general subject of human values and the contribution that each decision makes to these values. The solution of this problem may belong to the domain of dynamic optimization subject to uncertainty in which: need, urgency and overall benefits, opportunities, costs and risk play a significant role to organize the sequence of implementation. These must be prioritized with respect to general or strategic criteria. That is why the subject of criteria and values takes on particular significance. Our greatest challenge is the unknown future and the new decisions and uncertainties it presents us with. Scenario construction is a useful tool for us to deal with the future and its dynamics.

Acknowledgements

I am grateful to my friends Eizo Kinoshita for material in section 5-6, Kirti Peniwati for reading and commenting on the chapter and Luis Vargas for the relationship between the supermatrix and input-output and help in summarizing responses to the references given below, and to Diederik Wijnmalen for reading the manuscript and making valuable suggestions for changes.

Chapter 6
Automatic Decision-Making: Neural Firing and Response

6-1. Introduction

In contrast with conscious decision-making, there are numerous subconscious decisions that we make without thinking about them. Some are biological and are made by different parts of our body to keep it alive and functioning normally. Others are a result of repetition and training that we can then do without thinking about them. The mathematics of conscious decisions with the Analytic Hierarchy and Network Processes is discrete, and has been discussed in the first three parts published on the subject. The mathematics of subconscious decisions is continuous. Here, we generalize the discrete mathematics of conscious decisions to the continuous case and develop it in some depth to apply to the synthesis of firings in the brain.

It is true that many decisions we make subconsciously arise out of our physical and biological needs and derive from the pressure to survive physically. We also make subconscious decisions in developing skills like swimming, riding a bicycle, driving a car, and playing the piano. What we learn to do consciously with frequent repetition becomes a habit and we do it without thinking about it. An automatic decision is a decision that is made intuitively and subconsciously. It is automatic when it is repeated as a habit either mentally or physically as a result of learning. It is known through its manifestation rather than driven by instinct, although it is difficult to draw a sharp distinction between the two. When we fall short in our physical habits relative to known standards, our mind analyzes the causes of such incompatibility in terms of actions needed and their priorities, and implements them to improve performance. Strengthening a habit (a sequence of actions) involves analysis, decisions and implementation to close the gap and improve compatibility to meet standards. Unless a person has been trained to make decisions mentally as a habit, doing it consciously without much thinking and fast, as if it lies between habit and continuous perception to constantly modify the habit that decision is likely to be subject to many errors. Making successive intelligent strokes in swimming or pedaling a bicycle are examples of decisions that involve uniformity (periodicity) of action and require one to be trained to make them without hesitation. They are spontaneous decisions in which reason, that may have initially served to establish behavior through conscious interaction, now acquires a more automatic and intuitive relationship and becomes a habit. Making important rational decisions is an intellectual activity requiring much reflection and thinking and being able to change one's mind, in ways that are not characteristic of automatic decisions. We need to reason and think to make rational decisions and check the environment to include the good and the undesirable in our deliberations. These decisions do not belong to the subliminal category because they require reflection and the connecting of many different, often new factors, and they require creativity. They involve such substantial variety and variations that they cannot be made automatically. If they are worked out in advance for implementation they can be automated and made by a machine, but they are not precisely what interests the developers of decision-making theories today.

While "thinking" is generally carried out in the neo-cortex of the brain, feelings and emotions are associated more with the autonomic (sympathetic and parasympathetic) nervous system that in part is known to operate independently of the conscious thought processes of the brain. There is very little conscious control over many activities of the autonomic nervous system. It is as if there are two persons in each of us. One that looks out at the physical environment to give us information for survival, and another that looks inside to keep our biological system running.

Even when our understanding is holistic and intuitive, it is fragmentary and needs to be laid out in detail and made complete by connecting the related parts within a structure and using a conscious thought process to bring analytical thinking and memories in the brain together with the intuition and experience of the autonomic nervous system. The elements and connections may not be complete enough to create meaning so an individual will make them coherent by adding or deleting elements and connections to fill the gaps in his/her perception that then may or may not be consistent with reality. Thus one's perceptions or mental models are essentially a combination of observations about reality and the assumptions that are built in the mind to make the data meaningful. To learn we have no other way but to patch together our thinking and modeling to understand complexity from the incomplete pieces that we have.

The mathematics of rational or reasoned decision making must involve feedback to make decisions with a finite but possibly large number of criteria and alternatives. Feedback network decisions are a generalization of hierarchic decision-making. They use both a structure and a synthesis of priorities of influence within the framework of a matrix, known as a supermatrix because its entries are themselves matrices whose columns are priority vectors. To capture the overall priorities of the elements to determine which one is the best, the matrix is first transformed into a stochastic matrix by prioritizing the influence of its clusters (collections of homogeneous elements) according to their influence on other clusters and then using these priorities to weight the corresponding blocks of the supermatrix. The supermatrix is thus made stochastic. It is then raised to limiting powers to capture all the transitivities of influence among the elements. According to Perron-Frobenius theory, instead of raising the matrix to powers, one can also solve the principal eigenvalue problem for that supermatrix to obtain the overall priorities and find the best one to adopt for a decision. Such an approach is then generalized to the case of synthesis of many types of influence and further to benefits and opportunities and costs and risks.

6-2. Automatic Decisions as a Generalization of Rational Complex Decisions

When we think of any decision we also think of a decision maker. What else besides our entire conscious mind makes decisions and how does it do it? One might answer by looking outward at a group of people that can work together to debate and structure their problem carefully in the context of benefits, opportunities, costs and risks and then collectively provide judgments that are then synthesized to obtain a representative decision for the entire group. But one can also look inward and conclude that there is another kind of group decision-making.

Our mind is a child of our brain that is made of a group of tens of billions of neurons. Each neuron performs its task by firing in response to a stimulus it receives. It needs a sufficiently strong stimulus signal to fire but it has a choice to fire or not to fire and in making this choice it is an automatic decision maker. In making the decision to fire or not to fire a neuron compares the intensity of signals it receives. If it fires, there is an electric signal generated by the firing process that passes to other neurons in a feedback process. These electrical signals are synthesized into feelings, perceptions and ideas. The process of electricity being converted to images and sounds and convey ideas is not unfamiliar to us who live in the age of technology. Not too long before the nineteenth century when electricity was discovered, it would have been very difficult to accept and understand how ideas can be passed by something like electric signals. Descartes thought of brain operation in terms of hydraulics because those were the best ideas he had to think with. Along with our technology we have concepts from mathematics that make it possible to conceptualize and understand the fundamental reasoning that may underlie the explanation about how neurons produce feelings, perceptions and ideas. Among them is the idea of a dense set, as the rational numbers are dense in the real numbers. Because they are a dense set the rational numbers can be used to come arbitrarily close to any real number. Because there are so many neurons to perform each function, neural firings can be represented by functions that are dense in a very general space of functions that represent the real world as it appears to us. This makes it possible for us to view the world along the lines of decision-making and its generalization. Our presentation here is brief and meager, but it is possible to pursue it in greater depth and I have tried to do that in my book on the brain [57]. There it is shown how such dense functions can represent a small part of two symphonies, one by Mozart and another by Haydn, from the neural firing that results from hearing, and similarly they can represent various pictures that result from neural firings caused by visual stimuli.

The discrete mathematics of conscious decision-making generalizes to the continuous case where both stimulus and response are continuous. There are two related ways to formulate the problem. The first involves a functional equation. Some brain researchers have observed that neural firing corresponds to damped periodic oscillation. Whatever aspect of the real world we consider, sight, sound, touch, taste, smell, heat and cold, gravitational pull, and many others occurring simultaneously at each instant, their corresponding stimuli are impacting our senses over and over. The neurons of the brain respond to external stimuli with electric firings. These firings differ in their frequency and separation from stimulus to stimulus and from neuron to neuron and are combined to obtain a synthesis of the stimuli to which each neuron responded by firing. This synthesis gives us a miniaturized (proportionate) response to the stimulus simply because we cannot respond to every stimulus with its actual intensity, such as the explosion of a bomb. Survival requires that we be able to control the environment as best we can from our miniaturized responses to what we perceive the stimuli to be.

We can describe our responses to stimuli mathematically as follows. A stimulus S of magnitude s, is received as a similarity transformation as, where $a > 0$ is referred to as a dilation of s. The dilation is a stretching if $a > 1$, and a contraction if $a < 1$. Without such proportionality, it would be impossible to establish a meaningful relationship between the dimensions of the object in the mind as we conceptualize it and what its real dimensions are. An effective response $w(as)$ to a perturbed stimulus s must be faithful in capturing the magnitude of the stimulus after it is received and needs to be proportional to responding to that original stimulus without perturbation, namely $w(as) \propto w(s)$. Responding to a stimulus correctly and proportionately in their firings are decisions that our neurons can make automatically.

The question is: What kind of response function $w(s)$ to a stimulus of magnitude s satisfies the functional equation $w(as) = bw(s)$ required by such proportionality? It turns out that this functional equation is also a necessary condition for solving the equation we obtain by generalizing the discrete eigenvalue decision problem. Before turning to that generalization we note that if there are several stimuli our overall response to them needs to also satisfy a proportionality relation. It may be that the stimulus is an oscillatory electric signal that is better characterized by amplitude and angle. In that case, instead of a real variable *s,* the stimulus is better characterized by a complex variable z and the parameters a and b may themselves take on complex number values and the solution would be a complex valued function.

The foregoing functional equation can be generalized to the following equation (with real or complex variables and parameters) that gives the response to several stimuli:

$$w(a_1 s_1,...,a_n s_n) = bw(s_1,...,s_n)$$

There is a way to formulate the problem of automatic decisions that relates to the stimulus-response equation $w(as) = bw(s)$. It involves generalizing the discrete, eigenvalue-oriented decision-making of the AHP to the continuous case where Fredholm's equation is the continuous version of the discrete eigenvalue formulation. In that generalization it turns out that the functional equation $w(as) = bw(s)$ is a necessary condition for Fredholm's integral equation of the second kind to be solvable. Instead of finding the eigenvector of a pairwise comparison matrix one uses the kernel of an operator. Operations on the matrix translate to operations on the kernel. From the matrix formulation leading to the solution of a principal eigenvalue problem

$$\sum_{j=1}^{n} a_{ij} w_j = \lambda_{\max} w_i, \sum_{i=1}^{n} w_i = 1$$

we have

$$\int_a^b K(s,t)\, w(t)\, dt = \lambda_{\max}\, w(s) \quad \text{or} \qquad \lambda \int_a^b K(s,t) w(t) dt = w(s)$$

$\int_a^b w(s) ds = 1$, where the positive matrix A is replaced by a positive kernel $K(s,t) > 0$ and the eigenvector w by the eigenfunction $w(s)$. Note that the entries in a matrix depend on the two variables i and j that assume discrete values. Thus the matrix itself depends on these discrete variables and its generalization, the kernel function, depends on two (continuous) variables. The reason for calling it a kernel is the role it plays in the integral, where without knowing it we cannot determine the exact form of the solution. The standard way in which the first equation is written is to move the eigenvalue to the left hand side which gives it the reciprocal form. In general, by abuse of notation, one continues to use the symbol λ to represent the reciprocal value and with it one includes the familiar condition of normalization $\int_a^b w(s)ds = 1$. Here also, the kernel $K(s,t)$ is said to be 1) consistent and therefore also reciprocal, if $K(s,t)$ $K(t,u)= K(s,u)$, for all s, t and u, or 2) reciprocal, but perhaps not consistent, if $K(s,t)\,K(t,s) = 1$ for all s,t.

A value of λ for which Fredholm's equation has a nonzero solution $w(t)$ is called a characteristic value (or its reciprocal is called an eigenvalue) and the corresponding solution is called an eigenfunction. An eigenfunction is determined to within a multiplicative constant. If $w(t)$ is an eigenfunction corresponding to the characteristic value λ and if C is an arbitrary constant, we see by substituting in the equation that $Cw(t)$ is also an eigenfunction corresponding to the same λ. The value $\lambda = 0$ is not a characteristic value because we have the corresponding solution $w(t) = 0$ for every value of t, which is the trivial case, excluded in our discussion. The material immediately below is also found with proofs in my book on the brain referenced at the end of the paper.

Theorem 1 K(s,t) is consistent if and only if it is separable of the form:

$$K(s,t) = k(s)/k(t)$$

Theorem 2 If K(s, t) is consistent the solution of Fredhom's equation is given by

$$w(s) = \frac{k(s)}{\int_S k(s)ds}$$

We note that this formulation is general and applies to all situations where a continuous scale of relative measurement is needed. We now determine the form of $k(s)$ and also of $w(s)$.

In the discrete case, the normalized eigenvector was independent of whether or not all the elements of the pairwise comparison matrix A are multiplied by the same constant a, and thus we can replace A by aA and obtain the same eigenvector. Generalizing this result to the continuous case we have:

$$K(as, at)=aK(s,t)=k(as)/k(at)=a\,k(s)/k(t)$$

This means that K is a homogeneous function of order one.

Theorem 3 A necessary and sufficient condition for $w(s)$ to be an eigenfunction solution of Fredholm's equation of the second kind, with a consistent kernel that is homogeneous of order one, is that it satisfy the functional equation

$$w(as)=bw(s), \text{ where } b=\alpha a.$$

What we want in the continuous case is a general solution for all consistent kernels. I know of no general (non-iterative) method for solving an integral equation in closed form in an unknown kernel, and our kernel here, although it is consistent, is unknown. Fortunately we can obtain the general solution in the real and then again in the complex domains by solving the functional equation $w(as) = bw(s)$ that is a necessary condition for the solvability of the integral equation. In both cases we have the general single-valued and also the general multi-valued solutions. In the single-valued case we have, in particular, the general continuous and also the general differentiable solutions. In the case of complex valued functions of a complex variable we have the general everywhere analytic solutions (except perhaps at 0). The general solutions look essentially different according to whether $|a| \neq 1$ or $|a|=1$ (for positive real variables the case $a=1$ is trivial). Let us illustrate briefly how the real-valued solution is obtained. There is not room in this chapter to give all the details.

If we substitute $s=a^u$ in the equation we have:

$$w(a^{u+1}) - bw(a^u) = 0.$$

Again if we write $w(a^u) = b^u p(u)$, we obtain:

$$p(u+1) - p(u)=0$$

This is a periodic function of period one in the variable u (such as cos $u/2\pi$). Note that if the parameters a and s are real, then so is u which may be negative even if a and s are both assumed to be positive. Finally we have

$$w(s) = b^{\log s/\log a} p(\frac{\log s}{\log a})$$

The right hand side of this equation is a damped periodic function.

The general complex solution of our functional equation is:

$$w(z) = Cb^{[\log|z| / \log|a|]} g(z)$$

where $C > 0$. The [ ] in the above expression denotes the "closest integer from below" function, and g is an arbitrary solution of $g(az)=g(z)$.

Our solution that represents response to a force, which serves as a stimulus, through relative scales is general and has applicability to all phenomena whose measurement is based, for example, on ratio scales as in physics. When we speak of response subject to ratio scales, it is not only response of the brain to a stimulus, but also the response of any object to a force or influence to which it is subject.

Pursuing our generalization of discrete comparisons, and adopting the paradigm that neurons are decision makers that perform reciprocal comparisons in milliseconds, how to synthesize the firings of many neurons requires that we adopt the geometric mean again as a generalization of the discrete case. Without going into the details of such synthesis, we note that outcome of products of functions of the form $w(s) = b^{\log s/\log a}\, p(\frac{\log s}{\log a})$ is again a function of the same form with different parameters a and b because the product of two periodic functions of period one is also a periodic function of period one and similarly if one were to use the complex form of the solution for the synthesis of electric signals as in the brain. A significant observation is that rather than adding signals, due to the reciprocal property, they are multiplied which is likely to be at odds with what people have been considering in the literature so far. One needs to pursue this idea and its validation in greater depth. In addition, synthesis of the solution of the several stimuli problem would also have to be considered.

The solution of Fredholm's equation of the second kind derived above for a single variable is defined in the frequency domain or transform domain in Fourier analysis as it is based on the flow of electric charge. Stimuli received by the brain from nature are transformed to chemical and electrical neural activities that result in summation and synthesis. This is transformed to awareness (of physical nature) by converting the electrical synthesis to a space-time representation. The way the brain goes back and forth from a pattern of stimuli to its electro-chemical synthesis and then to a representation of its response to that spatio-temporal pattern is by applying the Fourier transform to the stimulus and the inverse Fourier transform to form its response. We must now take its transform to derive the solution in the space-time domain. In general we have for the Fourier transform $f(w)$ of a function $F(x)$

$$f(\omega) = \int_{-\infty}^{+\infty} F(x)\, e^{-2\pi i \omega x}\, dx = Ce^{\beta\omega}\; P(\omega)$$

Its inverse transform is the inverse Fourier transform of a convolution of the two factors in the product given by

$$F(x) = \int_{-\infty}^{+\infty} f\ (\omega)\ e^{2\pi i\omega x}\, d\omega$$

which we now apply to our solution.

Since our solution is a product of two factors, the inverse transform can be obtained as the convolution of two functions, the inverse Fourier transform of each of which corresponds to that of just one of the factors.

Now the inverse Fourier transform of $e^{-\beta u}$ is given by

$$\frac{\sqrt{(2/\pi)}\beta}{\beta^2+\xi^2}$$

Also from the theory of Fourier series, we know that we can write

$$P(u) = \sum_{k=-\infty}^{\infty} \alpha_k\ e^{2\pi iku}$$

whose inverse Fourier transform involves the familiar Dirac delta function and is given by:

$$\sum_{k=-\infty}^{\infty} \alpha_k \delta\,(\xi - 2\pi\, k)$$

The product of the transforms of the two functions is equal to the Fourier transform of the convolution of the two functions themselves that we just obtained by taking their individual inverse transforms. We have, to within a multiplicative constant:

$$\int_{-\infty}^{+\infty} \sum_{k=-\infty}^{\infty} \alpha_k \delta\,(\xi - 2\pi\, k) \frac{\beta}{\beta^2+(x-\xi)^2}\, d\xi = \sum_{k=-\infty}^{\infty} \alpha_k \frac{\beta}{\beta^2+(x-2\pi k)^2}$$

Consider the important special case where

$$P(u)= \cos u/2\pi=(1/2)(e^{iu/2\pi} + e^{-iu/2\pi}).$$

In this case of a real variable and real parameters, it is desirable to take our periodic part to be a familiar trigonometric function that satisfies the same conditions. The first plausible candidate is the cosine function. In fact there are infinitely many periodic functions that can be used for P. For example, the only real periodic functions satisfying the functional equation $f(2x) = -1+2\,(f(x))^2$ are $f\ (x)= -1/2$ (identically) and also $f(x)=\cos cx\ ,\ c > 0$. This is a characterization of the cosine function under the assumption of periodicity and continuity in a neighborhood of zero, by a functional equation.

What we have done so far is to be concerned with the inverse Fourier transform. We now need to take its inverse to develop expressions for the response. The Fourier transform is the continuous generalization of expanding functions in Fourier series. With it one is able to represent a function by taking its transform and get the function back by taking the inverse transform. Thus one goes from a pattern presented as a stimulus to an energy representation of it (vibrations caused by the pattern), and back from the representation to the pattern.

The inverse Fourier transform of $w(u)=Ce^{-\beta u}\cos u/2\pi$, $\beta > 0$ is given by:

$$C\left[\frac{1}{\beta^2+(x+2\pi)^2}+\frac{1}{\beta^2+(x-2\pi)^2}\right]$$

When the constants in the denominator are small relative to x we have C_1/x^2 that we believe is why in optics, gravitation (Newton) and electricity (Coulomb) our response to the forces is according to inverse square laws. This is the same law of nature in which an object responding to a force field must decide to follow that law by comparing infinitesimal successive states through which it passes. If the stimulus is constant, the exponential factor in the general response solution is constant, and the solution would be periodic of period one. When the distance x is very small, the result varies inversely with the square of the parameter $\beta>0$.

The space-time Fourier transform of the general complex valued solution

$$w(z) = Cb^{[\log|z|/\log|a|]}g(z)$$

is a combination of Dirac distributions.

$$(1/2\pi)\log a\sum_{-\infty}^{\infty}a'_n\left[\frac{(2\pi n+\theta(b)-x)}{(\log a|b|+(2\pi n+\theta(b)-x)}\;i\right].\delta(2\pi n+\theta(b)-x) \quad (15)$$

where $\delta(2\pi n+\theta(b)-x)$ is the Dirac delta function. This is supporting evidence in favor of our eigenvalue model to deal with judgments and decisions as a result of the workings of neurons that do their work by impulse firings.

6-3. Generalization to Multiple Stimuli

With multiple stimuli we have the functional equation

$$w(a_1 z_1, \ldots, a_n z_n) = b\,w(z_1, \ldots, z_n)$$

whose solution for the real variable case (change z's to s's) with $b > 0$, $a_k > 0$, and $s_k > 0$, is $w(s_1,\ldots,s_n) = b^{\sum_{k=1}^{n}(\log s_k/\log a_k)/k} P\left(\frac{\log s_1}{\log a_1},\ldots,\frac{\log s_n}{\log a_n}\right)$, (k = 1, . . . , n), where P is an arbitrary periodic function of period one of n variables, that is,

$$P(u_1+1,\ldots,u_n+1) = P(u_1,\ldots,u_n)$$

Solution of the functional equation in the complex domain due to Karol Baron [57] is

$$w(z_1,\ldots,z_N)$$

$$= z_1^{k_1}\ldots z_N^{k_N}\ G(|z_1|,\ldots,|z_M|,\frac{\log|z_{M+1}|}{\log|a_{M+1}|},\ldots,\frac{\log|z_N|}{\log|a_N|}, \arg z_1,\ldots,\arg z_N)$$

where G is a doubly periodic function with periods

$$(0, \underset{M}{\ldots}, 0, 1, \underset{M-N}{\ldots}, 1, \arg a_1,\ldots,\arg a_N)$$

and $(0, \ldots, 0, \underset{(n+l)}{2\pi}, 0, \ldots, 0)$ for $l \in \{1, \ldots, N\}$. It is known that a single-valued analytic function cannot possess more than two linearly independent periods.

For a **continuum number of stimuli** let $K(\mathbf{X},\mathbf{Y})$ be a compact reciprocal kernel i.e. $K(x,y)K(y,x) = 1$, for all $x\varepsilon\mathbf{X}$ and $y\varepsilon\mathbf{Y}$, where **X** and **Y** are compact subsets of the reals. We have the equation $w(\mathbf{X}) = \lambda\int_{\Omega} K(\mathbf{X};\mathbf{Y})w(\mathbf{Y})$.

Formally, we write the general solution in the form of a product integral:

$$w(\mathbf{X}) = [\exp\int_{\Omega}(\log x/\log a)dx]P(\frac{\log\mathbf{X}}{\log a})$$

Table 6-1 provides a summary of the eigenvalue formulation of the paired comparisons process in both the discrete and continuous cases.

Table 6-1: Mathematical Formulation and Solution of the Paired Comparisons Process

Discrete	Continuous
$A=(a_{ij})$, A consistent that is $a_{ij}a_{jk}=a_{ik,}$ then $a_{ij}=w_i/w_j$ and $\sum_{j=1}^{n} a_{ij}w_j = nw_i, i=1,\ldots,n, \sum_{i=1}^{n} w_i = 1$	$K(s,t)$ consistent that is $K(s,t)K(t,u)=K(s,u)$ then $K(s,t)=k(s)/k(t)$ and $\lambda \int_a^b K(s,t)w(t)dt = w(s), \int_a^b w(s)ds = 1$
$A=(a_{ij}), A$ reciprocal that is $a_{ji}=1/a_{ij}$ but not consistent, then $\sum_{i=1}^{n} a_{ij}w_j = \lambda_{\max} w_i, \sum_{i=1}^{n} w_i = 1$	$K(s,t)$ reciprocal that is $K(s,t)K(t,s)=1$, but not consistent, then $\lambda \int_a^b K(s,t)w(t)dt = w(s), \int_a^b w(s)ds = 1$
Principal eigenvector solution of $Aw=\lambda_{\max} w$	Eigenfunction solution also solution of functional equation $w(as)=bw(s)$; $w(s)=b^{\log s/\log a} p(\frac{\log s}{\log a})$ or more simply $w(u)=e^{\alpha u} p(u), \alpha=\log b,$ $u=\log s/\log a$ In the complex domain a single valued solution of the functional equation: $w(az)=bw(z)$, is $w(z)=cb^{\log\|z\|/\log\|a\|} g(z)$ where $g(z)$ is an arbitrary solution of $g(az)=g(z)$
Hierarchic Composition gives rise to multilinear forms $w_i^h = \sum_{i_2,\cdots,i_{h-1}=1}^{N_{h-1},\cdots,N_1} w_{i_1 i_2}^{h-1} \cdots w_{i_{h-2} i_{h-1}}^{2} w_{i_{h-1}}^{1} \quad i_1 \equiv i$	Hierarchic composition in the case of a finite number of criteria is a particular case of the multiple stimuli solution. It is a product integral in the case of a continuum number of criteria, as in the case of a continuum number of stimuli
Network composition also gives rise to convergent series of multilinear forms	Continuum composition - same as with hierarchic composition

6-4. The Hypermatrix of the Brain

How do we maintain an ongoing record of the signals transmitted in the brain that can also be updated, revised, and synthesized to capture the transient information that is communicated through neural firings?

The approach we follow to represent interactions in the brain is a result of representing the network of neurons by a graph, whose nodes represent the neurons themselves, and whose synaptic connections with other neurons are arcs or line segments that connect the nodes. Electric potentials are measured across the arcs. We assign the potentials direction so that they are read in a positive direction. In the opposite direction we assign them a zero value. Thus we represent the neurons of the brain conceptually by listing them in a column on the left as illustrated in the supermatrix in Table 6-2 and listing them again in a row above the columns of the matrix. We assume that for convenience we have arranged the neurons into components, which correspond to subcomponents or layers and these in turn according to the components or modules to which they belong. One can then enter a zero or a one in each column of the matrix to indicate whether a neuron in a row synapses with a neuron in a column. In fact, instead of the number one, a positive integer can be used to indicate the number of synapses that a neuron on the left has with a neuron at the top of the matrix. In that case each column of the matrix would represent the number of synapses of all neurons with a given neuron represented at the top of the matrix. That would be the most elementary way to represent the connections of the brain. It all hangs together in one piece, because every element is connected to some other element. Such a representation in a matrix can be modified by multiplying its nonnegative integer entries by the damped periodic oscillations of period one corresponding to the neuron with which the synapses are associated. In neural terminology, summing the elements in a column corresponds to spatial summation at an instant of time.

The different components of the hypermatrix are represented as block supermatrices. The control subsystems are connected to the supermatrices, which they control, and among themselves, and are also connected to higher-level control components. We shall see in the next section that the outcome obtained from the hypermatrix is somewhat different from that of the supermatrix. The *i,j* block of this matrix is a supermatrix shown in Table 6-2.

Figures 6-1 and 6-2 below are hard-worked-on but rudimentary applications of the hypermatrix to modules and submodules of the brain to illustrate what we have in mind. We warn the reader that we are simply using some knowledge and imagination to brave the complexity. The size of the hypermatrix to describe the brain would be of the order of 100 billion by 100 billion (we have not consulted the Cray Research people about whether the development of their supercomputers comes close to satisfying the dicta of brain computing). It is far beyond our capability to handle a matrix of such a size, or know enough about the physical reality of the brain and its synapses to create the entries in the matrix. Figure 6-2 shows the supermatrix of vision as part of the hypermatrix.

Table 6-2: A Supermatrix Entry of the Hypermatrix

$$W^{mn} = \begin{array}{cc} & \begin{array}{cccc} c_1^n & c_2^n & \cdots & c_M^n \\ e_{11}e_{12}\cdots e_{1n_1} & e_{21}e_{22}\cdots e_{2n_2} & & e_{N1}e_{N2}\cdots e_{Nn_N} \end{array} \\ \begin{array}{cc} c_1^m & \begin{array}{c} e_{11} \\ e_{12} \\ \vdots \\ e_{1m_1} \end{array} \\ c_2^m & \begin{array}{c} e_{21} \\ e_{22} \\ \vdots \\ e_{2m_2} \end{array} \\ \vdots & \vdots \\ c_M^m & \begin{array}{c} e_{M1} \\ e_{M2} \\ \vdots \\ e_{Mm_M} \end{array} \end{array} & \begin{bmatrix} W_{11} & W_{12} & \cdots & W_{1N} \\ W_{21} & W_{22} & \cdots & W_{2N} \\ \vdots & \vdots & \vdots\,\vdots\,\vdots & \vdots \\ W_{M1} & W_{M2} & \cdots & W_{MN} \end{bmatrix} \end{array}$$

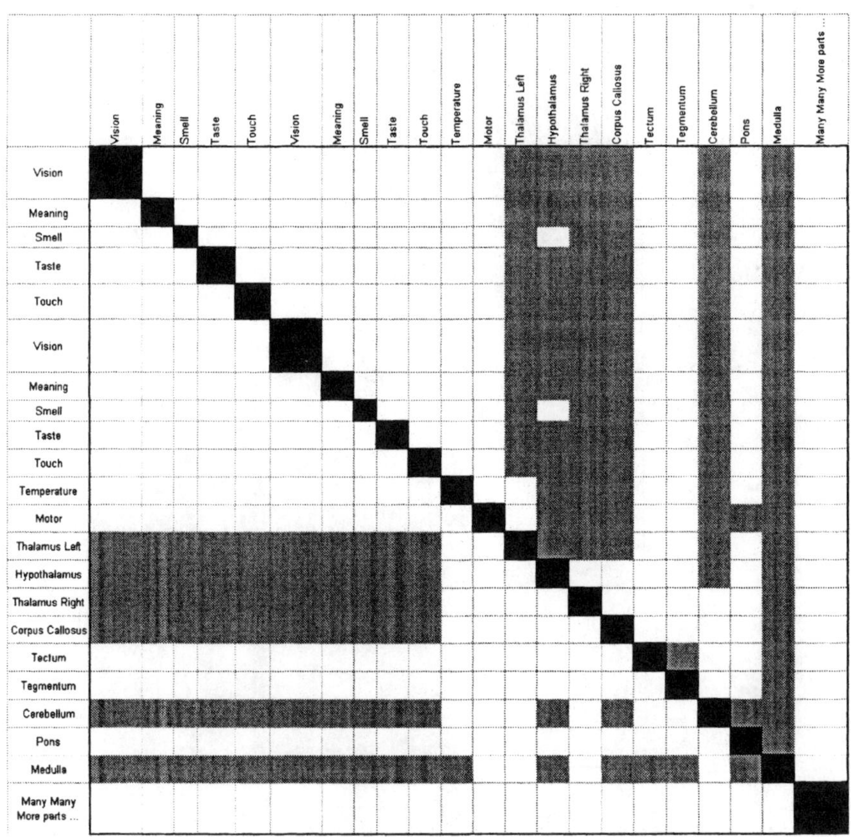

Figure 6-1: Hypermatrix of the Brain

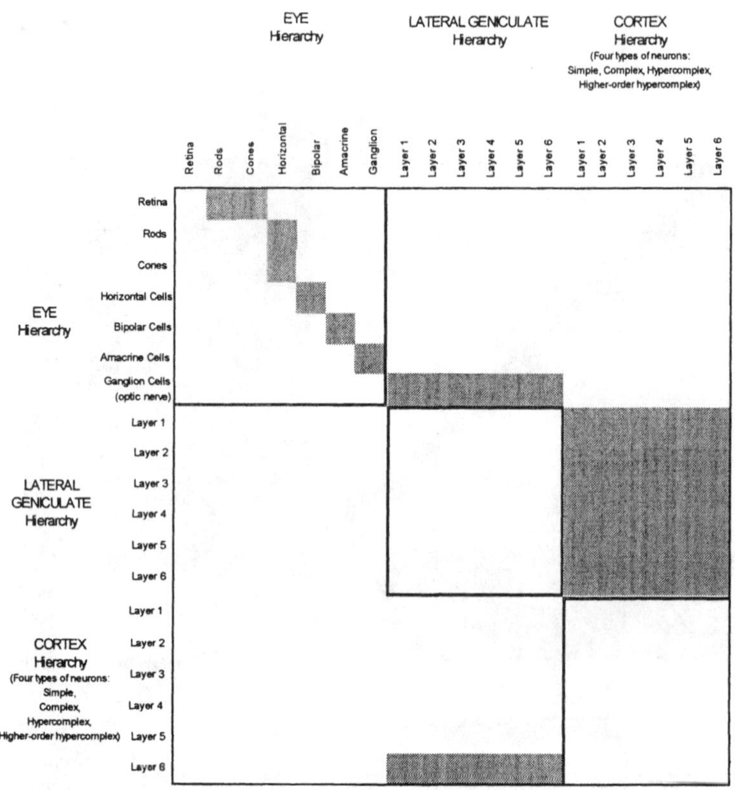

Figure 6-2: Supermatrix of Vision

6-5. Synthesis

The most significant observation about the brain, which consists of many individual neurons, is that it primarily synthesizes the firings of individual neurons into clusters of information and these in turn into larger clusters and so on, leading to an integrated whole.

Due to their sequential nature, the firings of a neuron that precede other neurons would be lost unless there is something like a field in which all the firings fit together to form a cohesive entity which carries information. Is there a field in the brain and where is it? We believe that the process of analytic continuation in the theory of functions of a complex variable provides insight into how neurons seem to know one another. *Analytic continuation has the striking consequence that something happening on a very small piece of a connected open set*

completely determines *what is happening in the entire set, at great distances from the small piece.* On page 373, Kuffler and Nicholls (1976) in their often cited book [29] say, ***"The nervous system appears constructed as if each neuron had built into it an awareness of its proper place in the system."*** That is what analytic continuation in the theory of functions of complex variables does. By a means similar to analytic continuation neurons are conditioned to fall on a unique path to continue information that connects with information processed by adjacent neurons with which a given neuron is connected.

By raising the hypermatrix to powers one obtains transitive interactions. This means that a neuron influences another neuron through intermediate neurons. All such two-step interactions are obtained by squaring the matrix. Three step interactions are obtained by cubing the matrix and so on. By raising the matrix to sufficiently large powers, the influence of each neuron on all the neurons with which one can trace a connection, yields the transient influence of neurons in the original hypermatrix Multiplying the hypermatrix by itself allows for combining the functions that represent the influence from pre-synaptic to post-synaptic neurons to accumulate all the transitive influences from one neuron to another and allow for feedback. I sometimes suspect that something like taking the Hadamard (element wise) product of the hypermartrix with itself is a more accurate description of how electricity travels down different paths in the matrix to synthesize signals because only multiplication to obtain the geometric mean takes place in this operation, a different story of synthesis than the one described above as a generalization of operations on the supermatrix of the ANP.

The Fourier transform that expresses the result of firing and the density of the resulting firings give us the desired synthesis. Depending on what parts of the brain are operational and participating in the synthesis, different physical and behavioral attributes are observed to take place, including consciousness related to the Fourier transform of the single-valued sensory functions.

6-6. Formation of Images and Sounds with Dirac Distributions

Complex valued functions cannot be drawn as one does ordinary functions of three real variables. The reason is that complex functions contain an imaginary part. Nevertheless, one can make a plot of the modulus or absolute value of such a function. The basic assumption we made to represent the response to a sequence of individual stimuli is that all the layers in a network of neurons are identical, and each stimulus value is represented by the firing of a neuron in each layer. A shortcoming of this representation is that it is not invariant with respect to the order in which the stimuli are fed into the network. It is known in the case of vision that the eyes do not scan pictures symmetrically if they are not symmetric, and hence our representation must satisfy some order invariant principle. Taking into account this principle would allow us to represent images independently of the form in which stimuli are input into the network. For example, we recognize an image even if it is subjected to a rotation, or to some sort of deformation. Thus, the invariance principle must include affine and similarity transformations. This invariance would allow the network to recognize images even when they are not identical to the ones from which it recorded a given concept, e.g., a bird. The next step would be to use the network representation given here with additional conditions to uniquely represent patterns from images, sounds and perhaps other sources of stimuli such as smell. Our representation focuses on the real part of the magnitude rather than the phase of the Fourier transform. Tests have been made to see the effect of phase and of magnitude on the outcome of a representation of a complex valued function. There is much more blurring due to change in magnitude than there is to change in phase. Thus we focus on representing responses in terms of Dirac functions, sums of such functions, and on approximations to them without regard to the coefficients in (15).

The functions result from modeling the neural firing as a pairwise comparison process in time. It is assumed that a neuron compares neurotransmitter-generated charges in increments of time. This leads to the continuous counterpart of a reciprocal matrix known as a reciprocal kernel. A reciprocal kernel $\boldsymbol{K}$ is an integral operator that satisfies the condition $\boldsymbol{K}(s,t)\boldsymbol{K}(t,s) = 1$, for all s and t. The response function $w(s)$ of the neuron in spontaneous activity results from solving the homogeneous equation (4). If

$$\lim_{\xi \to 0} K(\xi s, \xi t)$$

exists, where $\boldsymbol{K}$ is a compact integral operator defined on the space $L_2[0,b]$ of Lebesgue square integrable functions. If the reciprocal kernel $\boldsymbol{K}(s,t)0$, on ϱs, $\dot{t}b$, is Lebesgue square integrable and continuously differentiable, then

$$w(t) = t^{\alpha} e^{g(t)} / \int_0^b t^{\alpha} e^{g(t)} dt$$

satisfies (4) for some choice of $g(t)$. Because finite linear combinations of the functions $\{t^{\alpha} e^{-\beta t}, \alpha, \beta \geq 0\}$ are dense in the space of bounded continuous functions $\mathbf{C}[0,b]$ we can approximate $t^{\alpha} e^{g(t)}$ by linear combinations of $t^{\alpha} e^{-\beta t}$ and hence we substitute $g(t) = -\beta t, \beta \geq 0$, in the eigenfunction $w(t)$. The density of neural firing is not completely analogous to the density of the rational numbers in the real number system. The rationals are countably infinite, the number of neurons is finite but large. In speaking of density here we may think of making a sufficiently close approximation (within some prescribed bound rather than arbitrarily close).

We use the functions:

$$\{t^{\alpha} e^{-\beta t}, \alpha, \beta \geq 0\}$$

to represent images and sounds.

Before we describe how the network can be used to represent images and sounds, we summarize the mathematical model on which the neural density representation is based.

Neural responses are impulsive and hence the brain is a discrete firing system. It follows that the spontaneous activity of a neuron during a very short period of time in which the neuron fires is given by:

$$w(t) = \sum_{k=1}^{R} \gamma_k (t - \tau_k)^{\alpha} e^{-\beta(t-\tau_k)}$$

if the neuron fires at the random times τ_k, k=1, 2 ,..., R. Empirical findings support the assumption that R and the times τ_k, k=1, 2,..., R are probabilistic. However, the parameters α and β vary from neuron to neuron, but are constant for the firings of each neuron. Non-spontaneous activity can be characterized as a perturbation of background activity. To derive the response function when neurons are stimulated from external sources, we consider an inhomogeneous equation to represent stimuli acting on the neuron in addition to existing spontaneous activity. Thus, we solve the inhomogenous Fredholm equation of the 2nd kind given by:

$$w(s) - \lambda_0 \int_0^b K(s,t)\, w(t)\, dt = f(s)$$

This equation has a solution in the Sobolev space $W_p^k(\Omega)$ of distributions (in the sense of Schwartz) in $\mathbf{L}_p(W)$ whose derivatives of order k also belong to the space $\mathbf{L}_p(W)$, where W is an open subset of $\mathbf{R}^n$.

We created a 2-dimensional network of neurons consisting of layers. For illustrative purposes, we assume that there is one layer of neurons corresponding to each of the stimulus values. Thus, if the list of stimuli consists of n numerical values, we created n layers with a specific number of neurons in each layer. Under the assumption that each numerical stimulus is represented by the firing of one and only one neuron, each layer of the network must also consist of n neurons with thresholds varying between the largest and the smallest values of the list of stimuli. We also assumed that the firing threshold of each neuron had the same width. Thus, if the perceptual range of a stimulus varies between two values θ_1 and θ_2, and each layer of the network has n neurons, then a neuron in the ith position of the layer will fire if the stimulus value falls between

$$\theta_1 + (i-1)\frac{\theta_2 - \theta_1}{n-1} \quad \text{and} \quad \theta_1 + i\frac{\theta_2 - \theta_1}{n-1}.$$

6-7. PICTURE EXPERIMENT

In the graphics experiment the bird and rose pictures required 124 and 248 data points, respectively, whereas the sound experiment required 1000 times more data points. Once the (x, y) coordinates of the points were obtained, the x-coordinate was used to represent time and the y-coordinate to represent response to a stimulus. The numerical values associated with the drawings in Figures 6-3 and 24 were tabulated and the numbers provided the input to the neurons in the networks built to represent the bird and the rose. This task is computationally demanding even for such simple geometric figures as the bird and the rose. For example, for the bird picture, the stimuli list consists of 124 values, and we would need 124^2=15376 neurons, arranged in 124 layers of 124 neurons each The network and the data sampled to form the picture given in Figure 6-4, were used to create a 124x124 network of neurons consisting of 124 layers with 124 neurons in each layer. Each dot in the figures is generated by the firing of a neuron in response to a stimulus falling within the neuron's lower and upper thresholds.

Figure 6-3: Bird

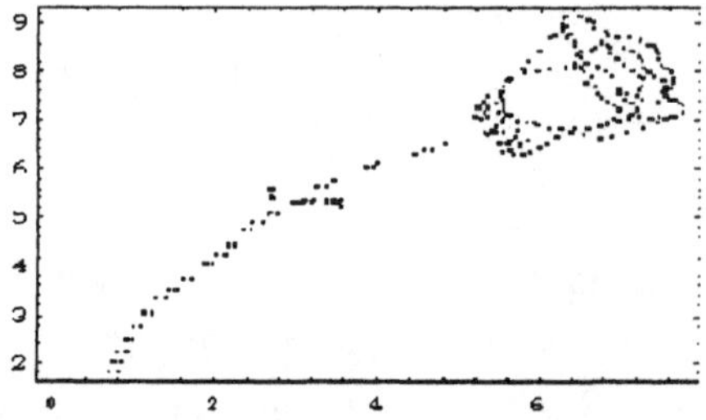

Fig 6-4: Rose

6-8. SOUND EXPERIMENT

In the sound experiment we first recorded with the aid of Mathematica the first few seconds of Haydn's symphony no.102 in B-flat major and Mozart's symphony no. 40 in G minor. The result is a set of numerical amplitudes between -1 and 1. Each of these amplitudes was used to make neurons fire when the amplitude falls within a prescribed threshold range. Under the assumption that each neuron fires in response to one stimulus, we would need the same number of neurons as the sample size, i.e., 117,247 in Haydn's symphony and 144,532 in Mozart's symphony. Our objective was to approximate the amplitude using one neuron for each amplitude value, and then use the resulting values in Mathematica to play back the music. A small sample of the numerical data for Mozart's symphony is displayed in Figure 6-5.

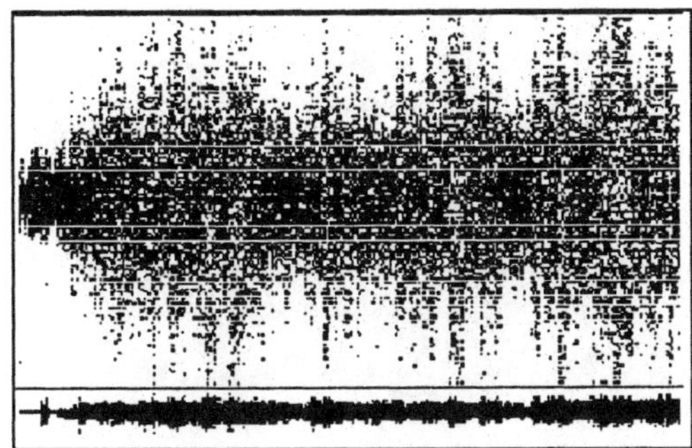

Figure 6-5: Mozart's Symphony No. 40

6-9. Theory for a Compatibility Index and its Generalization to the Continuous Case

In the AHP/ANP the question arises as to how close one priority vector is to another priority vector. When two vectors are close, we say they are *compatible.* The question is how to measure compatibility in a meaningful way. It turns out that consistency and compatibility can be related in a useful way. Our development of a compatibility measure uses the idea of the Hadamard or element-wise product of two matrices.

Let us show first that the priority vector $w = (w_1, \ldots ,w_n)$ is completely compatible with itself. Thus we form the matrix of all possible ratios $W=(w_{ij})=(w_i/w_j)$ from this vector. This matrix is reciprocal, that is $w_{ji} = 1/w_{ij}$. The Hadamard product of a reciprocal matrix W and its transpose W^T is given by:

$$WoW^T = \begin{pmatrix} w_1/w_1 & \cdots & w_1/w_n \\ \vdots & & \vdots \\ w_n/w_1 & \cdots & w_n/w_n \end{pmatrix} \circ \begin{pmatrix} w_1/w_1 & \cdots & w_n/w_1 \\ \vdots & & \vdots \\ w_1/w_n & \cdots & w_n/w_n \end{pmatrix} = \begin{pmatrix} 1 & \cdots & 1 \\ \vdots & & \vdots \\ 1 & \cdots & 1 \end{pmatrix} = \begin{pmatrix} 1 \\ \vdots \\ 1 \end{pmatrix} (1 \cdots 1) \equiv ee^T$$

The sum of the elements of a matrix A can be written as $e^T Ae$. In particular we have $e^T AoA^T e = n^2$ for the sum of the elements of the Hadamard product of a matrix and its transpose. Thus a matrix is completely compatible with itself. Now we have an idea of how to define a measure of compatibility for two matrices A and B. It is given by $\frac{1}{n^2} e^T AoB^T e$. Note that a reciprocal matrix of judgments that is inconsistent is not itself a matrix of ratios from a given vector. However, such a matrix has a principal eigenvector and thus we speak of the compatibility of the matrix of judgments and the matrix formed from ratios of the principal eigenvector. We have the following theorem for a reciprocal matrix of judgments and the matrix W of the ratios of its principal eigenvector:

Theorem : $\frac{1}{n^2} e^T Ao\, W^T e = \frac{\lambda_{\max}}{n}$

Proof: From $Aw = \lambda_{max} w$ we have $\sum_{j=1}^{n} a_{ij} w_j = \lambda_{\max} w_i$

and $$\frac{1}{n^2} e^T AoW^{\mathrm{T}} e = \frac{1}{n^2} \sum_{i=1}^{n} \sum_{j=1}^{n} a_{ij} \frac{w_j}{w_i} = \frac{\lambda_{\max}}{n}$$

We want this ratio to be close to one or in general not much more than 1.1 and be less than this value for small size matrices. It is in accord with the idea that a 10% deviation is at the upper end of acceptability.

Table 6-3 gives information on compatibility and consistency for different size judgment matrices.

Table 6-3: Relationship Between Consistency and Compatibility for a Different Number of Elements

Number of Elements (n)	Compatibility Index (S.I.)	λ_{max}	$C.I. = \dfrac{\lambda_{\max} - n}{n - 1}$	$R.I.$	$C.R. = \dfrac{C.I}{R.I}$
3	1.017	3.052	0.026	0.52	0.05
4	1.053	4.214	0.071	0.89	0.08
5	1.089	5.444	0.111	1.11	0.10
6	1.104	6.625	0.125	1.25	0.10
7	1.116	7.810	0.135	1.35	0.10
8	1.123	8.980	0.140	1.40	0.10
9	1.129	10.160	0.145	1.45	0.10

EXAMPLE

Consider the vectors $\left[\frac{4}{7},\frac{2}{7},\frac{1}{7}\right]^T$ and $\left[\frac{3}{4.6},\frac{1}{4.6},\frac{.6}{4.6}\right]^T$, are they compatible?

We form the matrices A and B of ratios from these two respective vectors. We then take their Hadamard (or element-wise) product. We obtain

$$\begin{pmatrix} 1 & 2 & 4 \\ 1/2 & 1 & 2 \\ 1/4 & 1/2 & 1 \end{pmatrix} \circ \begin{pmatrix} 1 & 1/3 & 1/5 \\ 3 & 1 & 3/5 \\ 5 & 5/3 & 1 \end{pmatrix} = \begin{pmatrix} 1 & 2/3 & 4/5 \\ 3/2 & 1 & 6/5 \\ 5/4 & 5/6 & 1 \end{pmatrix}$$

and $$\frac{1}{n^2} e^T A \text{ o } B^T e = \frac{9\frac{1}{4}}{9} = 1.028$$

and by our measure of compatibility the two vectors are considered to be close or compatible.

As another example for the following Hadamard product we have

$$\begin{pmatrix} 1 & 2 & 4 \\ 1/2 & 1 & 2 \\ 1/4 & 1/2 & 1 \end{pmatrix} \circ \begin{pmatrix} 1 & 2 & 4 \\ 1/2 & 1 & 2 \\ 1/4 & 1/2 & 1 \end{pmatrix} = \begin{pmatrix} 1 & 4 & 16 \\ 1/4 & 1 & 4 \\ 1/16 & 1/4 & 1 \end{pmatrix}$$

and $$\frac{1}{n^2} e^T AoB^T e = \frac{27\frac{9}{16}}{9} = 3.063$$

The two eigenvectors of A and B^T are

$$\left(\frac{4}{7}, \frac{2}{7}, \frac{1}{7}\right)^T \textit{and} \left(\frac{1}{7}, \frac{2}{7}, \frac{4}{7}\right)^T$$

Their matrices of ratios show that they are not compatible.

It is easy to show that given the vector $[.05\ \ .15\ \ .30\ \ .50]^T$ the vector $[.08\ \ .22\ \ .25\ \ .45]^T$ is close to it, whereas the vector $[.03\ \ .25\ \ .10\ \ .62]^T$ is not close.

6-10. USES OF COMPATIBILITY

Compatibility can be used to assess how close the composite outcome of a set of alternatives by an individual is from that of a group composite outcome. The latter can be obtained by taking the geometric mean of the composite outcome of several individuals. After assessing the compatibility of the matrix of ratios of each individual with that of the group, one can suggest to each individual which of his ratios is the most incompatible with that of the group and propose changes in his overall thinking to make it more compatible. Conversely, members of a group may want to reconsider their own judgments after learning from that individual who has a different perspective. Through such revision and recalculation of the group outcome, one may be able to obtain a group decision that is compatible with each member. A similar approach may be applied to test the compatibility of individual outcomes with that of a group whose outcome is derived by combining individual judgments in each matrix.

Here are two simple examples that demonstrate the validity of the pairwise comparisons matrix to which the reader may apply the compatibility index.

Relative Weights of Objects: The matrix in Table 6-4 gives the estimated pairwise comparisons of the weights of the five objects lifted by hand, made by the then President of the Diners Club, a friend of the author. The two vectors appear to be very close but are they compatible?

Table 6-4: Pairwise Comparisons of the Weights of Five Objects

Weight	Radio	Type-writer	Large Attaché Case	Projector	Small Attaché Case	Eigen-vector	Actual Relative Weights
Radio	1	1/5	1/3	1/4	4	.09	.10
Typewriter	5	1	2	2	8	.40	.39
Large Attaché Case	3	1/2	1	1/2	4	.18	.20
Projector	4	1/2	2	1	7	.29	.27
Small Attaché Case	1/4	1/8	1/4	1/7	1	.04	.04

Relative Electric Consumption of Household Appliances: In Table 6-5 we have paired comparisons done by students in electrical engineering estimating the consumption of electricity of common household appliances. How compatible are the derived and actual vectors? The hairdryer is of such a small magnitude that it probably should have been left out of the other homogeneous comparisons.

Table 6-5: Relative Electricity Consumption (Kilowatt Hours) of Household Appliances

Annual Electric Consumption	Elec. Range	Refrig	TV	Dish Wash	Iron	Radio	Hair Dryer	Eigen-vector	Actual Relative Weights
Electric Range	1	2	5	8	7	9	9	.393	.392
Refrigerator	1/2	1	4	5	5	7	9	.261	.242
TV	1/5	1/4	1	2	5	6	8	.131	.167
Dishwasher	1/8	1/5	1/2	1	4	9	9	.110	.120
Iron	1/7	1/5	1/5	1/4	1	5	9	.061	.047
Radio	1/9	1/7	1/6	1/9	1/5	1	5	.028	.028
Hair-dryer	1/9	1/9	1/8	1/9	1/9	1/5	1	.016	.003

COMPATIBILITY IN THE CONTINUOUS CASE

The rational numbers are known to be dense in the real numbers. The question is whether, because of this, inconsistency and incompatibility on the rational numbers generalize to inconsistency and incompatibility on the real numbers. We know that the rational numbers have measure zero and thus it seems that inconsistency on the rational numbers need not imply inconsistency (incompatibility) on the real numbers. To study this subject one can retreat to discrete steps and computations, and sometimes the space can be made discrete over a mesh to apply a discrete computing device.

We now derive a compatibility index in the continuous case along the lines discussed for the discrete case. We consider the solution of the equation $w(as) = bw(s)$ given by $w(s) = b^{\log s/\log a} p(\frac{\log s}{\log a})$ and rewrite it as

$$w(s) = e^{\log b^{\log s/\log a}} p(\frac{\log s}{\log a}) = e^{\alpha u} p(u), \alpha = \log b, u = \log s / \log a$$

We have for the compatibility index of two such functions with their respective parameters:

$$\frac{1}{T^2}\int_0^T\int_0^T \frac{e^{\alpha_1 u} p(u)}{e^{\alpha_2 u} p(u)} \frac{e^{\alpha_2 v} p(v)}{e^{\alpha_1 v} p(v)} du dv = \frac{1}{T^2} \frac{e^{(\alpha_1-\alpha_2)T} - 1}{\alpha_1 - \alpha_2} \frac{1 - e^{-(\alpha_1-\alpha_2)T}}{\alpha_1 - \alpha_2}$$

$$= \frac{1}{T^2} \frac{e^{(\alpha_1-\alpha_2)T} - 1 - 1 + e^{-(\alpha_1-\alpha_2)T}}{(\alpha_1 - \alpha_2)^2} = \left(\frac{e^{(\alpha_1-\alpha_2)T/2} - e^{-(\alpha_1-\alpha_2)T/2}}{(\alpha_1 - \alpha_2)T}\right)^2$$

$$= \frac{1}{4}\left(\frac{e^{(\alpha_1-\alpha_2)T/2} - e^{-(\alpha_1-\alpha_2)T/2}}{(\alpha_1 - \alpha_2)T/2}\right)^2 = \frac{1}{4}\left(\frac{e^{\gamma} - e^{-\gamma}}{\gamma}\right)^2 \to 1 \text{ as } |\gamma| \to 0$$

Use for such a compatibility measure has not been determined in practice as in the discrete case. But it is clear that it would be very useful to find such examples with their functions.

6-11. Conclusions

We have sketched the relationship between discrete rational decision-making and automatic partly instinctive decisions. It is fortunate that much of the mathematics needed to do this kind of thinking had already been discovered by mathematicians of the 19th and 20th centuries. It is certain that new mathematics is needed for deeper investigation of this important subject. The relatively new mathematical field of functional equations with several books written on it is helpful in this respect because it allows us to formulate problems that we believe to be realistic and provides us with solutions that we can study for their meaning and practicality.

I am grateful to my colleagues Janos Aczel, the world expert in functional equations, for his help in developing some of the material on functional equations in this chapter, to Kirti Peniwati for editorial help, to Luis Vargas for discussions in the continuous case of the compatibility index and to Rozann Saaty for her patient editorial help.

Chapter 7
Dynamic Decisions: Decisions as Functions of Time

7-1. Introduction

Because good decisions depend on the conditions of the future, and because conditions vary over time, to make a good decision requires judgments of what is more likely or more preferred over different time periods. There are at least three ways to deal with dynamic decisions. One is to include in the structure itself different factors that indicate change in time such as scenarios and different time periods and then carry out paired comparisons with respect to the time periods using the fundamental scale of the AHP. The second is to do paired comparisons as rates of relative change with respect to time. This is done at different points of time as representatives of intervals to which they belong. These intervals can have different lengths. For each representative point one needs to provide a pairwise judgment about the relative rate of change of one alternative over another and derive mathematical functions for that matrix of comparisons for one of the time periods. The third is to do what I proposed in my first book on the AHP and that is to use functions for the paired comparisons and derive functions from them. It is usually difficult to know what functions to use and what they mean. Ideas and examples are presented towards the development of a theory for dynamic decision-making.

The Analytic Hierarchy Process (AHP) for decision-making is a theory of relative measurement based on paired comparisons used to derive absolute scales in the form of normalized ratio scales whose elements are then used as priorities. Matrices of pairwise comparisons are formed either by providing judgments to estimate dominance using absolute numbers from the 1 to 9 fundamental scale of the AHP, or by directly constructing the pairwise dominance ratios using actual measurements. The AHP can be applied to both tangible and intangible criteria based on the judgments of knowledgeable and expert people, although how to get measures for intangibles is its main concern. The weighting and adding synthesis process applied in the hierarchical structure of the AHP combines multidimensional scales of measurement into a single "uni-dimensional" scale of priorities. In the end we must fit our entire world experience into our system of priorities if we are going to understand it.

Sound decision making not only requires that we look ahead as a process of thinking and planning, but also that our structures be flexible to include change so that we can constantly revise our decision because the system itself is in imbalance resulting in a non-stationary optimum. Thus optimizing inefficiently by selecting a best decision at a given time can only be a sub-optimum over a long-range time horizon because of the fundamental influence of change in any survivable system. There are three ways to cope with this problem. The first is to make the best choice according to short, mid and long term merits with a feedback loop or a holarchy used to prioritize them according to their benefits, opportunities, costs and risks evaluated in terms of strategic criteria used in general to guide all our decisions [10, 11]. The other is to make the judgments mathematically depend on time and express them as functions, discussed in this paper. The third and less practical way is to revise a decision every once in while. Although many decisions can be tested in advance through sensitivity analysis to determine their long term stability, revision after implementation can be both controversial and costly. One may have to abandon an already finished resource intensive alternative for another such costly alternative. In politics, we circumvent doing it by electing new leaders with the perspective we want, so they can focus on making better decisions for pressing needs in society.

So far most of us have had no way to combine dollars with yards or pounds to trade them off. We would be truly multi-dimensional if we could combine the different dimensions into a single dimension that represents our priority of importance. That is precisely what the AHP and ANP help us do in a more or less precise way, depending on the level of experience that we bring to bear on a decision problem. Until recently, the AHP and ANP have been **static** in that they have used numbers and derived numbers to represent priorities. What we need is to make them dynamic by using numbers or functions and then deriving either numbers that represent functions like expected values, or deriving functions directly to represent priorities over time. My aim here is to extend the AHP/ANP to deal with time dependent priorities; we may refer to them as DHP/DNP (Dynamic Hierarchy Process/Dynamic Network Process). At this point we may not know enough to develop the necessary fundamental scale of functions to use in making paired comparisons of intangibles. But if nothing else DHP and DNP work with tangibles now and we need to weigh and trade off tangibles as functions of time.

Time dependent decision-making that we call dynamic decision-making is a subject that we need today. So far we have thought of our decisions as known alternatives to choose from. But these alternatives may evolve over time along with our preferences for them like stocks in the stock market whose prices constantly change over time. Our actions need to vary over time like a medicine capsule that releases different amounts of chemical at different times. Time dependent decisions are a reality and not a complicated idea that we can ignore. At a minimum they are needed in technical design problems in which the influences of several tangible design factors change over time and tradeoffs must be made among them to enable the system to respond differently and continuously over the time of its operation. But the power and potential of the subject lie in its use of judgment to make comparisons to derive relative real valued functions for intangibles from paired comparisons. Because we can do that for real numbers we can also do it for complex numbers. They have a modulus (magnitude) and an argument (direction), each of which is real. That is where we need to go later to derive relative complex functions from paired comparison expert judgments. The modulus is estimated in the usual way of comparing magnitudes and the argument or angle is estimated along the lines of rate of change comparison given below. In this way the two parts of a complex number are derived from paired comparisons.

There are essentially two analytic ways to study dynamic decisions: structural, by including scenarios and time periods as elements in the structure that represents a decision, and functional, by explicitly involving time in the judgment process. A possible third way would be a hybrid of these two.

The **structural** method is most familiar today and it involves using scenarios or time periods as factors in the hierarchic or network structure of a decision, and then making appropriate judgments. Generally contrast scenarios such as optimistic, status quo and pessimistic, or more specific ones such as different values for the economy or the stock market are put near or at the top of a hierarchy. The likelihood of the scenarios is first determined in terms of higher level criteria under the goal such as economic, political, social and technological, that are themselves prioritized according to their prevailing influences over a certain time horizon. Judgments are provided for the behavior of the alternatives with respect to the factors encountered under each scenario (see Wind and Saaty). Synthesis reveals the best alternative to follow in view of the mix of potential scenarios. For more detail about this method see my book on Analytical Planning where contrast scenarios are discussed. The other structural method is to put actual time periods at the "bottom" of the structure, prioritize them and finally combine their priorities by, for example, using the idea of expected value. This method was used in estimating when the US economy would recover and is illustrated in the next section.

The second approach where the judgments themselves change with time is **functional** in the literal sense. Whatever the structure may be, time dependent judgments are provided using functions from which priorities are then obtained and synthesized as one generally does with the AHP/ANP. We have two problems to solve when using dynamic judgments in the AHP/ANP. The first is what scale to use to represent dynamic judgments and how in this case it can be made to satisfy the axiom of homogeneity. The second is how to generate the principal eigenvector of a matrix whose order is more than four. Because 7 is an upper bound on producing results with reliable consistency, it is sufficient to find ways to derive the principal eigenvector of a matrix of order seven or less. This task can also be done in two ways, analytically and numerically. This paper is about both these ways but particularly about the mathematics of the functional way. In making pairwise comparisons we estimate how many times one element is more important than another with respect to a common property by forming their ratios if we know their measurements and get an expert to tell us when we do not have their exact measurements. Each judgment is expressed with a number.

Suppose now that the measurements are a function of time. If we know the functions, we can form their ratios, but if we do not, what kind of typical functions can we use to represent ratios in a standard way just as we use numbers in a standard way. If humans have an intrinsic ability to look at the future of two stocks whose values appreciate over time and can say that on the whole one would be a better investment than the other, then one would like to capture this intuitive understanding by some standard functions to apply in all situations where we have to deal with intangibles over time. We have to do this kind of thinking even if we do not know much about the exact future. Like the US building a 60 billion dollar anti-missile system based on imagined threats over a future time horizon that may not materialize. The decision would be a function of time going forward or pulling back as the need may be. What are typical functions to use in describing in an uncertain way the ratio of anticipated variations of two functions over time? I will discuss and illustrate my proposed approach to this problem.

7-2. A Structural Dynamics Example

We have already encountered examples in which time periods are identified and prioritized with respect to higher level criteria as in the examples of the turn around of the US economy. Here time itself becomes descriptively one of the factors to be considered in the development of priorities without using mathematics to represent judgments as functions of time analytically. The use of scenarios in planning is another example of how time horizons can be introduced into the structure of decisions.

7-3. Functional Dynamics: Numerical Solution of the Principal Eigenvalue Problem by Raising the Matrix to Powers – A Basic 3 x 3 Example

Because priorities are obtained in the form of the principal eigenvector and because this vector is obtained by raising the paired comparisons matrix to powers, particularly in this case, we do not need to solve equations. We are fortunate in this special and rare case to do that. In the AHP one simply composes by multiplying and adding functions. So, in principle, there is no major theoretical difficulty in making decisions with dynamic judgments. In the ANP the problem is to obtain the limiting result of powers of the supermatrix with dynamic priorities. Because of its size, for the foreseeable future, the supermatrix would have to be solved numerically. It may even turn out in the long run that this is the more efficient way to obtain priorities from the supermatrix even when we have analytic expressions to represent priorities introduced in the usual way in the supermatrix to raise it to powers to obtain its limit for various values of time.

We remind the reader that if one has the principal eigenvector of a matrix, to test for consistency one obtains its principal eigenvalue by forming the scalar product of the principal eigenvector and the vector of column sums of the matrix. Generally, given an eigenvector, this is also the way to obtain its corresponding eigenvalue. The typical form of a judgment matrix in dynamic form is:

$$A(t) = \begin{bmatrix} a_{11}(t) & a_{12}(t) & \cdots & a_{1n}(t) \\ a_{21}(t) & a_{22}(t) & \cdots & a_{2n}(t) \\ \vdots & \vdots & \vdots & \vdots \\ a_{n1}(t) & a_{n2}(t) & \cdots & a_{nn}(t) \end{bmatrix}$$

$a_{ij} > 0, a_{ji}(t) = a_{ij}^{-1}(t)$. As in the discrete case, when $A(t)$ is consistent, we have $a_{ij}(t) = w_i(t)/w_j(t)$.

The basic idea with the numerical approach is to obtain the time dependent principal eigenvector by simulation. One expresses the judgments functionally but then derives the eigenvector from the judgments for a fixed instant of time, substitutes the numerical values of the eigenvectors obtained for that instant in a supermatrix, solves the supermatrix problem and derives the priorities for the alternatives. Repeating the process for different values of time one generates a curve for the priorities of the alternatives and then approximates these values by curves with a functional form for each component of the eigenvector. It is sufficient to illustrate this entire procedure for one matrix.

Let us consider the 3 by 3 matrix with dynamic coefficients shown below. The rows of the two Tables 7-1 below the matrix give the principal eigenvector for the indicated values of t. They are then plotted in the diagram below and an algorithm is used to find the analytic expressions for the best fitting curves for the three components of the eigenvector. This entire process can be made automatic in software for dynamic judgments.

$$A(t)=\begin{bmatrix} 1 & a(t) & b(t) \\ 1/a(t) & 1 & c(t) \\ 1/b(t) & 1/c(t) & 1 \end{bmatrix} \quad \begin{array}{l} a(t)=0.1+t^3 \\ b(t)=1+2t^2 \\ c(t)=1+\frac{1}{2}e^t \end{array}$$

Table 7-1: Eigenvectors for Different Values of Time for Matrix Above

t	a(t)	b(t)	c(t)
0	0.1	1	1.5
0.05	0.100125	1.005	1.525636
0.1	0.101	1.02	1.552585
0.15	0.103375	1.045	1.580917
0.2	0.108	1.08	1.610701
0.25	0.115625	1.125	1.642013
0.3	0.127	1.18	1.674929
0.35	0.142875	1.245	1.709534
0.4	0.164	1.32	1.745912
0.45	0.191125	1.405	1.784156
0.5	0.225	1.5	1.824361
0.55	0.266375	1.605	1.866627
0.6	0.316	1.72	1.911059
0.65	0.374625	1.845	1.95777
0.7	0.443	1.98	2.006876
0.75	0.521875	2.125	2.0585
0.8	0.612	2.28	2.11277
0.85	0.714125	2.445	2.169823
0.9	0.829	2.62	2.229802
0.95	0.957375	2.805	2.292855
1	1.1	3	2.359141

t	w1	w2	w3
0	0.12202	0.648329	0.229651
0.05	0.122032	0.650441	0.227527
0.1	0.122939	0.65207	0.224991
0.15	0.125189	0.652457	0.222354
0.2	0.129205	0.650917	0.219878
0.25	0.135356	0.646922	0.217721
0.3	0.143922	0.640169	0.215909
0.35	0.155057	0.630604	0.214339
0.4	0.168789	0.618394	0.212817
0.45	0.185024	0.603858	0.211119
0.5	0.203569	0.587395	0.209036
0.55	0.224166	0.569422	0.206412
0.6	0.246511	0.550334	0.203156
0.65	0.270281	0.530484	0.199235
0.7	0.29515	0.510183	0.194667
0.75	0.320802	0.489692	0.189507
0.8	0.346935	0.469231	0.183833
0.85	0.373278	0.448984	0.177738
0.9	0.399583	0.4291	0.171317
0.95	0.425637	0.4097	0.164664
1	0.451256	0.390876	0.157868

The following expressions are best least-squares fits in some technical sense of each set of numerical data for the components shown in Table 7-1 and plotted in Figure 7-1.

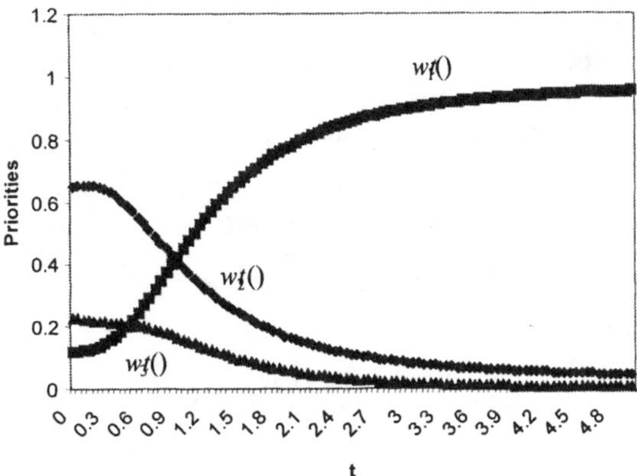

Figure 7-1: A Plot of the Numerical Estimate of the Components of the Principal Right Eigenvector

$$w_1(t) \approx \frac{1}{\sqrt{2\pi}} \int_{-\infty}^{-0.053+1.151\ln t} e^{-\frac{z^2}{2}} dz, \quad t > 0.4$$

$$w_2(t) \approx \frac{1}{\sqrt{2\pi}} \int_{-\infty}^{-0.344-0.905\ln t} e^{-\frac{z^2}{2}} dz, \quad t > 0.4$$

$$w_3(t) \approx e^{-0.956-0.979t}, \quad t > 0.4$$

7-4. Functional Dynamics: Analytic Solution of the Principal Eigenvalue Problem – Solving Algebraic Equations of Degree *n*

Because we need to solve for the principal eigenvector, Perron theory gives us a way to obtain it more simply than by solving a high order algebraic equation or even by raising the matrix to arbitrarily large powers. On p. 20 of Horn and Johnson's "Matrix Analysis" there is a brief discussion of the classical adjoint. Let $M = A - \lambda_{max}(T)I$ I be an n by n matrix, where A is the pairwise comparisons matrix and I is the identity matrix. What we now show is only useful when we know $\lambda_{max}(T)$. Let M' be the matrix whose entry in the ith row and j^{th} column is $(-1)^{i+j}$ times the (n-1 by n-1) determinant of the matrix obtained by removing the ith column and j^{th} row of M. Note the row/column transposition. Then $M M' = \det(M)\, I$. Now M has rank n-1. We note that in our situation, because its characteristic polynomial is of degree n and vanishes at $\lambda_{max}(T)$, the rank of M cannot be more than n-1. By Perron, $\lambda_{max}(T)$ is unique and cannot again be the root of a determinant of an n-1 minor of M and the rank of M is precisely n-1. Thus $MM' = 0$ and every column of M' is an eigenvector of M (belongs to the kernel of M). Since the kernel of M is one-dimensional, all of the columns of M' must be proportional. They are also nonzero vectors because the rank of M is n-1, that is "some" n-1 by n-1 minor is nonsingular. This gives us another way of getting the principal right eigenvector of A when we know $\lambda_{\max}(T)$. But for the supermatrix we already know that $\lambda_{\max}(T)=1$ which follows from:

$$\max\sum_{j=1}^{n} a_{ij} \geq \sum_{j=1}^{n} a_{ij}\frac{w_j}{w_i} = \lambda_{\max} \quad \text{for max } w_i$$

$$\min\sum_{j=1}^{n} a_{ij} \leq \sum_{j=1}^{n} a_{ij}\frac{w_j}{w_i} = \lambda_{\max} \quad \text{for min } w_i$$

Thus for a row stochastic matrix we have $1=\min\sum_{j=1}^{n} a_{ij} \leq \lambda_{\max} \leq \max\sum_{j=1}^{n} a_{ij} = 1$, thus λ_{ma}

The same type of argument applies when a matrix is column stochastic.

Here is an example of the foregoing ideas. The matrix A, its principal right eigenvector and its eigenvalues are:

$$\begin{bmatrix} 1 & 2 & 3 & 4 & 5 \\ \frac{1}{2} & 1 & 2 & 3 & 4 \\ \frac{1}{3} & \frac{1}{2} & 1 & 2 & 3 \\ \frac{1}{4} & \frac{1}{3} & \frac{1}{2} & 1 & 2 \\ \frac{1}{5} & \frac{1}{4} & \frac{1}{3} & \frac{1}{2} & 1 \end{bmatrix} \begin{pmatrix} 0.418539 \\ 0.262518 \\ 0.159923 \\ 0.097253 \\ 0.061767 \end{pmatrix} \begin{Bmatrix} 5.06808 \\ 0.00498879+0.582755i \\ 0.00498879-0.582755i \\ -0.0390289+0.068286i \\ -0.0390289-0.068286i \end{Bmatrix}$$

$\lambda_{\max}(A) = 5.06808$

The matrix $M = A - \lambda_{\max}(T)I$ is given by:

$$\begin{bmatrix} -4.06808 & 2 & 3 & 4 & 5 \\ \frac{1}{2} & -4.06808 & 2 & 3 & 4 \\ \frac{1}{3} & \frac{1}{2} & -4.06808 & 2 & 3 \\ \frac{1}{4} & \frac{1}{3} & \frac{1}{2} & -4.06808 & 2 \\ \frac{1}{5} & \frac{1}{4} & \frac{1}{3} & \frac{1}{2} & -4.06808 \end{bmatrix}$$

Its adjoint matrix M' is:

$$\begin{bmatrix} 136.49 & 214.908 & 353.393 & 580.105 & 924.877 \\ 85.6099 & 134.796 & 221.657 & 363.855 & 580.105 \\ 52.1526 & 82.116 & 135.031 & 221.657 & 353.393 \\ 31.7155 & 49.9371 & 82.116 & 134.796 & 214.908 \\ 20.1428 & 31.7155 & 52.1526 & 85.6099 & 136.49 \end{bmatrix}$$

Note that $MM' = 0 =$

$$\begin{bmatrix} -3.62\times10^{-12} & 8.35\times10^{-14} & 4.35\times10^{-14} & 3.83\times10^{-13} & 1.63\times10^{-13} \\ 1.96\times10^{-14} & -3.61\times10^{-12} & 2.97\times10^{-14} & 1.20\times10^{-14} & 1.98\times10^{-14} \\ 2.10\times10^{-14} & -2.05\times10^{-14} & -3.69\times10^{-12} & -9.44\times10^{-14} & 1.09\times10^{-13} \\ -2.64\times10^{-14} & -2.58\times10^{-14} & 1.58\times10^{-14} & -3.69\times10^{-12} & 4.67\times10^{-14} \\ 1.36\times10^{-14} & 2.35\times10^{-14} & 3.04\times10^{-14} & 2.93\times10^{-14} & -3.66\times10^{-12} \end{bmatrix}$$

Any column of M' such as the first gives principal right eigenvector given above in normalized form.

A technical problem that arises in this approach is that because of the time dependence of the coefficients of the matrix, it is difficult to generate the eigenvector of priorities in symbolic form if the order of the matrix is more than four. The reason is that in these cases one must solve a polynomial equation to obtain the principal eigenvalue and derive the corresponding principal eigenvector and we have expressions given below for both of these for $n \leq 4$. But for $n > 4$ the story is complicated and has a long history in our time.

In this paper we give the analytic solution to derive the eigenvector for up to a 4x4 matrices and also give the solution of the quintic equation for the eigenvalues in closed form. The reader interested in this problem can contact this author for more general information on the solution of the quintic, sextic and septic equations. A technical problem that arises in this approach is that because of the time dependence of the coefficients of the matrix, it is difficult to generate the eigenvector of priorities in symbolic form if the order of the matrix is more than four. The reason is that in these cases one must solve a polynomial equation to obtain the principal eigenvalue and derive the corresponding principal eigenvector and we have expressions given below for both of these for $n \leq 4$. But for $n > 4$ the story is complicated and has a long history in our time.

Mathematica is a good program for providing the eigenvalues and the eigenvectors of matrices of large order. It would also be useful if one were to use it for time dependent judgments by taking different times, entering these numerical values of time, solving an entire decision problem numerically, and repeating the process. In the end the several decision-outcome values can be approximated by time dependent curves.

QUADRATIC CASE

To obtain the eigenvalue and eigenvectors of a 2 by 2 matrix, we must solve the problem

$$\begin{bmatrix} 1 & a(t) \\ 1/a(t) & 1 \end{bmatrix} \begin{bmatrix} w_1(t) \\ w_2(t) \end{bmatrix} = \lambda_{\max} \begin{bmatrix} w_1(t) \\ w_2(t) \end{bmatrix}$$

for which we know that $\lambda_{\max}(t) = 2$ because the matrix is consistent. For the eigenvector we need to solve the system of equations:

$$w_1(t) + a(t)w_2(t) = 2w_1(t)$$
$$w_1(t)/a(t) + w_2(t) = 2w_2(t)$$

The first equation yields

$w_1(t) = a(t)w_2(t),$ and because $w_1(t) + w_2(t) = 1,$ we have for our solution $w_1(t) = a(t)/[1 + a(t)], w_2(t) = 1/[1 + a(t)].$

CUBIC CASE

$$\lambda_{\max} = (a_{13}/a_{12}a_{23})^{1/3} + (a_{12}a_{23}/a_{13})^{1/3} + 1$$

If we define $\Delta = a_{12}a_{23} + a_{13}(\lambda_{\max} - 1)$ and

$$D = a_{12}a_{23} + a_{13}(\lambda_{\max} - 1) + (\lambda_{\max} - 1)a_{23} + (a_{13}/a_{12}) - 1 + (1 - \lambda_{\max})^2$$

we have

$$w_1 = \frac{\Delta}{D}$$

$$w_2 = \frac{(\lambda_{\max} - 1)a_{23} + (a_{13} / a_{12})}{D}$$

$$w_3 = \frac{-1 + (1 - \lambda_{\max})^2}{D}$$

QUARTIC CASE

If we define

$$B = \left(\frac{a_{23}a_{34}}{a_{24}} + \frac{a_{24}}{a_{23}a_{34}}\right) + \left(\frac{a_{12}a_{24}}{a_{14}} + \frac{a_{14}}{a_{12}a_{24}}\right) + \left(\frac{a_{12}a_{23}}{a_{13}} + \frac{a_{13}}{a_{12}a_{23}}\right) + \left(\frac{a_{13}a_{34}}{a_{14}} + \frac{a_{14}}{a_{13}a_{34}}\right)$$

$$C = 3 - \left(\frac{a_{12}a_{23}a_{34}}{a_{14}} + \frac{a_{14}}{a_{12}a_{23}a_{34}}\right) - \left(\frac{a_{12}a_{24}}{a_{13}a_{34}} + \frac{a_{13}a_{34}}{a_{12}a_{24}}\right) - \left(\frac{a_{14}a_{23}}{a_{13}a_{24}} + \frac{a_{13}a_{24}}{a_{14}a_{23}}\right)$$

Then

$$\lambda_{\max} = \left[-8 + \frac{B^2}{2} + 8C + \sqrt{\left[-\frac{4}{3}(C+3)\right]^3 + (8 - \frac{B^2}{2} - 8C)^2}\right]^{1/3} + \left[-8 + \frac{B^2}{2} + 8C - \sqrt{\left[-\frac{4}{3}(C+3)\right]^3 + (8 - \frac{B^2}{2} - 8C)^2}\right]^{1/3}$$

and

$$w_1 = \frac{\overline{w_1}}{Q}, w_2 = \frac{\overline{w_2}}{Q}, w_3 = \frac{\overline{w_3}}{Q}, w_4 = \frac{\overline{w_4}}{Q}$$

where

$$Q = (\lambda_{\max} - 1)^3 + (a_{14} + a_{34} + a_{24})(\lambda - 1)^2 + \left[(a_{12}a_{24} - 3) + (a_{13} + a_{23})a_{34} + (\frac{1}{a_{12}} + \frac{1}{a_{13}})a_{14} + \frac{a_{24}}{a_{23}}\right](\lambda_{\max} - 1)$$
$$+ \left[(a_{12}a_{23}a_{34} - a_{12} - a_{14} - a_{24} - a_{34}) + (\frac{a_{13}a_{24}}{a_{23}} + \frac{a_{13}a_{34}}{a_{12}}) + \frac{a_{14}a_{32} + a_{12}a_{24}}{a_{13}} + \frac{a_{14} - a_{13}}{a_{12}a_{23}}\right]$$

$$\overline{w_1} = a_{14}(\lambda_{\max}-1)^2 + (a_{12}a_{24} + a_{13}a_{34})(\lambda_{\max}-1) + (a_{12}a_{23}a_{34} + \frac{a_{13}a_{24}}{a_{23}} - a_{14})$$

$$\overline{w_2} = a_{24}(\lambda_{\max}-1)^2 + (a_{23}a_{34} + \frac{a_{14}}{a_{12}})(\lambda_{\max}-1) + (\frac{a_{13}a_{34}}{a_{12}} + \frac{a_{14}a_{23}}{a_{13}} - a_{24})$$

$$\overline{w_3} = a_{34}(\lambda_{\max}-1)^2 + (\frac{a_{24}}{a_{23}} + \frac{a_{14}}{a_{13}})(\lambda_{\max}-1) + (\frac{a_{14}}{a_{12}a_{23}} + \frac{a_{12}a_{24}}{a_{13}} - a_{34})$$

$$\overline{w_4} = (\lambda_{\max}-1)^3 - 3(\lambda_{\max}-1) - (\frac{a_{12}a_{23}}{a_{13}} + \frac{a_{13}}{a_{12}a_{23}})$$

REMARK It is easy to see from this solution that if any coefficient is increased (decreased) in a given row of the pairwise comparison matrix, the value of the eigenvector component corresponding to that row is increased (decreased) relative to the remaining components. This property holds for a reciprocal matrix.

THE QUINTIC AND HIGHER ORDER CASES

Algebraic Equations by Theta Constants, in Tata Lectures on Theta II, D. Mumford, ed., pp. 3.261-3.272, Birkhaüser, Boston, 1984, do not require the use of Tschirnhausen transformations. Let $f(x) = a_0x^n + a_1x^{n-1} + ... + a_n = 0, a_0 \neq 0$ be an algebraic equation irreducible over a subfield of the complex numbers. A root of this equation can be expressed in terms of theta functions of zero argument involving the period matrix derived from one of two types of hyper-elliptic integrals.

Bernd Sturmfels gives the solution of the quintic equation in term using the finest of the 2^{n-1} triangulations of the hypergeometric differential equations and corresponding 2^{n-1} series solutions. The roots of the quintic $a_5x^5 + a_4x^4 + a_3x^3 + a_2x^2 + a_1x + a_0 = 0$ one of which is the principal eigenvalue that may also be obtained in other ways are given by an infinite series and the question about such expansions is whether the series always converge. We have:

$$X_{1,-1} = -\left[\frac{a_0}{a_1}\right], X_{2,-1} = -\left[\frac{a_1}{a_2}\right] + \left[\frac{a_0}{a_1}\right], X_{3,-1} = -\left[\frac{a_2}{a_3}\right] + \left[\frac{a_1}{a_2}\right],$$

$$X_{4,-1} = -\left[\frac{a_3}{a_4}\right] + \left[\frac{a_2}{a_3}\right], X_{5,-1} = -\left[\frac{a_4}{a_5}\right] + \left[\frac{a_3}{a_4}\right].$$

Each bracket represents a power series with a monomial in the bracket as its first term:

$$\left[\frac{a_0}{a_1}\right]=\frac{a_0}{a_1}+\frac{a_0^2 a_2}{a_1^3}-\frac{a_0^3 a_3}{a_1^4}+2\frac{a_0^3 a_2^2}{a_1^5}+\frac{a_0^4 a_4}{a_1^5}-5\frac{a_0^4 a_2 a_3}{a_1^6}-\frac{a_0^5 a_5}{a_1^6}+\ldots$$

$$\left[\frac{a_1}{a_2}\right]=\frac{a_1}{a_2}+\frac{a_1^2 a_3}{a_2^3}-\frac{a_1^3 a_4}{a_2^4}-3\frac{a_0 a_1^2 a_5}{a_2^4}+2\frac{a_1^3 a_3^3}{a_2^5}+\frac{a_1^4 a_5}{a_2^5}-5\frac{a_1^4 a_3 a_4}{a_2^6}+\ldots$$

$$\left[\frac{a_2}{a_3}\right]=\frac{a_2}{a_3}-\frac{a_0 a_5}{a_3^2}-\frac{a_1 a_4}{a_3^2}+2\frac{a_1 a_2 a_5}{a_3^3}+\frac{a_2^2 a_4}{a_3^3}-\frac{a_2^3 a_5}{a_3^4}+2\frac{a_2^3 a_4^2}{a_3^5}+\ldots$$

$$\left[\frac{a_3}{a_4}\right]=\frac{a_3}{a_4}-\frac{a_2 a_5}{a_4^2}+\frac{a_3^2 a_5}{a_4^3}+\frac{a_1 a_5^2}{a_4^3}-3\frac{a_2 a_3 a_5^2}{a_4^4}-\frac{a_0 a_5^3}{a_4^4}+4\frac{a_1 a_3 a_5^3}{a_4^5}+\ldots$$

$$\left[\frac{a_4}{a_5}\right]=\frac{a_4}{a_5}.$$

7-5. Value of Pairwise Comparisons – an Example

The following example shows that by making pairwise comparisons we learn much more about the detail of a dynamic priority function than if we were to simply guess at each component of the eigenvector components individually.

FAMILY SPENDING TIME AT HOME

Let us consider the simple case of a family with a father, a mother, and a child. Obviously the amount of time the child spends at home will depend on his age. An infant will spend the same amount of time at home as the mother and then, as he grows older, he will spend progressively less time at home compared to the mother. We assume that the mother docs not go out to work.

If we were to compare the length of time spent at home by mother and child and plot this relation as a function of time (i.e., as the child grows older), we would get the type of curve shown in Figure 7-2.

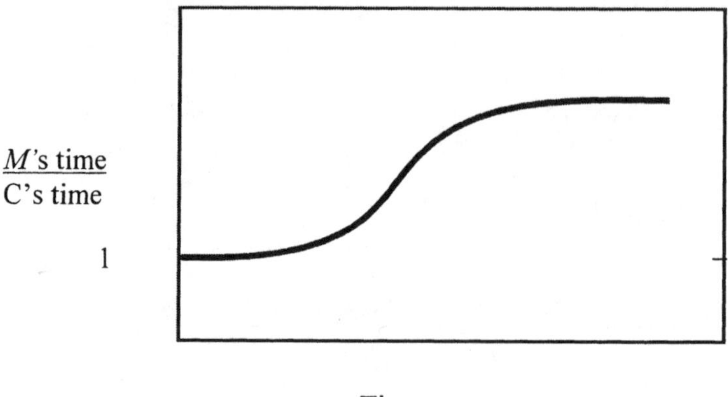

Figure 7-2: Relative Time at Home – Mother to Child

Thus the curve begins with the home maker mother and child spending the same amount of time, then the ratio of mother's to child's time increases until it levels off by the time the child is in her/his mid-teens. Comparison of father to child times yields a relationship that is a mirror image of the above -reflected about a horizontal axis halfway up the curve. This is illustrated in Figure 7-3. The relative length of time spent by father and mother would not vary too much and could be expected to be fairly constant.

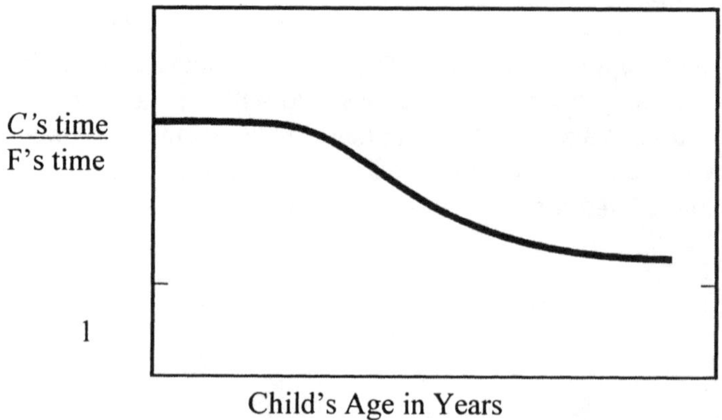

Figure 7-3: Relative Time at Home – Child to Father

If we were to make a pairwise comparison of the different lengths of time spent at home by the different members of the family, we would get a sequence of comparison matrices each corresponding to a particular period of time.

Consider the time period corresponding to the child's age 0-4 years. If we were to exclude, say, eight hours of the night, we would expect the mother and child to spend about two to three times the length of time the father spends at home. The mother and child would of course spend the same amount of time.

This would give rise to the following matrix:

$$\begin{array}{c} \\ F \\ M \\ C \end{array} \begin{array}{c} \begin{array}{ccc} F & M & C \end{array} \\ \begin{bmatrix} 1 & 1/2.5 & 1/2.5 \\ 2.5 & 1 & 1 \\ 2.5 & 1 & 1 \end{bmatrix} \end{array}$$

$$\lambda_{max} = 3.0, \quad \text{C.I.} = 0.0, \quad \text{C.R.} = 0.0$$

This yields the following eigenvector for their relative times at home:

F: 0.167
M: 0.417
C: 0.417

That would seem to be a reasonable estimate of the proportions of time each spends at home. Around the age of four the child begins school, so there is a sudden change in the relative proportions of time spent at home by mother and child and by father and child.

Moving to the time dependent situation, we can express the varying proportions in a single matrix as shown below:

$$\begin{array}{c} \\ F \\ M \\ C \end{array} \begin{array}{c} \begin{array}{ccc} F & M & C \end{array} \\ \begin{bmatrix} 1 & 1/2 & 1/(3-\ln t/2) \\ 2 & 1 & 0.4+\ln t/2 \\ 3-\ln t/2 & 1/(0.4+\ln t/2) & 1 \end{bmatrix} \end{array}$$

The variable t denotes the child's age ranging between 4 and 16 years. This matrix, along with the previous one, gives rise to the curves in Figure7-4, Figure 7-5, and Figure 7-6 that depict the corresponding pairwise comparisons as time varies from zero to 16 years.

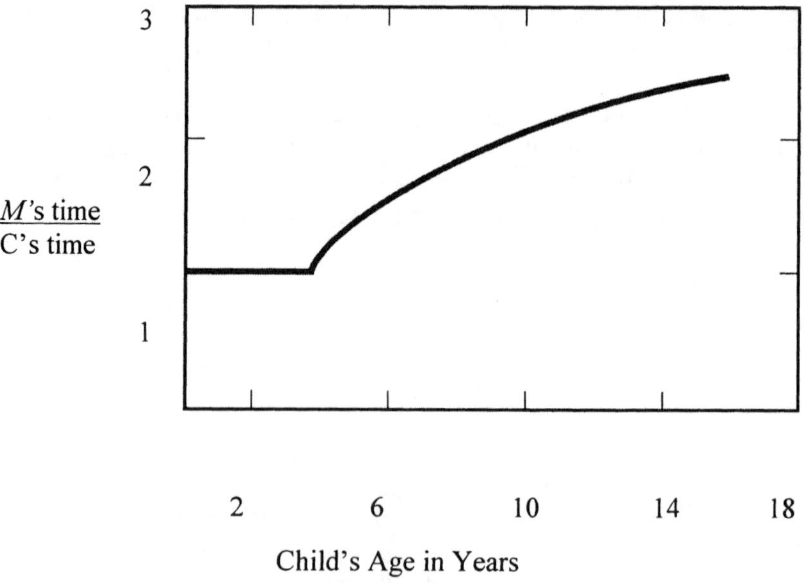

Figure 7-4: Mother to Child: age 0-16 years

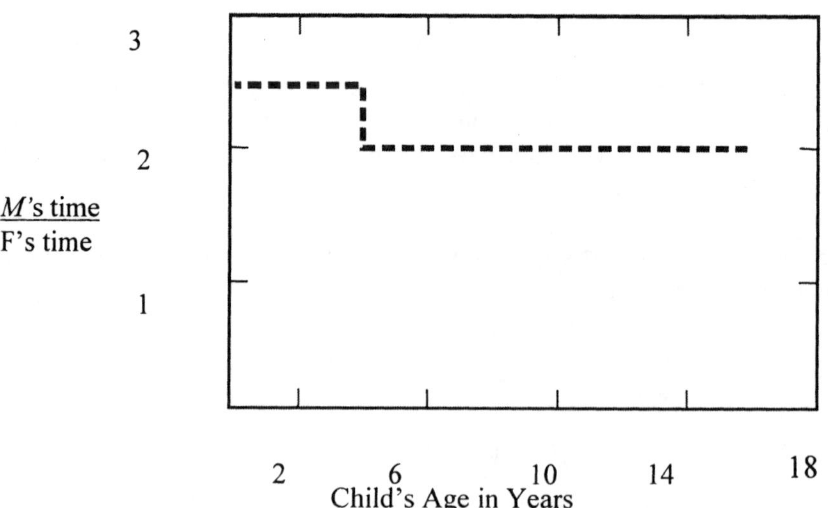

Figure 7-5: Mother to Father: Age 0-16 years

The solution of the maximum eigenvalue problem corresponding to these pairwise comparison curves for $(4 \le t \le 16)$ is

$$\lambda_{\max} = 1 + \left[\frac{2}{(3 - \ln t/2)(0.4 + \ln t/2)} \right]^{1/3} + \left[\frac{(3 - \ln t/2)(0.4 + \ln t/2)}{2} \right]^{1/3}$$

The corresponding eigenvector is given by

$$w_1 = \Delta / D; w_2 = \left[(\lambda_{\max} - 1)(0.4 + \ln t/2) + \frac{2}{3 - \ln t/2} \right] / D; w_3 = \left[-1 + (-2)^2 \right] / D$$

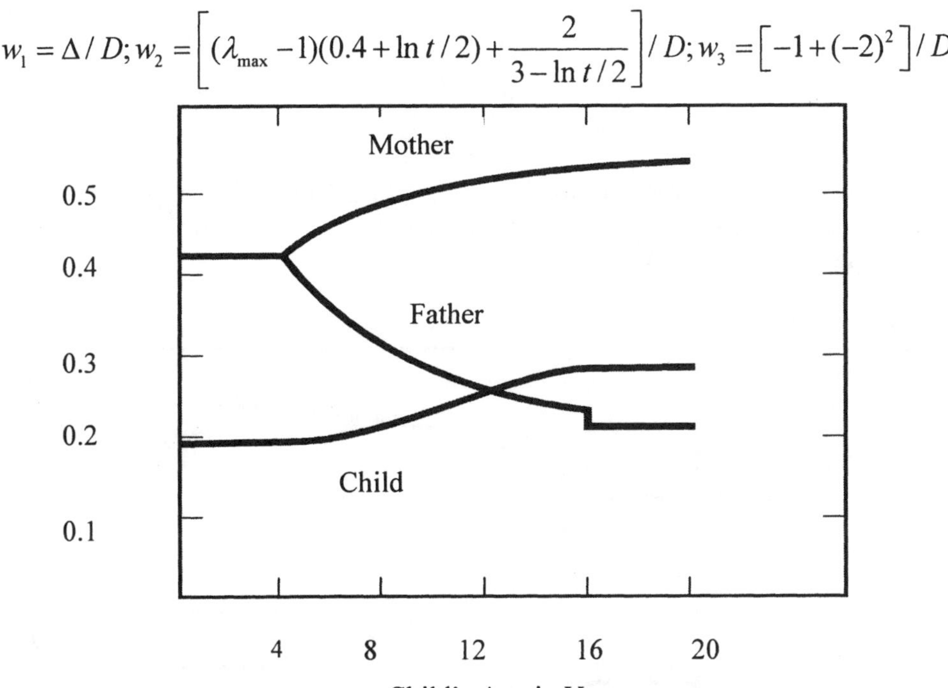

Figure 7-6: Child to Father: age 0-16 years

where

$$\Delta = 0.5(0.4 + \ln t/2) + \frac{\lambda_{\max} - 1}{3 - \ln t/2}$$

$$D = (\lambda_{\max} - 0.5)(0.4 + \ln t/2) + \frac{\lambda_{\max} + 1}{3 - \ln t/2} - 1 + (1 - \lambda_{\max})^2$$

As the child finishes school, he begins spending even less time at home than the father. The proportions once again become fairly constant and are reflected in the following (consistent) pairwise comparison matrix:

$$\begin{array}{c} \\ F \\ M \\ C \end{array} \begin{array}{c} \begin{array}{ccc} F & M & C \end{array} \\ \begin{bmatrix} 1 & 0.5 & 1.25 \\ 2 & 1 & 2.5 \\ 0.8 & 0.4 & 1 \end{bmatrix} \end{array}$$

$\lambda_{max} = 3.0$, C.I. = 0.0, C.R. = 0.0

The eigenvector solution is given by:

F: 0.263
M: 0.526
C: 0.211

Plotting these results together for $0 \leq t \leq 4$, $4 \leq t \leq 16$, and $16 \leq t$ gives a realistic representation of the relative time, with respect to all others, which each spends at home (see Figure 7-7).

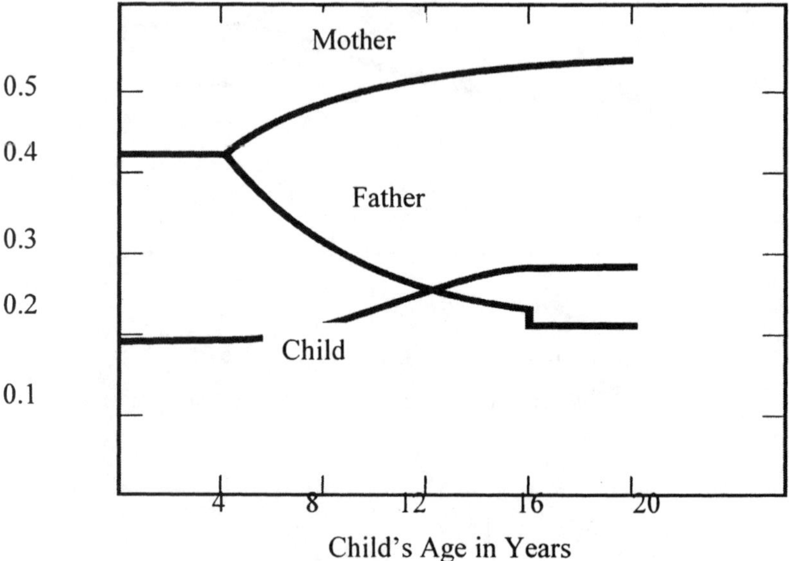

Figure 7-7: Relative Proportion of Time Spent at Home

7-6. Pairwise Comparison Judgments and Scale – General Discussion

Recall that in making paired comparisons of intangibles, we use the smaller or lesser element as a unity and estimate the larger one as a multiple of it. We can also do that in dynamic judgments by simply introducing a function to estimate how many times more is the larger element than the unit. In this case there may be a change of unit of the comparison if the larger element becomes the smaller and must serve as the unit. Just as we used absolute numbers to enter into the comparison matrix in the static case, we need to enter basic functions to represent judgments in the dynamic case. What typical functions can we use that would, for example, approximate well the functions of the family example above? I do not have a conclusive answer to that question, if indeed there is an answer to it. For the pairwise comparison judgments one may attempt to fit one of the functions given in Table 7-2 to the dynamic judgments. These functions have been left in parametric form so that the parameter may be set for the particular comparison, hopefully meeting the homogeneity requirement of the1-9 scale used in the discrete case as a limit on the range of values. They, and combinations of them, reflect our intuitive feeling about relative change in trend: constant, linear, polynomial, logarithmic, exponential, oscillatory, and finally discrete that allows for sudden change like a Dirac delta function.

The following is an example given by Andreichicov and Andreichicova, [1]. They assumed that the preferences for alternatives at the bottom of Figure 7-8, with respect to the criteria in the fourth hierarchy level, would remain constant in the future. However, they assumed that preferences for the factors located at the second hierarchy level would vary.

The relative importance of the criteria for each actor also would be subject to modification in the future. The filling of pairwise comparison matrices as the dynamic task was made as follows. There were $(n\text{-}1)$ cells in a matrix selected, where the functions describing changes of appropriate preferences were made. The preferences at the time coincided with preferences in the static task. At the following instants the values for the other $(n^2\text{-}2n\text{+}1)$ preferences were calculated on the basis of the $(n\text{-}1)$ functions given (*Auto*). Thus there was no problem of inconsistency during solution of the dynamic problem. Forming the functions was produced experimentally with the help of the software developed by the authors.

Table 7-2: This Author's Idea of a Mathematician's Formulation of a Dynamic Judgment Scale

Time-dependent importance intensity	Description	Explanation
a	Constant for all t, $1 \le a \le 9$ an integer	No change in relative standing
$a_1 t + a_2$	Linear relation in t, increasing or decreasing to a point and then a constant value thereafter. Note that the reciprocal is a hyperbola.	Steady increase in value of one activity over another
$b_1 \log(t+1)+b_2$	Logarithmic growth up to a certain point and constant thereafter	Rapid increase (decrease) followed by slow increase (decrease)
$c_1 e^{c_2 t} + c_3$	Exponential growth (or decay if c_2 is negative) to a certain point and constant thereafter (not reciprocal of case c_2 is negative is the logistic S-curve)	Slow increase (decrease) followed by rapid increase (decrease)
$d_1 t^2 + d_2 t + d_3$	A parabola giving a maximum or minimum (depending on d_1 being negative or positive) with a constant value thereafter. (May be modified for skewness to the right or left)	Increase (decrease) to maximum (minimum) and then decrease (increase)
$e_1 t^n \sin(t + e_2) + e_3$	Oscillatory	Oscillates depending on n, n > 0 ($n \le 0$) with decreasing (increasing) amplitude
Catastrophes	Discontinuities indicated	Sudden changes in intensity
Polynomials are known in general to approximate to continuous functions on a closed interval arbitrarily closely.		

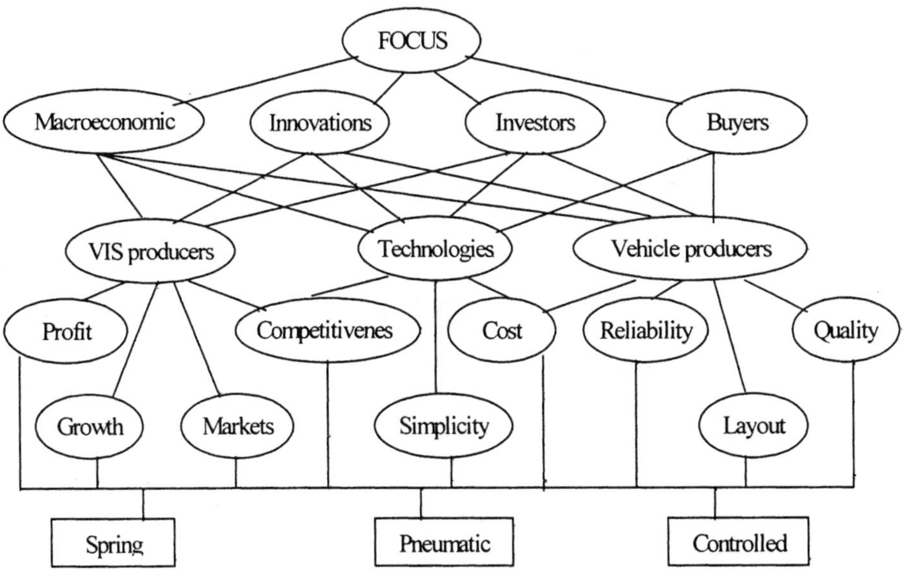

Figure 7-8: Hierarchy for Dynamic Evaluation

Table 7-3: Priority Vectors for Criteria in the Static Problem

	Macroeconomic	*Innovations*	*Investments*	*Buyers*
FOCUS	0.380	0.085	0.466	0.069
	VIS producers	Vehicles producers	Technologies	
Macroeconomic	0.109	0.582	0.309	
Innovations	0.105	0.258	0.637	
Investments	0.167	0.740	0.094	
Buyers	0.167	0.833		
	Profit	Growth	Competitiveness	Markets
VIS producers	0.532	0.097	0.186	0.186
	Quality	Cost	Reliability	Layout
Vehicles producers	0.143	0.402	0.054	0.402
	Competitiveness	Cost	Simplicity	
Technologies	0.333	0.333	0.333	

The dynamic paired comparison matrices were as in Table 7-4. Table 7-5 gives the priority vectors for the alternatives in the static case.

Table 7-4: Dynamic Paired Comparison Matrices

FOCUS	*Macroeconomic*	*Innovations*	*Investments*	*Buyers*
Macroeconomic	1	$1/0.25e^{0.6t}$	Auto	$1/(0.2-0.05t+0.08t^2)$
Innovations	$0.25e^{0.6t}$	1	$0.2-0.18t+0.15t^2$	Auto
Investments	auto	$1/(0.2-0.18t+0.15t^2)$	1	Auto
Buyers	$0.2-0.05t+0.08t^2$	Auto	Auto	1

VIS producers	*Profit*	*Growth*	*Competitiveness*	*Markets*
Profit	1	$1/(0.2+0.05t+0.025t^2)$	$1/0.333e^{0.43t}$	$1/0.333e^{0.43t}$
Growth	$0.2+0.05t+0.025t^2$	1	Auto	Auto
Competitiveness	$0.333e^{0.43t}$	Auto	1	Auto
Markets	$0.333e^{0.43t}$	Auto	Auto	1

Vehicles producers	*Quality*	*Cost*	*Reliability*	*Layout*
Quality	1	$0.333+0.4t+0.04t^2$	$3-1.15t+0.18t^2$	$0.333+0.15t$
Cost	$1/(0.333+0.4t+0.04t^2)$	1	Auto	Auto
Reliability	$1/(3-1.15t+0.18t^2)$	Auto	1	Auto
Layout	$1/(0.333+0.15t)$	Auto	Auto	1

Table 7-5: Priority Vectors for Alternatives in the Static Problem

	Coil spring	*Pneumatic*	*Controlled*
Profit	0.648	0.230	0.122
Growth	0.143	0.429	0.429
Competitiveness	0.075	0.333	0.592
Markets	0.109	0.582	0.309
Quality	0.066	0.319	0.615
Cost	0.751	0.178	0.070
Reliability	0.637	0.105	0.258
Layout	0.105	0.258	0.637
Simplicity	0.751	0.178	0.070

The other paired comparison matrices were the same as in the static problem. The results are shown in Figure 7-9 and 7-10.

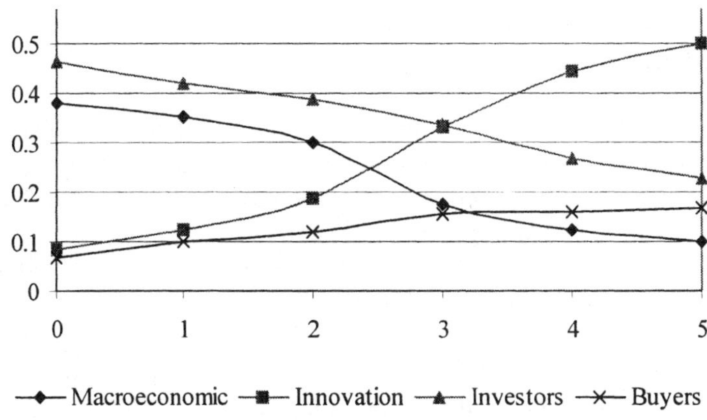

Figure 7-9: Change in Factor Priorities over Time

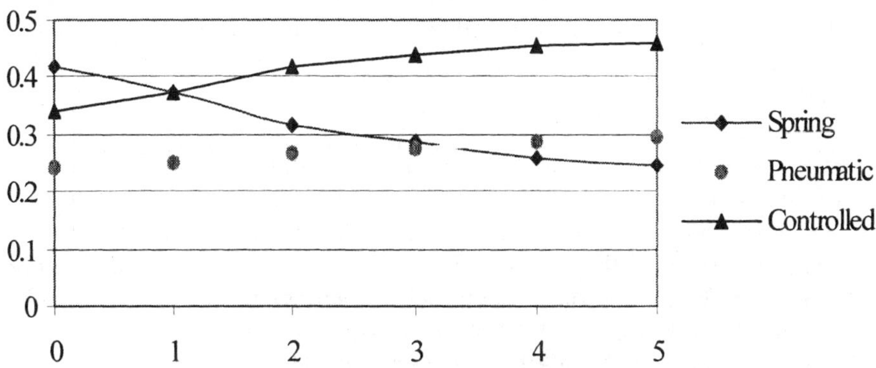

Figure 7-10: Change in Each Alternative's Priorities over Time

The priority of innovation in Russia is expected to increase in the future. The buyer's priority will also increase slightly. The investor's importance and macroeconomic influence will decrease. These modifications and the changes in the importance of the criteria for producers will result in a change in the order established for the alternatives. The spring coil, which is simple and cheap, moves from first place to last place. The best alternative in the future will be VIS controlled, which has high vibroisolation quality and high cost. The low priority of the pneumatic VIS in both cases might be explained by its relatively high cost and low reliability.

7-7. Fundamental Scale of Relative Change - On the Rate of Change of Intangibles!

Let us now turn to a more practical way of creating a fundamental scale that is in harmony with any person's way of looking ahead to make comparisons. As in the discrete case, because we have intangibles we have no functions to describe their behavior absolutely, but we can compare them to derive scales of relative change over time. We have no problem to deal with tangibles whose behavior over time is known though a function-of-time expression for each.

The question is how to generalize this idea to the dynamic case. Two kinds of data need to be generated. One is the initial point $x(0)$ of the curve of relative change. Here we ask the same question as in the discrete case: which of the two dominates the other with regard to a common attribute they share? The other question has to do with their perceived relative change: which of the two is perceived to change more than the other with respect to a common attribute they share? This second question is answered with perhaps different estimates for different time periods.

As in the discrete case, an individual has the ability to recognize distinctions among high, medium and low and for each of these also three distinctions of high, medium and low. In the case of static judgments that deal with numbers we had the nine values of the fundamental scale 1-9. We assume for the moment that when we compare two (tangible) activities each described by a curve as a function of time that we can make these nine distinctions in their rates of change relative to one another. How can each of these curves vary so that we would be able to divide the relative variation between them into recognizable nine categories over time? We note that in the simplest case where both functions are linear in time and their relative variation expressed by their ratio is a hyperbola over time. A hyperbola has a simple but rather sophisticated interpretation. What are different possible interpretations of variations (ratios) between two functions? To deal with such concepts effectively we need to think of time in two ways, the hard way, as a tangible measured on a clock and make judgments over known, perhaps uniform, time intervals, or the soft way, as an intangible divided according to our feelings about it such as short term, mid term and long term. This author's idea of a practical-minded person's representation of a dynamic judgment scale of relative changes is shown in Table 7-6.

Table 7-6: Formulation of a Dynamic Judgment Scale

Comparison of A over B	
Extreme Increase	↑
Very Strong Increase: x(t) = 2.414t	↗
Strong Increase: x(t) = t	↗
Moderate Increase ; x(t) = 0.414t	↗
Equal; x(t) = 1	→
Moderate Decrease: x (t)=-0.414t	↘
Strong Decrease: x (t)=-t	↘
Very Strong Decrease: x (t)=-2.414t	↘
Extreme Decrease	↓

Comparison of A over B	Slope of Line $\left(0 \le \theta \le 90^\circ\right)$	Slope of Line $\left(0 \le \theta \le 45^\circ\right)$	Slope of Line $\left(0 \le \theta \le 22.5^\circ\right)$
Extreme Increase	∞	1	0.414
Very Strong Increase	2.414	0.668	0.303
Strong Increase	1	0.414	0.199
Moderate Increase	0.414	0.199	0.098
Equal	0	0	0
Moderate Decrease	-0.414	-0.199	-0.098
Strong Decrease	-1	-0.414	-0.199
Very Strong Decrease	-2.414	-0.668	-0.303
Extreme Decrease	$-\infty$	-1	-0.414

An application of it over time is shown in Table 7-7.

Table 7-7: Different Possible Formulations and Variations Using the Basic Scale in Table 7-6

Time Horizons	Short-term	Mid-term	Long-term	Combined Over the Three Horizons	Functional Form
Comparison of A over B	→	↗	↘	→↗↘	$a_{12}(t)=\begin{cases} x_1(0) & 0\le t\le t_1 \\ x_1(0)+0.414(t-t_1) & t_1<t\le t_2 \\ x_1(0)+0.414(t_2-t_1) & t_2<t\le t_3 \\ -2.414(t-t_2) & \end{cases}$
Comparison of A over C	↘	↘	↗	↘↘↗	$a_{13}(t)=\begin{cases} x_2(0)-t & 0\le t\le t_1 \\ x_2(0)+1.414t_1-2.414t & t_1<t\le t_2 \\ x_2(0)+1.414t_1-4.828t_2+2.414t & t_2<t\le t_3 \end{cases}$
Comparison of B over C	↓	→	↑	↓→↑	$a_{23}(t)=\begin{cases} x_3(0)t_1(t_1+t)^{-1} & 0\le t\le t_1 \\ \frac{1}{2}x_3(0) & t_1<t\le t_2 \\ \frac{1}{2}x_3(0)\dfrac{t_3+t}{t_3+t_2} & t_2<t\le t_3 \end{cases}$

As in the 1-9 scale, time horizons may be divided into 9 periods starting with the present time and relative increases and decreases further refined. Here a function representing judgments may descend below $x(t) = 1$ and thus the coefficient may include a description of both dominance and being dominated. Its transpose is the reciprocal function. Because we do not wish to use upward or downward arrows for an entire judgment over a time horizon interval, we can replace such a "Dirac" type function by a curve that rises or falls sharply and continuously over the interval. Examples are $(t-a)^{-1}, |t-a|^{-1}$ *and* $(t-a)^{-2}$. Homogeneity needs to be maintained not only for magnitudes but also for the angle of relative change. The angle span for homogeneity may be less than 90 degrees. Perhaps it should be closer to a radian $360/2\pi = 57.296^\circ$ and its division into ranges of just noticeable increases in slope or angle. There needs to be a theoretical way to justify the bound on the homogeneity of relative change. When exceeded, one may have to use clustering as in the comparison of different magnitudes.

Note that because the time horizons are not well specified over time, instead of connecting their end points to make a continuous curve, one may select the mid point of a time horizon to draw each line segment and take their points of intersection as the positions where the composite curve connects. A better alternative is to divide each of short, midterm and long-term into three intervals sand provide judgments of relative change by the above scale for each. This is time consuming but more accurate even if one were to repeat the same judgments over success intervals.

We now show by an example that real life situations reveal themselves along similar lines to the line segments we combined to put together decisions made over short, medium and long term time horizons. The example has to deal with the earnings and projected electricity use by the three companies involved (taken from the internet) as shown in Figure 7-11.

$$\begin{array}{cc} \textit{Short Term} & \begin{array}{ccc} \textit{IBM} & \textit{MSFT} & \textit{AT\&T} \end{array} \\ \begin{array}{c} \textit{IBM} \\ \textit{MSFT} \\ \textit{AT\&T} \end{array} & \begin{bmatrix} 1 & 1.499-0.0103t & 2.955-0.0089t \\ & 1 & 1.969+0.0079t \\ & & 1 \end{bmatrix} \end{array}$$

$$\begin{array}{cc} \textit{Medium Term} & \begin{array}{ccc} \textit{IBM} & \textit{MSFT} & \textit{AT\&T} \end{array} \\ \begin{array}{c} \textit{IBM} \\ \textit{MSFT} \\ \textit{AT\&T} \end{array} & \begin{bmatrix} 1 & 1.476+0.0056t & 2.797+0.089t \\ & 1 & 1.899+0.1125t \\ & & 1 \end{bmatrix} \end{array}$$

$$\begin{array}{cc} \textit{Long Term} & \begin{array}{ccc} \textit{IBM} & \textit{MSFT} & \textit{AT\&T} \end{array} \\ \begin{array}{c} \textit{IBM} \\ \textit{MSFT} \\ \textit{AT\&T} \end{array} & \begin{bmatrix} 1 & 1.733-0.089t & 2.943+0.0104t \\ & 1 & 1.668+0.0175t \\ & & 1 \end{bmatrix} \end{array}$$

Plots of estimated dynamic priorities versus actual are shown in Figure 7-12.

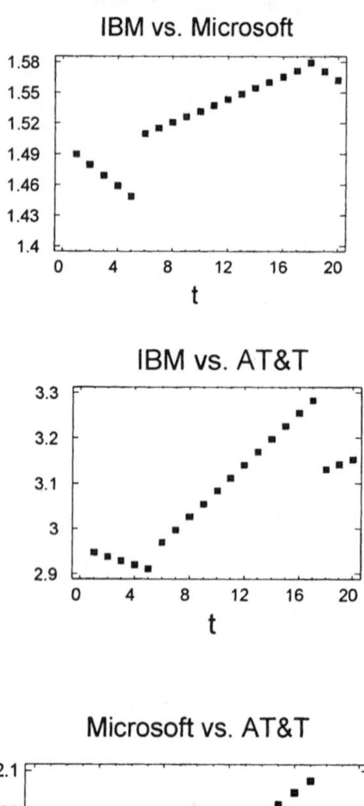

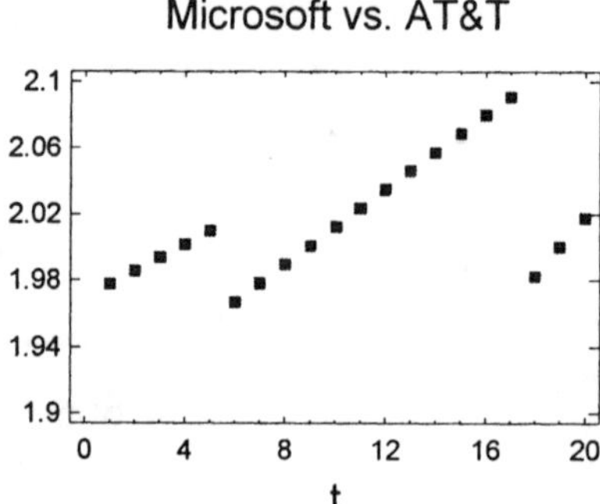

Figure 7-11: Relative Earnings of Software Companies

Judgments fitted with linear approximations:

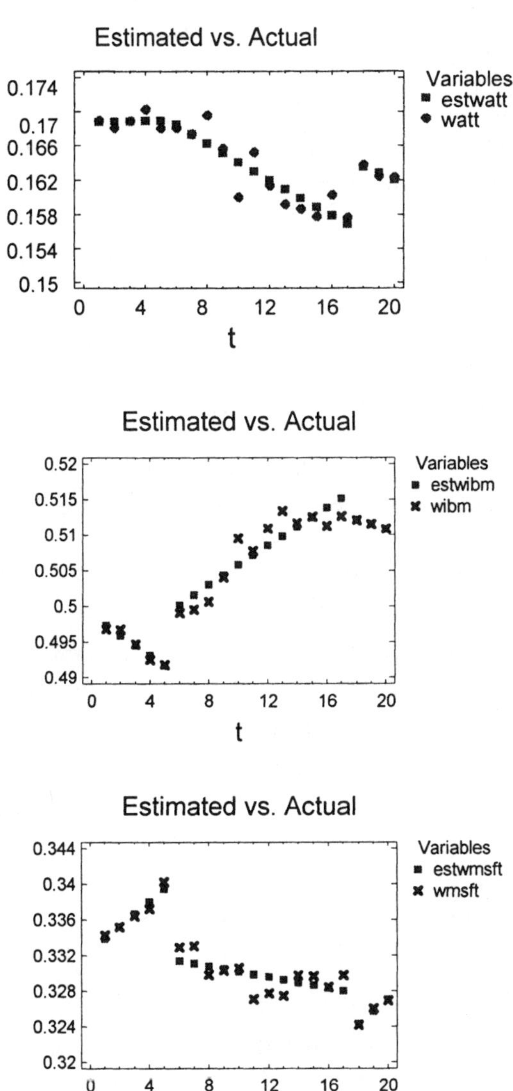

Figure 7-12: Estimated versus Actual Relative Values for the Three Companies

It may be possible to aggregate a judgment function into a number by assuming that each discrete judgment on a curve arises from different observations about a future determined not by a point but by an interval of time. In that case one uses the geometric mean of all these judgments leading to a product integral. As in the discrete case where we have for the product **of the judgments** $x_1, x_2, \ldots, x_p$:

$$x_1 x_2 \cdots x_p = e^{\log x_1 x_2 \cdots x_p} = \prod_{i=1}^{p} e^{\log x_i} = e^{\sum_{i=1}^{p} \log x_i} \longrightarrow e^{\int \log x(\alpha) d\alpha}$$

This product reduces to a product integral yielding a single number for an answer, for our case we replace α by t and $x(\alpha)$ by $x(t)$ in the integral above to obtain a number for each judgment.

Finally, one can use the criterion $a_{ij} w_j / w_i >> 1$ of the AHP or the gradient approach (more complex in the dynamic case) to improve overall consistency. One would possibly be dealing with nonlinear inequalities.

7-8. A Complete Example with Paired Comparisons

Let us consider the case of tangibles. We have two people, the first is a years older than the second, where $a = 30$. As seen in Figure 7-13, as time lapses the difference between their ages remains constant. However, the ratio of their ages in the (1,2) position in the paired comparison matrix below is a hyperbola given by $(a+t)/t = 1 + a/t$ as shown in Figure 7-14. Initially the ratio is infinite when $t = 0$. As time lapses this ratio converges asymptotically to the line $x(t) = 1$. The pairwise comparison matrix formed by taking the ratios of the functions of age of the two people is given by:

$$\begin{bmatrix} 1 & (a+t)/t \\ t/(a+t) & 1 \end{bmatrix}$$

which has the normalized principal right eigenvector :

$$w_1(t) = (a+t)/(a+2t), w_2(t) = t/(a+2t).$$

The ideal mode solution is $1, t/t+a, t > 0, a \geq 0$, with a graph comprised of a horizontal line and a curve as shown in Figure 7-15. Figure 7-16 is a plot of the normalized eigenvector components.

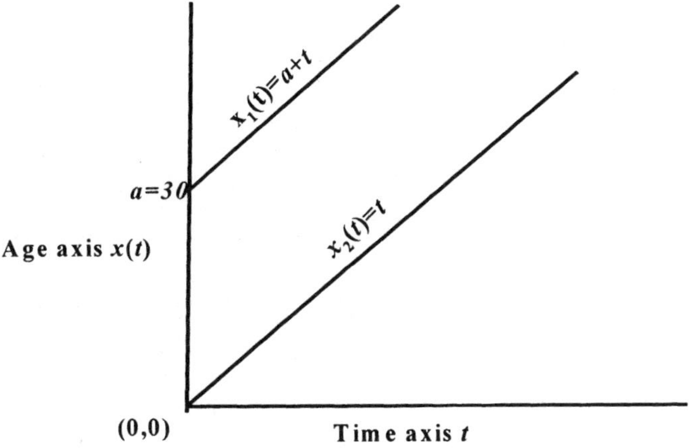

Figure 7-12: Age as a Function of Time

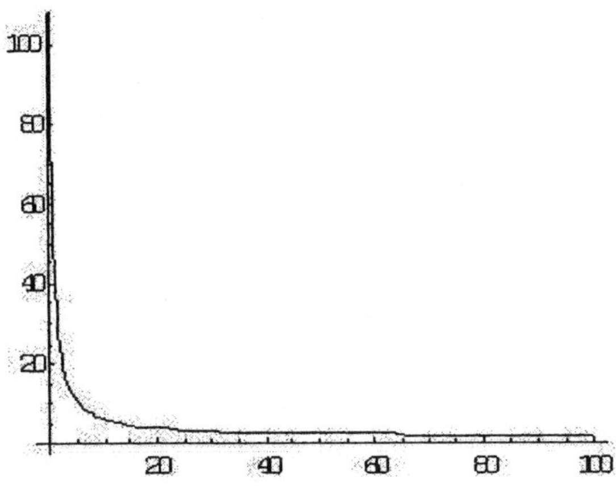

Figure 7-13: Hyperbola; $x_1(t)/x_2(t) = 1 + 30/t$

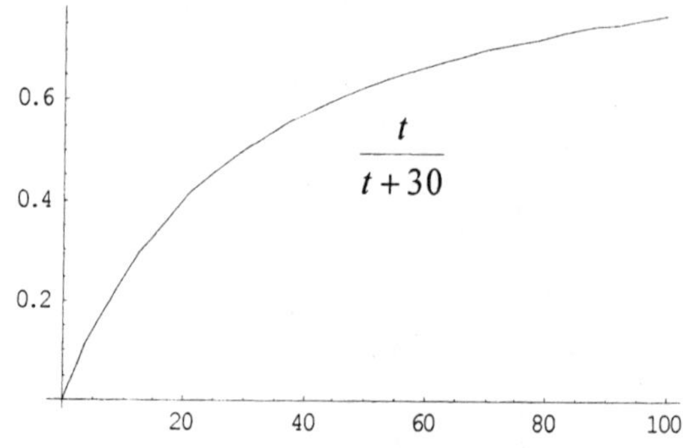

Figure 7-14: $x_1(t)/x_2(t) = t/(t+30)$

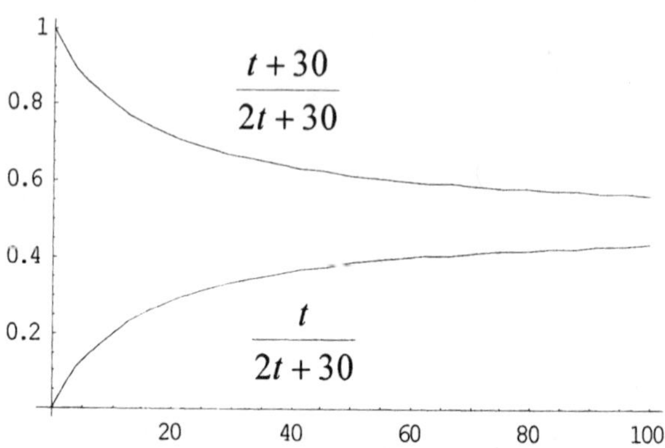

Figure 7-15: Graph of Normalized Time Dependent Eigenvector $w_1(t), w_2(t)$ with $a = 30$

We continue our illustration of a multicriteria problem by considering another attribute besides age that is measurable over time, and that is strength. Let us assume that strength increases to a certain value ≤ 1 and then decreases with age eventually to zero at death as in Figure 7-18. Assume that Figure 7-18 describes the strengths of the two individuals and that the corresponding equations are:

$$y_1(t) = 1 - \frac{1}{2500}(t-20)^2, y_2(t) = 1 - \frac{1}{2500}(t-50)^2$$

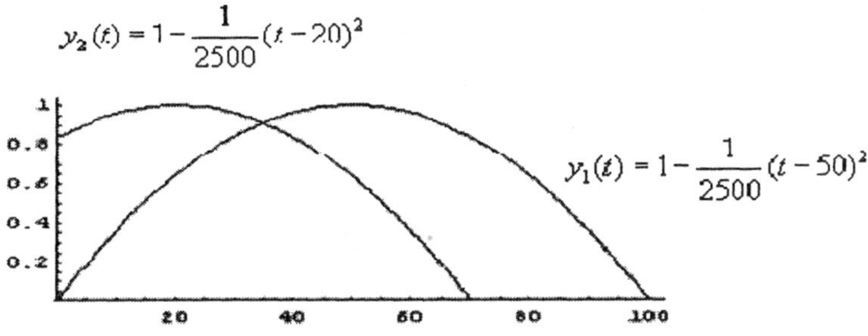

Figure 7-16: Graph of the Two Strength Functions $[y_1(t), y_2(t)]$

Forming the ratios of the functions that represent the relative strengths of the individuals we have the paired comparison matrix below:

$$\begin{bmatrix} 1 & \frac{y_1(t)}{y_2(t)} \\ \frac{y_2(t)}{y_1(t)} & 1 \end{bmatrix}$$

The above matrix has a normalized eigenvector of $[y_1(t), y_2(t)]$ which gives the solution vector $[u_1(t), u_2(t)]$ with:

$$u_1(t) = 1 - \frac{1}{2500}(t-20)^2 / [1 - \frac{1}{2500}(t-20)^2 + 1 - \frac{1}{2500}(t-50)^2],$$

$$u_2(t) = 1 - \frac{1}{2500}(t-50)^2 / [1 - \frac{1}{2500}(t-20)^2 + 1 - \frac{1}{2500}(t-50)^2]$$

The graph of this time dependent eigenvector solution of strength is shown in Figure 7-17.

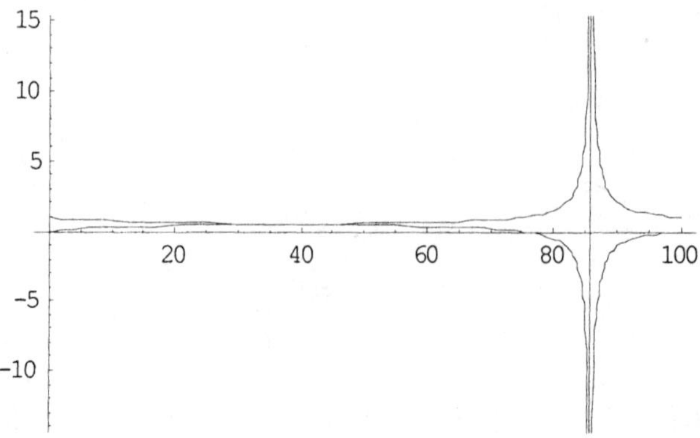

Figure 7-17: Time Dependent Eigenvector Solution of Strength Graph $[u_1(t), u_2(t)]$

We obtain the composite vector of the two alternatives, age and strength, by combining the two vectors obtained for age and strength.

Finally let us assume that the two criteria, age and strength, are equally important so we can weight and add the two vectors $w_1(t), w_2(t)$ with $a = 30$ and $[u_1(t), u_2(t)]$ We might also have given the criteria time dependent weights to do the weighting and adding. We have the following solution for our final composite vector $[z_1(t), z_2(t)]$. Its graph is shown in Figure 7-18.

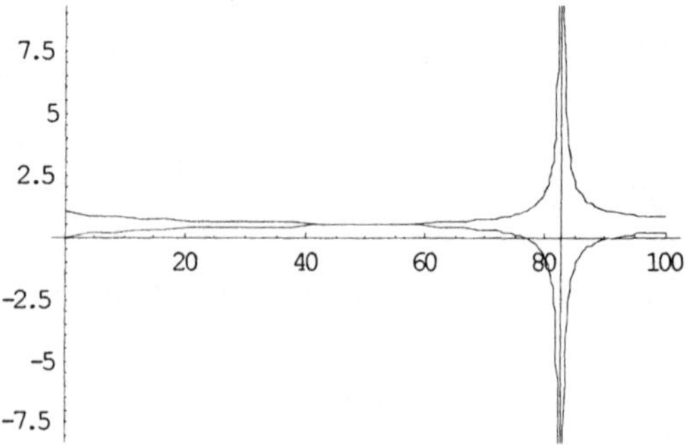

Figure 7-18: Graph of Synthesized Solution $[z_1(t), z_2(t)]$

$$z_1(t) = [\frac{1}{2}(30+t)/(30+2t)] + \frac{1}{2}[1 - \frac{1}{2500}(t-20)^2]/[1 - \frac{1}{2500}(t-20)^2 + 1 - \frac{1}{2500}(t-50)^2],$$

$$z_2(t) = [\frac{1}{2}t/(30+2t)] + \frac{1}{2}[1 - \frac{1}{2500}(t-50)^2]/[1 - \frac{1}{2500}(t-20)^2 + 1 - \frac{1}{2500}(t-50)^2].$$

7-9. Historical Facts

Solution of the cubic and the quartic became common knowledge through the publication of the *Ars Magna* of Geronimo Cardano (1501-1576). But Cardano was not the original discoverer of the solution of either the cubic or the quartic. Generally the solution of the cubic is attributed to the Italian professor Scipione del Ferro (1465-1526), from Bologna, one of the oldest of the medieval universities and a school with a strong mathematical tradition.

The solution of the quartic is attributed to Ludovico Ferrari (1522-1565). The names of Niccolo Fontana (1500-1557) the stammerer (Tartaglia) is also associated with the solution of the cubic because he elaborated on Del Ferro's solution and became addicted to solving cubic equations. It was from Ferrari in 1547-48 that the history of this spectacular discovery became public knowledge. Ferrari reduced the solution of the general bi-quadratic equation to that of a cubic equation. It was Cardano who considered negative numbers and called them "fictitious".

Nearly 250 years later it became known form the works of Abel and Ruffini and from Galois theory that a quatric is the largest degree equation for which one can obtain the roots (eigenvalues in our problem) in the form of radicals. This means that the roots can be expressed as a finite formula involving only the four arithmetic operations and the extraction of roots. We have already given symbolic expressions for the principal eigenvalue and eigenvector in symbolic form for $n \leq 4$ in my first book on the AHP. Still even in these cases, it is a relatively complicated process to weight and synthesize time dependent priorities for the alternatives. Once we have the outcome, we can analyze its rate of change with respect to time by taking its derivative.

The mathematics to do this in general symbolic form is not here yet, nor is PC computer technology necessarily up to the task. To solve a quintic equation in symbolic form in order to get the principal eigenvalue we are told by the chart distributed in 1994 by Wolfram Research on the quintic equation that it requires a trillion bytes, or one gigabyte of storage. One wonders what solving higher order equations would require. The upshot is that we can do time dependent AHP/ANP numerically by simulation. One would express the judgments functionally but then derive the eigenvector from the judgments for a fixed moment of time, put the outcome in a supermatrix, solve the problem and derive the outcome for the alternatives. Repeating the process for different values of time generates a curve for the priorities. One then approximates these values by curves with a functional form for each coefficient.

THE QUINTIC AND HIGHER ORDER CASES

The poster distributed by Wolfram Research in 1994 gives a nice introduction to the classical methods for symbolic computation of the roots of an algebraic equation. All algebraic equations of degree 4 and less can be solved using only square and cubic roots. Solutions of algebraic equations using radicals are called radical solutions. Abel (1802-1829) proved that the general equation of degree higher than four could not be solved using radicals. Galois (1811-1832) provided a method to characterize equations that are solvable by radicals. His method involved the development of group theory to determine the effect of permuting the roots of the equation on functions of the roots. The solution of the quartic equation can be related to the 4! = 24 symmetries of the tetrahedron, and those of the quintic equation to the 5! = 120 symmetries of the icosahedron. The general quintic equation can be solved by Kiepert's algorithm (Auflðsung der Gleichungen vom Fünften Grades, J. für Math., 87, 114-133, 1878) using theta series (see below; power series, sometimes also called Taylor series have the form, $\sum_{n=0}^{\infty} c_n t^n$,Laurent series the form $\sum_{n=-\infty}^{\infty} c_n t^n$, and Puiseux series often encountered in this connection the form $\sum_{n=-\infty}^{\infty} c_n t^{n/k}$ k, a fixed natural number) . The fact that radicals cannot be used in all cases of the quintic and higher order equations leads to the question as to what type of functions are needed to solve equations of higher degree than 4. Hyperradicals is the term used for such functions. Hermite, for example, showed that elliptic modular functions provide solutions to the quintic equation. Tschirnhausen transformations are often used to simplify the form of an algebraic equation, solve it in the reduced form and then apply the inverse transformation to obtain the solution of the general equation. Actually, the equation $a_0 x^n + a_1 x^{n-1} + \ldots + a_{n-1} x + a_n = 0, a_0 \neq 0$ is reduced to $z^n + b_1 z^{n-4} + \ldots + b_{n-1} x + b_n = 0$ with three fewer terms, and thus the quintic equation takes the form $z^5 + b_4 z + b_5 = 0$. Theta functions are periodic functions that can be represented by series whose convergence is extraordinarily rapid. Jacobi and Abel in 1827 studied these functions for the first time. We have,

$$\theta_2(z,q) = 2\sum_{n=0}^{\infty} q^{(n+1/2)^2} \cos(2n+1)z$$

$$\theta_3(z,q) = 1 + 2\sum_{n=0}^{\infty} q^{n^2} \cos 2nz$$

The elliptic modular function φ(z) is given by:

$$\varphi(z)=\sqrt[8]{\frac{\theta_2(0,z)^4}{\theta_3(0,z)^4}}$$

Camille Jordan proved in 1870 that an algebraic equation of any degree can be solved in terms of modular functions. The following theorem of H. Umemura (Resolution of Algebraic Equations by theta Constants, in Tata Lectures on Theta II, D. Mumford, ed., pp. 3.261-3.272, Birkhaüser, Boston, 1984.) does not require the use of Tschirnhausen transformations. Let $f(x)=a_0x^n+a_1x^{n-1}+...+a_n=0, a_0\neq 0$ be an algebraic equation irreducible over a subfield of the complex numbers. A root of this equation can be expressed in terms of theta functions of zero argument involving the period matrix derived from one of two types of hyperelliptic integrals.

7-10. Conclusions

It appears that independently from whether people like to do or can do dynamic comparisons, there would always be technological problems with mathematical engineering design that require the use of AHP/ANP in dynamic form. The first applications may not be taxing to our ingenuity to deal with functions instead of numbers, but it is certain that soon after they will and I expect that extensions of this paper will make that appear even more plausible.

Perhaps one of the advantages of dynamic judgments may be that the requirement of homogeneity is given up to the mathematics of the functions one uses. It seems to me that while this may be reasonable for technical but not behavioral problems. One may be able to compare the relation between two machines constructed in a systematic way so that their relative behavior is predetermined. In that case homogeneity is not needed as a requirement on the fundamental scale.

One thing we have to learn to do is to create a scale that is truly associated with our intuition so that we can use it in the natural and spontaneous way people have learned to use the scale 1-9 that is associated with verbally expressed judgments. Intuitively I think this is a considerable worthy challenge of our effort to extend the AHP/ANP. My appreciation goes to Luis G. Vargas for his dexterous and caring help with several tables and figures and for a part of our joint work on the brain.

Chapter 8
Allocation of Intangible Resources: Analytic Hierarchy Process and Linear Programming

8-1. Introduction

An intangible is an attribute that has no scale of measurement. Intangibles such as effort and skill arise in conjunction with resource allocation but are not usually included directly in a mathematical allocation model because of the absence of a unit of measurement to attach numbers to them. But there is a nontrivial way to quantify intangibles through relative measurement and derive priorities for them. It then becomes possible to combine these priorities with normalized measures of tangibles to allocate resources. To perform such allocation, a linear programming model is transformed to an equivalent model with coefficients and variables measured in relative terms. The priorities derived include among them relative values of the tangible resources as given on measurement scales. The optimum solution gives the relative amount of each resource. The presence of tangible resources makes it possible to estimate the cost or value of the intangibles for that particular problem in proportion to their priorities. A detailed example is given to illustrate the ideas. (This chapter is a selection from a paper co-authored with my colleagues Klaus Dellmann and Luis Vargas.)

Intangible resources such as quality, care, attention, and intelligence are often needed to develop a plan, design a system or solve a problem. So far, resource allocation models have not dealt with intangibles directly, but only by assigning them worth usually measured in time and money. Our goal here is to show that although there is no scale of measurement for an intangible, it can be measured in relative terms side by side with tangibles and thus an absolute scale of priorities is derived for them. These priorities serve as coefficients in an optimization framework to derive relative amounts of resources to be allocated. For the intangible resources, because there is no unit of measurement, no absolute amount of a resource can be specified, but in the presence of tangibles, it becomes possible to compute their absolute equivalents because of the proportionality inherent in their priorities.

Our concern with the measurement of intangibles relates to the value of assets owned by corporations. While one may argue that the market value of a company including its intangible resources is concretely calculated from its tangible assets, intangibles become particularly significant when, for example, two companies merge, and synergy gives rise to new intangibles with potential positive and negative impact on the value of the combined company. Measuring such intangibles could help assess the wisdom of a merger. An example given later on illustrates this point.

8-2. On the Measurement of Intangibles

Webster's unabridged dictionary defines a tangible as something "conceived or thought of as definable or measurable," and an intangible as something "incapable of being defined or determined with certainty or precision." Thus measurement is central in transforming an intangible to become a tangible. A scale of measurement requires a unit. A unit is the single most important building block on which a scale is founded A measurement on a scale involves the numerical assignment of multiples and fractions of the unit of that scale. A scale is a set of objects, a numerical space and a mapping from the objects to the numbers invariant under some transformation. To construct the mapping *consistently* so that for example objects having more of the attribute being measured are assigned larger values, one must compare that measurement with all other measurements on *that scale that have been experienced. Thus it appears that comparison and* experience are an integral part of measurement. Let us see how to apply these ideas to formulate linear programming problems with intangible coefficients.

8-3. On Estimating Lp Coefficients

A linear programming (LP) model can be represented with relative measurement and hence, when measurement scales exist, the relative linear programming (RLP) model with measurements prescribed in relative terms, and the absolute linear programming (LP) model (the usual model with measurements on physical scales which Roberts [40] showed must belong to ratio scales) are the same to within a multiplicative constant. It is then possible to construct LP models using solely relative measurement to optimize the allocation of intangible resources.

	Traditional LP	$\Leftrightarrow$	Relative LP
Decision Variables:	$\bar{x} = (\bar{x}_1, \cdots, \bar{x}_n)^T$		$\bar{w} = (w_1, \cdots, w_n)^T$
Objective Function:	$\sum_j c_j x_j \rightarrow$	${}_R c_j = \dfrac{c_j}{\sum_k \lvert c_k \rvert}$	$\rightarrow \sum_j {}_R c_j w_j$

$$\text{Constraints: } \sum_j a_{ij}x_j \le b_i \rightarrow \left\{ \begin{array}{l} {}_Ra_{ij} = \dfrac{a_{ij}}{\sum_k |a_{ik}|} \\ {}_Rb_i = \dfrac{\frac{b_i}{\sum_k |a_{ik}|}}{\sum_h \frac{|b_h|}{\sum_k |a_{hk}|}} \\ w_j = \dfrac{x_j}{\sum_h \frac{|b_h|}{\sum_k |a_{hk}|}} \end{array} \right\} \rightarrow \sum_j {}_Ra_{ij}w_j \le {}_Rb_i$$

$$\text{Primal:} \quad \begin{array}{l} Max \sum_j c_j x_j \\ s.t.: \sum_j a_{ij}x_j \le b_i \\ x_j \ge 0 \end{array} \quad \Leftrightarrow \quad \begin{array}{l} Max \sum_j {}_Rc_j w_j \\ s.t.: \sum_j {}_Ra_{ij}w_j \le {}_Rb_i \\ w_j \ge 0 \end{array}$$

(note that *s.t.* stands for *subject to*)

$$\text{Dual:} \quad \begin{array}{l} Min \sum_i b_i y_i \\ s.t.: \sum_i a_{ij}y_i \ge c_j \\ y_i \ge 0 \end{array} \quad \Leftrightarrow \quad \begin{array}{l} Min \sum_i {}_Rb_i v_i \\ s.t.: \sum_i {}_Ra_{ij}v_i \ge {}_Rc_j \\ v_j \ge 0 \end{array}$$

It is significant to note that all the coefficients in the relative formulation are unit free, although their relative magnitudes are preserved. Thus the underlying magnitudes they represent can be compared in pairs.

There are three places where intangibles can arise in an LP problem. The most common is in the objective function in which the coefficients can be estimated as priorities, and the rest of the problem is formulated in the usual way. This problem presents no practical complications because the solution is the same if the objective function coefficients are given in relative terms tantamount to dividing by a constant.

If the problem already has tangible constraints, it is transformed into an RLP model. A new intangible constraint can be added by first deriving the coefficients, ${}_Ra_{ij}, j = 1,\ldots,n$ through paired comparisons, according to the relative use of that resource by the activities represented with the decision variables. Then one determines ${}_Rb_i, i = 1,\ldots,n$ by making paired comparisons as to the availability (or need) of the resources. If the problem has no tangible constraints, we simply compare the availability (or need) of the intangible resources involved to determine the ${}_{R}b_{i}$.

Incorporating a decision variable corresponding to an activity or resource for which there is no scale requires two steps: prioritizing the contribution of the variable to the objective and prioritizing the contribution of the activity or resource in the constraints. Intangibles in the decision variables are more difficult to treat because implementing a decision prescribed by the LP solution requires a unit. When tangibles are included, the unit may be applied through the priorities of the variables to the intangibles. Without a unit, we cannot interpret the absolute meaning of each component of the solution as we only have their relative values in the form of priorities.

8-4. Example

Two companies, A and B, entertain the possibility of merging because their management believes that their integration would create positive synergistic effects giving them increased competitive advantage in:

Markets: with positive impacts on image as a function of brand and quality.
Innovation, and
Cost Reduction: as a consequence of the integration of human resources from technical and managerial areas.

The areas in which management can concentrate its efforts, i.e., Markets, Innovation and Cost Reduction, use resources such as brand image (BIM), product quality (PQ), technical human resources (THR) and managerial human resources (MHR). When the merger takes place, each company would contribute differently to Markets, Innovation and Cost Reduction.

The companies have budgets allocated to technical (THR) and managerial (MHR) resources as shown in Table 8-1. The areas considered here, Markets, Innovation and Cost Reduction, use these resources at rates also given in Table 8-1. For example, Firm A uses 10, 70 and 20 percent, of the budget allocated to THR per unit effort allocated to Markets, Innovation and Cost Reduction, respectively. Similarly, Firm B uses 10, 80 and 20 percent of THR for every unit of effort allocated to Markets, Innovation and Cost Reduction, respectively.

Table 8-1: Budgets & Use of Resources Per Unit of Effort Allocated

	Markets	Innovation	Cost Reduction	THR($M)
FIRM A	0.1	0.7	0.2	182
FIRM B	0.1	0.8	0.1	455
				MHR($M)
FIRM A	0.3	0.1	0.6	435
FIRM B	0.4	0	0.6	155

Let w_{ij} be the amount of effort in area j (i.e., Markets, Innovation or Cost Reduction) contributed by company i. Let s_{ij} be the relative contribution of area j to the total worth of company i. We would like to determine w_{ij}, how much each company should contribute in each area so that the total worth of the company is maximized, i.e., $Z = Max\sum_{i,j} s_{ij} w_{ij}$.

To estimate the coefficients s_{ij}, we ask the question: Which area contributes more to the total worth of the company? The pairwise comparisons and the corresponding priorities are given in Table 8-2.

Table 8-2: Relative Contribution of Areas to the Total Worth of the Company

$$
\begin{array}{llll}
FirmA & MKTS \quad I \quad C & & Priorities \\
\begin{array}{r} Markets \\ Innovation \\ Costs \end{array} &
\begin{bmatrix} 1 & 2 & 2 \\ 1/2 & 1 & 1/2 \\ 1/2 & 2 & 1 \end{bmatrix} & \Rightarrow &
\begin{bmatrix} 0.49 \\ 0.20 \\ 0.31 \end{bmatrix}
\end{array}
$$

$$
\begin{array}{llll}
FirmB & MKTS \quad I \quad C & & Priorities \\
\begin{array}{r} Markets \\ Innovation \\ Costs \end{array} &
\begin{bmatrix} 1 & 1 & 2 \\ 1 & 1 & 2 \\ 1/2 & 1/2 & 1 \end{bmatrix} & \Rightarrow &
\begin{bmatrix} 0.40 \\ 0.40 \\ 0.20 \end{bmatrix}
\end{array}
$$

The companies then allocate effort expressed in monetary units according to the solution of the following LP models:

FIRM A

$$Max \quad 0.49w_{11} + 0.20w_{12} + 0.31w_{13}$$

s.t.

$$0.10w_{11} + 0.70w_{12} + 0.20w_{13} \leq 182$$
$$0.30w_{11} + 0.10w_{12} + 0.60w_{13} \leq 435$$
$$w_{ij} \geq 0;$$

FIRM B

$$Max \quad 0.40w_{21} + 0.40w_{22} + 0.20w_{23} \; s$$

.t.

$$0.10w_{21} + 0.80w_{22} + 0.10w_{23} \leq 455$$
$$0.40w_{21} + 0.60w_{23} \leq 155$$
$$w_{ij} \geq 0;$$

The constraints are specified in Table 8-1. The solutions of these models are given by:

FIRM A

$$w_{11} = 1431.5$$
$$w_{12} = 55.5$$
$$w_{13} = 0$$
$$Z_A = 711.98$$

FIRM B

$$w_{21} = 387.5$$
$$w_{22} = 520.3125$$
$$w_{23} = 0$$
$$Z_B = 363.125$$

If the companies merge, the resources merge and the efforts are now allocated by using the solution of the following LP model:

$$Max: \quad 0.49w_{11} + 0.20w_{12} + 0.31w_{13} + 0.40w_{21} + 0.40w_{22} + 0.20w_{23}$$

subject to:

$$0.10w_{11} + 0.70w_{12} + 0.20w_{13} + 0.10w_{21} + 0.80w_{22} + 0.10w_{23} \leq 637$$
$$0.30w_{11} + 0.10w_{12} + 0.60w_{13} + 0.40w_{21} + 0.60w_{23} \leq 590$$
$$w_{ij} \geq 0.$$

given by:

$$w_{11} = 1966.667$$
$$w_{12} = w_{13} = w_{21} = w_{23} = 0$$
$$w_{22} = 550.4167$$
$$Z_{A+B} = 1183.833$$

Note that the merger produces an objective function value that is greater than the sum of the individual objective functions:

$$Z_A + Z_B = 711.98{+}363.125 = 1075.105$$

vs.

$$Z_A = 1183.833$$

or an increase of 10.11 percent.

Assume now that we wish to allocate resources by considering two new resources, Brand Image and Product Quality. Because these resources are qualitative, we first prioritize the relative use of resources. Let ${}_R a_{ijk}$ be the relative amount of resource k used if a unit of effort is allocated to the jth area by the ith company. The question we need to ask here to estimate the relative amount of a resource k used is: Given a company and a resource, for example, Brand Image (BIM) and two areas (e.g., Markets and Innovation) which one uses that resource more and how much more?

$$\begin{matrix} BIM & MKTS & I & C \\ Markets \\ Innovation \\ Costs \end{matrix} \begin{bmatrix} 1 & 8 & 2 \\ 1/8 & 1 & 2 \\ 1/2 & 1/2 & 1 \end{bmatrix} \Rightarrow \begin{bmatrix} 0.666 \\ 0.167 \\ 0.167 \end{bmatrix} \quad (Firm \quad A)$$

$$\begin{matrix} BIM & MKTS & I & C \\ Markets \\ Innovation \\ Costs \end{matrix} \begin{bmatrix} 1 & 1 & 9 \\ 1 & 1 & 1/3 \\ 1/9 & 3 & 1 \end{bmatrix} \Rightarrow \begin{bmatrix} 0.60 \\ 0.20 \\ 0.20 \end{bmatrix} \quad (Firm \quad B)$$

The relative amounts for all the resources are given in Table 8-3.

Table 8-3: Matrix ${}_R A$ of Relative Use of Resources to Attain Objectives

	Firm A			Firm B		
	Markets	*Innovation*	*Cost Red.*	Markets	Innovation	*Cost Red.*
BIM	0.667	0.167	0.166	0.6	0.2	0.2
PQ	0.7	0.2	0.1	0.6	0.3	0.1
THR	0.1	0.7	0.2	0.1	0.8	0.1
MHR	0.3	0.1	0.6	0.4	0.0	0.6

Finally, we prioritize the relative importance of the resources. Let ${}_R b_{ik}$ be the relative amount of resource k available to company i. The question asked here is: Given a company and two resources (e.g., Brand Image and Product quality), which one is more abundant for that company, or is more important, and by how much? The following matrices of paired comparisons yield the priorities given in Table 8-4:

FIRM A

$$\begin{array}{c|cccc} & BIM & PQ & THR & MHR \\ \hline BIM & 1 & 3 & 2 & 1/2 \\ PQ & 1/3 & 1 & 1/2 & 1/4 \\ THR & 1/2 & 2 & 1 & 1/2 \\ MHR & 2 & 4 & 2 & 1 \end{array}$$

FIRM B

$$\begin{array}{c|cccc} & BIM & PQ & THR & MHR \\ \hline BIM & 1 & 1/2 & 1/3 & 1 \\ PQ & 2 & 1 & 1/2 & 2 \\ THR & 3 & 2 & 1 & 3 \\ MHR & 1 & 1/2 & 1/3 & 1 \end{array}$$

The priorities of the resources for each company and for the newly formed one are given in Table 8-4.

Table 8-4: RHS Coefficients

RHS Coefficients $_R\bar{b}$. Relative Importance of the Resources

FIRM A	BIM	PQ	THR	MHR
BIM	1	3	2	1/2
PQ	1/3	1	1/2	0.25
THR	1/2	2	1	1/2
MHR	2	4	2	1

FIRM B	BIM	PQ	THR	MHR
BIM	1	1/2	1/3	1
PQ	2	1	1/2	2
THR	3	2	1	3
MHR	1	1/2	1/3	1

RESOURCES	*Firm A*	*Firm B*	*Firms A+B*
Brand image (BIM)	*0.286*	*0.141*	0.2135
Product Quality (PQ)	*0.097*	*0.263*	0.18
Technical Human Resources (THR)	*0.186*	*0.455*	0.3185
Managerial Human Resources (MHR)	*0.431*	*0.141*	0.288

Thus, the LP model for company A is given by:

$$Max \quad 0.49w_{11} + 0.20w_{12} + 0.31w_{13}$$

subject to:

$$0.80w_{11} + 0.10w_{12} + 0.10w_{13} \leq 0.286$$
$$0.70w_{11} + 0.20w_{12} + 0.10w_{13} \leq 0.097$$
$$0.10w_{11} + 0.70w_{12} + 0.20w_{13} \leq 0.182$$
$$0.30w_{11} + 0.10w_{12} + 0.60w_{13} \leq 0.435$$
$$w_{ij} \geq 0;$$

and for company B is given by:

$$Max \quad 0.40w_{21} + 0.40w_{22} + 0.20w_{23}$$

subject to

$$0.60w_{21} + 0.20w_{22} + 0.20w_{23} \leq 0.141$$
$$0.60w_{21} + 0.30w_{22} + 0.10w_{23} \leq 0.263$$
$$0.10w_{21} + 0.80w_{22} + 0.10w_{23} \leq 0.455$$
$$0.40w_{21} + 0.60w_{23} \leq 0.155$$
$$w_{ij} \geq 0;$$

and for the combined company is given by:

$$Max: \quad 0.49w_{11} + 0.20w_{12} + 0.31w_{13} + 0.40w_{21} + 0.40w_{22} + 0.20w_{23}$$

s.t.:

$$0.3335w_{11} + 0.0835w_{12} + 0.083w_{13} + 0.30w_{21} + 0.10w_{22} + 0.10w_{23} \leq 0.2135$$
$$0.35w_{11} + 0.10w_{12} + 0.05w_{13} + 0.30w_{21} + 0.15w_{22} + 0.05w_{23} \leq 0.18$$
$$0.05w_{11} + 0.35w_{12} + 0.10w_{13} + 0.05w_{21} + 0.40w_{22} + 0.05w_{23} \leq 0.3185$$
$$0.15w_{11} + 0.05w_{12} + 0.30w_{13} + 0.20w_{21} + 0.30w_{23} \leq 0.288$$
$$w_{ij} \geq 0.$$

The solutions of these three LP models are given in Table 8-5 below. It is worth pointing out that with the merger, the objective function increased from 0.24686 + 0.25086 = 0.49772 to 0.57901 or 16.33 percent. The efforts are now shared by the two firms, with Firm A contributing to Markets and Cost Reduction and Firm B contributing to Innovation. In relative terms, Firm A will allocate

$$\frac{0.149423}{0.149423 + 0.885288} = 14.44\%$$

of its efforts to Markets and

$$\frac{0.885288}{0.149423 + 0.885288} = 85.56\%$$

to Cost Reduction, and Firm B will dedicate all its efforts to Innovation; and the resulting company should allocate, in relative terms: 9.4% to Markets, 34.96% to Innovation, and 55.64% to Cost Reduction.

Table 8-5: Solutions of the LP Models

FIRM A

0.667	0.167	0.166		0.140953461	0.286
0.7	0.2	0.1		0.097	0.097
0.1	0.7	0.2		0.182	0.182
0.3	0.1	0.6		0.435	0.435
0.49	0.19	0.32		0.246857692	
Solution: 0.022038	0.0555	0.704731			

FIRM B

0.6	0.2	0.2		0.141	0.141
0.6	0.3	0.1		0.180357	0.263
0.1	0.8	0.1		0.455	0.455
0.4	0	0.6		0.093429	0.141
0.4	0.4	0.2		0.250857	
Solution: 0	0.549286	0.155714			

FIRMS A+B

								RHS
	0.3335	0.0835	0.083	0.3	0.1	0.1	0.178937	0.2135
	0.35	0.1	0.05	0.3	0.15	0.05	0.18	0.18
	0.05	0.35	0.1	0.05	0.4	0.05	0.3185	0.3185
	0.15	0.05	0.3	0.2	0	0.3	0.288	0.288
OBJCOEF	0.49	0.19	0.32	0.4	0.4	0.2	Z= 0.57901	
Solution:	0.149423	0	0.885288	0	0.55625	0		

Alternatively, it is possible to translate these priorities into monetary values if there are some resources that are tangible and measured on a monetary scale. One must be careful and not assume that this translation can be done for all priorities in all circumstances. First, we convert the priorities of the intangible resources into monetary units by using one of the priorities of the tangible resources as the unit. For example, the priority of the tangible resource THR (0.3185) corresponds to the value $\frac{b_3}{\sum_j a_{3j}} = \frac{637}{1} = 637$. Hence, the monetary equivalent of the priority of the intangible resource Brand Image is given by: (0.2135/0.3185)*637 = 427, and similarly, for Product Quality we have (0.180/0.3185)*637 = 360. Had we used the tangible resource MHR, the monetary equivalents would have been 437 and 369, respectively. This happens when more than one tangible resource is involved in the prioritization of the intangible resources. To preserve the proportionality among the tangible resources one could have included for comparison just one of the tangible resources with the intangibles, and then adjusted the priorities of the remaining tangible resources accordingly. Alternatively, we could average over the monetary equivalents obtaining 432 and 364, respectively. Finally, the solution can be expressed in monetary values by applying the transformation $x_{ij} = w_{ij} \sum_i \frac{b_i}{\sum_{j,k} a_{ijk}}$. We have:

$$x_{11} = 0.149423(432 + 364 + 637 + 590) \approx 302$$

$$x_{13} = 0.885288(432 + 364 + 637 + 590) \approx 1{,}791$$

$$x_{22} = 0.55625(432 + 364 + 637 + 590) \approx 1{,}125.$$

$$x_{12} = x_{21} = x_{23} = 0$$

It is now possible to express the variables in terms of dollars and interpret this solution in terms of budgetary amounts allocated to different areas to fulfill a mission.

8-5. Conclusion

Priorities are absolute scale utilities. By deriving priorities on an absolute scale, it is possible to include intangibles with tangibles in the effort to optimize the allocation of scarce resources. In another example we have considered only intangibles, but the solution of the RLP formulation must be normalized to unity to give one a meaningful estimate of the relative magnitude of the resources to be allocated. We then transformed these relative magnitudes into a tangible resource through cross modality matching.

Appendix
Facts from Matrix and Graph Theory

In this appendix we have included some facts about matrix theory and graph theory that relate to the material of the book. We hope the reader will find them useful.

A-1. MATRICES

A matrix is a rectangular array of mn numbers arranged in m rows and n columns [8, 12, 20, 25, 30, 38]. The number, element, or entry of the matrix A in the ith row and jth column is denoted by a_{ij}. Thus we have for the m by n matrix A:

$$A = \begin{bmatrix} a_{11} & a_{12} & \cdots & a_{1n} \\ a_{21} & a_{22} & \cdots & a_{2n} \\ \vdots & & & \vdots \\ a_{m1} & a_{m2} & \cdots & a_{mn} \end{bmatrix}$$

Generally we denote the matrix A by (a_{ij}) and specify the number of its rows and columns. The subscripts i and j refer to the row and column, respectively, in which the entry is located. A is called a square matrix of order n if $m = n$. We shall be mostly interested in square $n \times n$ (n by n) matrices.

The rows and columns of A are called vectors. The matrix A may consist of a single row vector or a single column vector. In that case, a single subscript on this entry suffices. For example, $A \equiv (a_1, \cdots, a_n)$ is a row vector. The diagonal elements of a square matrix A of order n are a_{ii}, $i = 1, \ldots, n$. A *diagonal* matrix A has the property that $a_{ij} = 0$, for all i and j with $i \neq j$. If also all $a_{ii} = 0$ for all i, A is called the *zero* or *null* matrix and is denoted by boldface zero or by boldface capital $\mathbf{O}$. The unit or *identity* matrix I is a diagonal matrix with $a_{ij} = 1$ for $i = j$; and $a_{ij} = 0$ for $i \neq j$. The *transpose* of $A = (a_{ij})$, denoted by $A^T = (a_{ji})$, is defined by replacing the element in the i,j position of A by the element in the j,i position; that is, we interchange the rows and columns of A by reflecting around the main diagonal to obtain A^T. Since two matrices are equal if their corresponding elements are equal, we can define a *symmetric* matrix by $A = A^T$; that is $a_{ij} = a_{ji}$ for all i and j. A scalar multiple kA of a matrix $A = (a_{ij})$ is a matrix each of whose coefficients is equal to the product of each coefficient of A by a constant k. Thus we have $kA = (ka_{ij})$.

Let $A = (a_{ij})$ be an $n \times n$ matrix. Then A is nonnegative ($A \geq 0$) if $a_{ij} \geq 0$ for all i and j. A matrix A is positive ($A > 0$) if $a_{ij} > 0$ for all i and j. A matrix A is cogradient to a matrix B if there is a permutation matrix P such that $A = P^T BP$. A is reducible or decomposable if it is cogradient to a matrix of the form

$$\begin{bmatrix} B_1 & 0 \\ B_2 & B_3 \end{bmatrix}$$

where B_1 and B_3 are square submatrices. Otherwise A is irreducible or non-decomposable. By definition, a 1×1 matrix is irreducible. $A \geq 0$ is primitive if and only if there is an integer $m > 0$ such that $A^m > 0$. Otherwise it is imprimitive. A is column stochastic if $a_{ij} \geq 0$ and $\sum_{j=1}^{n} a_{ij} = 1$ for $j = 1, \ldots, n$. It is row stochastic if $\sum_{j=1}^{n} a_{ij} = 1$ for $i = 1, \ldots, n$. A is doubly stochastic if it is both column and row stochastic.

There are rules by which matrices A and B can be added, subtracted, multiplied, and "divided." These operations constitute an algebra of matrices, somewhat similar to the algebra of ordinary numbers, but care must be taken, as all the rules that work with ordinary numbers do not work with matrices, which have a more general algebra. Indeed, a matrix of order one by one is a single number, called a scalar, and all laws which apply to matrices in general must also apply to that special kind of matrix and hence to ordinary numbers. However, unlike multiplying numbers, matrix multiplication is non-commutative, and not every nonzero matrix has an inverse.

Historically, matrices arose as a shorthand method of listing coefficients of a system of equations, and the origins of matrix addition and multiplication may be related to operations on systems of equations. A general set of m equations in n unknowns is given by

$$\begin{aligned} a_{11}x_1 + a_{12}x_2 + \ldots + a_{1n}x_n &= y_1 \\ a_{21}x_1 + a_{22}x_2 + \ldots + a_{2n}x_n &= y_2 \\ \vdots \qquad\qquad\qquad \vdots \quad &\quad \vdots \\ a_{m1}x_1 + a_{m2}x_2 + \ldots + a_{mn}x_n &= y_m \end{aligned}$$

The writing of such a system can be made simple if the coefficients, the elements of the array (a_{ij}), are separated from the variables, the x_j. Then the x_j, which are repeated in each row, need be written only once; thus

$$\begin{bmatrix} a_{11} & a_{12} & \cdots & a_{1n} \\ a_{21} & a_{22} & \cdots & a_{2n} \\ \vdots & & & \\ a_{m1} & a_{m2} & \cdots & a_{mn} \end{bmatrix} \begin{bmatrix} x_1 \\ x_2 \\ \vdots \\ x_n \end{bmatrix} = \begin{bmatrix} y_1 \\ y_2 \\ \vdots \\ y_m \end{bmatrix}$$

If we write the x_j as a column, then the rule to reassemble the original system is: with every a_{ij} associate the corresponding x_j, i.e., $a_{3\,2}$ and x_2 yield $a_{3\,2}\,x_2$. That is, as you move across the rows of coefficients, move *down* the column of x's for the proper association. This simple operation is the basis for the general matrix multiplication rule.

We may refer to $(x_1, x_2, \ldots, x_n)$ as the vector x and $(y_1, y_2, \ldots, y_m)$ as the vector y. Notice that in general the number of elements in x is not the same as that in y. The product of an m by n matrix and a p by q matrix is only possible when $p = n$ and results in a matrix of size m by q. Thus if $q = 1$, that is, the second matrix is a vector, the product is also a vector. To prevent confusion, keep in mind that subscripted letters refer to elements of matrices or vectors and unsubscripted letters refer to a whole matrix or vector.

The system of lincar equations given above, known as an inhomogeneous system, may be simply represented as $Ax = y$. To solve this system, one can use the method of Gaussian elimination. By analogy with the solution of $ax = y$ whose solution is $x = y/a$ or $x = a^{-1}y$ for scalars, we find the inverse A^{-1} of the matrix A, that is, a matrix A^{-1} such that $AA^{-1} = A^{-1}A = I$. We then have $x = A^{-1}y$. An inefficient but time-honored procedure in computing the inverse of a matrix is to obtain its determinant and its adjoint. If $y = 0$, then a nonzero solution of the homogeneous equation $Ax = 0$ exists if and only if A^{-1} does not exist; otherwise

$x = A^{-1}0 = 0$ and $x = 0$ would be the only solution. It will be seen below that A^{-1} does not exist when the determinant of A is equal to zero. A final comment here is that in the Analytic Hierarchy Process we encounter a homogeneous equation of the form $(\lambda_{max}I - A)\, w = 0$. This equation has a nonzero solution w because λ_{max} is a root of the characteristic polynomial of A which is the determinant of $(\lambda I\text{-}A)$.

DETERMINANT OF A

To compute the determinant of a matrix, we need the recursive definitions of a minor and of a cofactor. The minor M_{ij} of a_{ij} is the determinant of the submatrix obtained by striking out the row and column of a_{ij}. The cofactor A_{ij} of a_{ij} is given by $A_{ij} = (-1)^{i+j} M_{ij}$. The determinant of A, often written as $|A|$, for a given i is:

$$|A| = \sum_{j=1}^{n} a_{ij} A_{ij}$$

or for a given j is:

$$|A| = \sum_{j=1}^{n} a_{ij} A_{ij}$$

Consider the matrix:

$$A = \begin{bmatrix} 2 & 0 & 0 & 4 \\ 3 & 1 & 1 & 2 \\ 6 & 4 & 1 & 0 \\ 4 & 2 & 2 & 1 \end{bmatrix}$$

Then

$$|A| = 2\begin{vmatrix} 1 & 5 & 2 \\ 4 & 1 & 0 \\ 2 & 2 & 1 \end{vmatrix} - 0\begin{vmatrix} 3 & 5 & 2 \\ 6 & 1 & 0 \\ 4 & 2 & 1 \end{vmatrix}$$

$$+1 = \begin{vmatrix} 3 & 1 & 2 \\ 6 & 4 & 0 \\ 4 & 2 & 1 \end{vmatrix} - 4 \begin{vmatrix} 3 & 1 & 5 \\ 6 & 4 & 1 \\ 4 & 2 & 2 \end{vmatrix}$$

$$= 2(-7) - 0\,(-11) + 1\,(-2) - 4\,(-10) = 24$$

To show how the process is extended to submatrices, we have, for example:

$$2 \begin{vmatrix} 1 & 5 & 2 \\ 4 & 1 & 0 \\ 2 & 2 & 1 \end{vmatrix} = 2 \left(1 \begin{vmatrix} 1 & 0 \\ 2 & 1 \end{vmatrix} - 5 \begin{vmatrix} 4 & 0 \\ 2 & 1 \end{vmatrix} + 2 \begin{vmatrix} 4 & 1 \\ 2 & 2 \end{vmatrix} \right)$$

A matrix whose determinant is zero is called singular.

ADJOINT OF A

Adjoint of $A = (A_{ij}) = (-1)^{i+j}$ cofactor of a_{ji} of A.

This gives

$$\begin{pmatrix} -7 & -20 & -29 & 68 \\ 11 & 28 & 49 & -100 \\ -2 & 8 & 2 & -8 \\ 10 & 8 & 14 & -32 \end{pmatrix}$$

for the adjoint of A. Finally the inverse of A is given by:

$$A^{-1} = \frac{Adjoint\ A}{|A|}$$

This approach is not to be used computationally, because it is inefficient. Its number of operations is of the order of one-third the fifth power of n, $0\left(\frac{n^5}{3}\right)$. It can be shown that $|AB| = |A||B|$, from which we can deduce that $|Adjoint\ A| = |A|^{n-1}$.

As noted above, determinants arise from the solution of equations by elimination. Thus in

$a_{11}x_1 = y_1$ we have $x_1 = \dfrac{y_1}{a_{11}}$

and in the system of two equations

$$a_{11}x_1 + a_{12}x_2 = y_1$$
$$a_{21}x_1 + a_{22}x_2 = y_2$$

by elimination in the first equation,

$$x_2 = \frac{y_1 - a_{11}x_1}{a_{12}}$$

and substitution in the second,

$$a_{21}x_1 + \frac{a_{22}}{a_{12}}(y_1 - a_{11}x_1) = y_2$$

followed by simplification,

$$\left(a_{21} - \frac{a_{11}a_{22}}{a_{12}}\right)x_1 = y_2 - \frac{a_{22}}{a_{12}}y_1$$

and solution

$$x_1 = \frac{a_{12}y_2 - a_{22}y_1}{a_{12}a_{21} - a_{11}a_{12}} = \frac{a_{22}y_1 - a_{12}y_2}{a_{11}a_{22} - a_{12}a_{21}}$$

$$= \frac{\begin{vmatrix} y_1 & a_{12} \\ y_2 & a_{22} \end{vmatrix}}{\begin{vmatrix} a_{11} & a_{12} \\ a_{21} & a_{22} \end{vmatrix}}$$

Here the determinant of $A = \begin{pmatrix} a_{11} & a_{12} \\ a_{21} & a_{22} \end{pmatrix}$ appears in the denominator. Similarly we have:

$$x_2 = \frac{\begin{vmatrix} a_{11} & y_1 \\ a_{21} & y_2 \end{vmatrix}}{\begin{vmatrix} a_{11} & a_{12} \\ a_{21} & a_{22} \end{vmatrix}}$$

This is a solution of the system by Cramer's rule, which again is computationally very inefficient. It replaces the coefficient of x_i by the vector of y's in the determinant of the numerator and calculates the determinant of the coefficient matrix in the denominator. The same approach can be generalized for the solution of an n by n system.

THE CHARACTERISTIC EQUATION: EIGENVALUES AND EIGENVECTORS

A proper vector (characteristic vector or eigenvector) of A is a nonnull vector $w = (w_1, \cdots, w_n)$ such that $Aw=\lambda w$ or $(1/\lambda)A$ transforms w to w, i.e., leaves w fixed. The values of λ corresponding to such a w are called the proper values (characteristic values or eigenvalues) of A. Thus w would be a proper vector or eigenvector if it is a nontrivial (nonzero) solution of $(\lambda I - A)w = 0$ for some number λ. The components of w constitute a solution(s) of a homogeneous linear system with matrix $\lambda I - A$. In fact, this system has the trivial solution $w_1 = \ldots = w_n = 0$. But in order that there be a nontrivial solution, the matrix $\lambda I - A$ must be singular, i.e., its determinant, $\det(\lambda I - A) = 0$, or simply $|\lambda I - A| = 0$. This determinant is an nth degree polynomial in λ. It has the form $\lambda^n - a_1\lambda^{n-1} + \cdots + (-1)^n|A|$ and is called the degree equation called the characteristic equation of A. The roots λ_I, $i = 1, \ldots, n$, of the characteristic equation $|\lambda I - A| = 0$ are the desired eigenvalues. The fundamental theorem of algebra assures the existence of n roots (not necessarily all distinct) for a polynomial equation of degree n. The eigenvectors are obtained by solving the corresponding systems of equations for each λ_i, $i = 1, \ldots, n$. Care must be taken in getting all the eigenvectors when there are multiple roots.

Note that in the characteristic polynomial the coefficient of λ^{n-1} is the sum of the diagonal elements of A. Thus

$$a_1 = \sum_{i=1}^{n} a_{ii} \equiv trace(A)$$

It is also true that the roots of the characteristic equation as roots of an nth degree equation satisfy

$$\sum_{i=1}^{n} \lambda_i = a_1 = trace(A)$$

and the last term in that equation is the product of the roots:

$$\prod_{i=1}^{n} \lambda_1 = |A|$$

We can see this by expanding the factorization $(\lambda-\lambda_1)(\lambda-\lambda_2)\cdots(\lambda-\lambda_n)$ of the characteristic polynomial. We note that the characteristic equation may have multiple roots, and hence the total number of distinct roots may be less than n. A multiple root λ_i of multiplicity k would appear in the factorization in the form $(\lambda-\lambda_i)^k$. For a simple root we have $k = 1$.

From $Aw=\lambda w$ and $A\lambda=\lambda A$, since λ is a constant, we have $A^2w=A(Aw)=A(\lambda w)=\lambda Aw=\lambda(\lambda w)=\lambda^2 w$. Thus, λ^2 is an eigenvalue of A^2 and similarly λ^k is an eigenvalue of A^k.

Consider the matrix

$$A = \begin{bmatrix} 1 & 2 \\ 3 & 4 \end{bmatrix}, \quad I = \begin{bmatrix} 1 & 0 \\ 0 & 1 \end{bmatrix}, \quad \lambda I = \begin{bmatrix} \lambda & 0 \\ 0 & \lambda \end{bmatrix}$$

$$(\lambda I - A) = \begin{bmatrix} 1-\lambda & 2 \\ 3 & 4-\lambda \end{bmatrix}$$

$$|\lambda I - A| = (I-\lambda)(4-\lambda)-6 = \lambda^2 - 5\lambda - 2 = 0$$

Since the characteristic equation is a quadratic, we solve it by using the well-known quadratic formula for the roots of such an equation. We have for the eigenvalues

$$\lambda_1 = \frac{5+\sqrt{33}}{2} \qquad \lambda_2 = \frac{5-\sqrt{33}}{2}$$

and to obtain the eigenvector corresponding to λ_1, we write $Aw=\lambda_1 w$, that is,

$$\begin{bmatrix} 1 & 2 \\ 3 & 4 \end{bmatrix} \begin{bmatrix} w_1 \\ w_2 \end{bmatrix} = \lambda_1 \begin{bmatrix} w_1 \\ w_2 \end{bmatrix}$$

or

$$w_1 + 2w_2 = \lambda_1 w_1$$

that is,

$$w_1 = -\frac{2}{1-\lambda_1} w_2$$

We also have

$$3w_1 + 4w_2 = \lambda_1 w_2$$

Since the matrix $\lambda_1 I - A$ is singular (its determinant is zero because its characteristic equation is evaluated at λ_1, one of the two roots), there is dependence between its rows, and hence the second equation yields no new information. Thus the eigenvector w is obtained by assigning an arbitrary value to w_2 and calculating w_1 from the above relation. Assigning w_2 the value 1, we have

$$w = \left[\frac{2}{\lambda_1 - 1}, 1 \right]$$

We can normalize w by making its coefficients sum to unity. We do this by dividing each coefficient by the sum w_1+w_2, which is $(\lambda_1+1)/(\lambda_1-1)$. The resulting normalized vector is

$$\left[\frac{2}{\lambda_1 + 1}, \frac{\lambda_1 - 1}{\lambda_1 + 1} \right]$$

Since multiplying by a constant does not affect the solution of $Aw=\lambda w$, we shall think of the eigenvectors w to be always given in normalized form. We may similarly obtain the eigenvector corresponding to λ_2.

Recall that a complex number is of the form $a+ib$ where $i=\sqrt{-1}$ and a and b are real. The modulus of such a number is denoted by $|a+ib|$ and is equal to $\left(a^2+b^2\right)^{1/2}$. The complex conjugate of $a+ib$ is $a-ib$ and $(a+ib)(a-ib)=a^2+b^2$. The eigenvalues of a real matrix, as the roots of any equation, may be complex numbers and occur in pairs as complex conjugates. If a matrix has real entries and is symmetric, all its eigenvalues are real and the eigenvectors corresponding to different eigenvalues are orthogonal in pairs. Thus, for example, if u and v are two such eigenvectors, then $uv^T = vu^T = 0$. The same is also true of a Hermitian matrix, which is a matrix of complex numbers in which a_{ji} is the complex conjugate of a_{ij}.

A theorem in matrix theory asserts that the eigenvalues of a matrix depend continuously on its entries (the same as proving that the roots of a polynomial depend continuously on its coefficients).

The eigenvalues, as the roots of any polynomial equation, are obtained by standard numerical methods, of which there are several. There are nowadays canned computer programs like MATHEMATICA, MAPLE, EISPACK, MATLAB, and LAPACK for getting these roots. When the equation is the characteristic equation of a matrix, these computer programs also find the eigenvectors.

Two well-known methods in the literature for obtaining the characteristic polynomial of a matrix, which is simply the determinant of ($\lambda I - A$), are those of U.J.J. Leverrier [32] and of D.K. Faddeev [20]. There is a more efficient way to obtain the roots $\lambda_1, \cdots, \lambda_n$ directly and use them to derive the characteristic polynomial $(\lambda-\lambda_1)\cdots(\lambda-\lambda_n)$.

A matrix $A = (a_{ij})$ is upper triangular if a_{ij}=0 for i>j. A is orthogonal if $A^TA=I$. Any matrix with real entries can be written as a product $A=QR$ where Q is orthogonal and R is upper triangular. An efficient way (not fully free of problems) for deriving the eigenvalues and eigenvectors of a matrix A is the QR algorithm developed in 1961 by J.G. Francis. The basic algorithm is described in Cullen [16].

1. INPUT: an n by n matrix A and allow m iterations.

2. Take $A_1 = A$

3. For $i = 1, 2, ..., m$, factor $A_i = Q_i R_i$ where $Q_i^T A_i = R_i, Q_i$ $_i$ is orthogonal and R_i is upper triangular.

4. Compute $A_{i+1} = R_i Q_i$.

5. OUTPUT: A_m orthogonally similar to $A = \left(A_m = Q_m^t \cdots Q_1^T A Q_1 \cdots Q_m\right)$ and close to upper triangular (the elements below the diagonal are close to zero).

The diagonal entries of A_m converge to the eigenvalues of A. The programs MATLAB and MATALG use EISPACK subroutines to compute the eigenvalues and eigenvectors.

ON IRREDUCIBILITY, PRIMITIVITY, CYCLICITY, AND STOCHASTICITY

Why do we need the irreducibility, primitivity, and cyclicity of matrices? Before the days of the computer it was necessary to work out the details of a mathematical theory in such a way as to make certain types of computations possible to obtain a limiting answer with a finite number of calculations when one could. *Thus irreducibility, needed in Frobenius' theorem, has to do with the fact that the principal eigenvalue $\lambda_{\max}$ of a nonnegative matrix is simple and therefore occurs only once. Primitivity ensures that there are no other roots whose moduli are equal to one. Imprimitivity deals with roots of unity and accounts for cycling.* Note that $\lambda_{\max}$ can be a simple root and a multiple root of a reducible matrix. In either case, there may be additional nth roots of unity. When the root is simple, the case of additional nth roots of unity is dealt with precisely as in the case of an irreducible matrix [13, 16].

Irreducibility and Graphs: $W \gneq 0$ is irreducible if and only if its directed graph is strongly connected. A connected graph is strongly connected if and only if every arc belongs to at least one cycle. The greatest common divisor (g.c.d.) c of the lengths of all cycles in a strongly connected graph is called the *index of imprimitivity* of that graph. The g.c.d. of the lengths of all cycles through any vertex is equal to c. The index of imprimitivity of an irreducible matrix is equal to the index of imprimitivity of its associated directed graph. Adding loops to the vertices of the graph does not affect its connectedness.

Lemma: W is irreducible if and only if $I+W$ is irreducible.

Proof: Adding loops to the vertices of the graph does not affect its connectedness.

Theorem: A necessary and sufficient condition for an $n \times n$ nonnegative matrix W to be irreducible is that $(I+W)^{n-1} > 0$.

Proof: The condition is necessary, for if $(I+W)^{n-1} > 0$, then every vertex in $I+W$ can be reached by a path of length $n-1$ from every other vertex and thus $I+W$ is irreducible. By the lemma, if $I+W$ is irreducible, then W is also irreducible. Conversely, by the lemma, $I+W$ is irreducible. Now $(I+W)^{n-1} \geq (I+W)^{n-1} > 0$, since in W every vertex can be reached by a path of at most length $n-1$ from any other vertex. Hence, except possibly for the diagonal elements, the entries of W^{n-1} are all positive. Adding I ensures that the diagonal is also positive.

The sum and product of two irreducible matrices and any power of an irreducible matrix are irreducible. If an integer power of a matrix is irreducible, then that matrix is irreducible.

Irreducibility and the Principal Eigenvalue: If W is an irreducible nonnegative matrix, its principal eigenvalue is a simple root of its characteristic equation.

The principal eigenvalue of an irreducible matrix dominates in modulus the principal eigenvalue of any of its submatrices (which lie on the main diagonal, called principal submatrices). For a nonnegative matrix, dominance or equality can hold. A nonnegative matrix W with principal eigenvalue λ_{max} is reducible if and only if λ_{max} is an eigenvalue of a principal submatrix of W. A nonnegative matrix W with a simple eigenvalue λ_{max} is irreducible if and only if both W and W^T have corresponding positive principal eigenvectors.

Irreducibility and the Principal Eigenvector: If W is an irreducible nonnegative matrix with principal eigenvalue λ_{max}, and $Aw=\lambda_{max}w$, then w is a scalar multiple of a positive vector. An irreducible nonnegative matrix has just one eigenvector w

whose components satisfy $\sum_{i=1}^{n} w_i = 1$. Its only eigenvalue with a positive

eigenvector is λ_{max}.

Irreducibility and Primitivity: If W is primitive of order n, then $m \lesssim n^2$-$2n$+2 where m is the first value for which W^m>0. A primitive matrix is irreducible. The product of primitive matrices may not be irreducible, and the product of reducible matrices may be positive and hence primitive. A positive power of a primitive matrix is primitive. An irreducible matrix is primitive if (1) it has a positive trace, or (2) it has a nonzero main diagonal. If the Hadamard (elementwise) product $W * W^2$ of an irreducible matrix W is nonzero, then W is primitive.

A matrix A is reducible if and only if at least one of the principal minors of order $n-1$ of the matrix $(\lambda_{max}I-A)$ is zero. A nonnegative matrix is reducible if and only if one entry on the main diagonal of its adjoint is equal to zero.

PERRON-FROBENIUS

Let W be an irreducible nonnegative matrix. Then W has an eigenvalue λ_{max} (called the principal eigenvalue) which is real, positive, and simple. For any other eigenvalue λ of W, we have $|\lambda| \leq \lambda_{max}$. To this principal eigenvalue λ_{max} there corresponds a nonnegative eigenvector (called the principal eigenvector) which is unique to within multiplication by a positive constant.

If W is primitive, then for any other eigenvalue λ of A we actually have $|\lambda| < \lambda_{max}$, and the eigenvector is strictly positive. If A is imprimitive (cyclic) with index (cycle) c, then there are exactly c eigenvalues λ_1, ..., λ_c with moduli equal to λ_{max}. These eigenvalues are all distinct and are given by

$$\lambda_1 = \lambda_{max}, \quad \lambda_2 = \lambda_{max} z, \quad \lambda_3 = \lambda_{max} z^2, \quad \ldots, \quad \lambda_{max} z^{c-1},$$

where z is the complex number $z = e^{22\pi i/2}, i = \sqrt{-1}.$

For example, the following graph (strictly speaking, the matrix of the graph) is irreducible because one can reach either of the two nodes from the other.

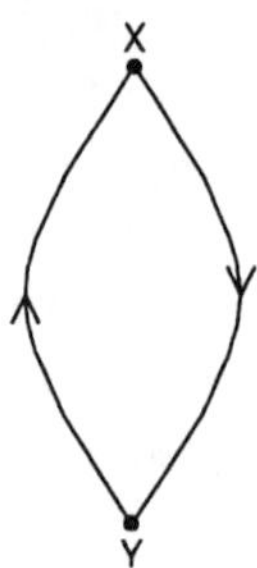

It also gives rise to cycling, as is obvious from the diagram. To see this algebraically, consider its matrix:

$$A = \begin{bmatrix} 0 & 1 \\ 1 & 0 \end{bmatrix}$$

We have

$$A^2 = \begin{bmatrix} 1 & 0 \\ 0 & 1 \end{bmatrix}, \begin{bmatrix} 0 & 1 \\ 1 & 0 \end{bmatrix}$$

In general

$$A^{2k} = \begin{bmatrix} 1 & 0 \\ 0 & 1 \end{bmatrix}, \quad A^{2k+1} = \begin{bmatrix} 0 & 1 \\ 1 & 0 \end{bmatrix}$$

and we have no unique limit result because the matrix is imprimitive (no power of it can be positive). If, on the other hand, we add a loop at X as shown in the graph below, we obtain a primitive matrix.

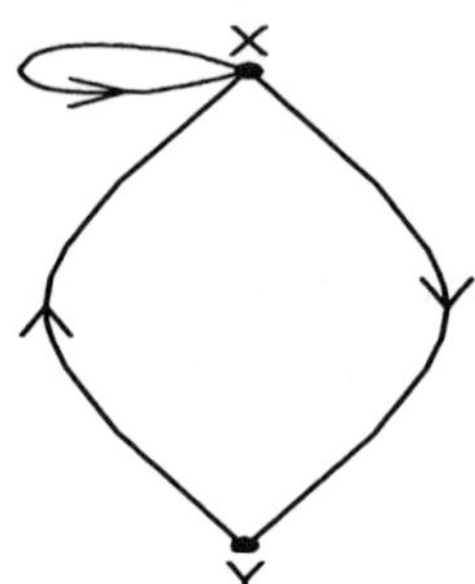

Here we have

$$A = \begin{bmatrix} 1 & 1 \\ 1 & 0 \end{bmatrix}, \quad A^2 = \begin{bmatrix} 2 & 1 \\ 1 & 1 \end{bmatrix}, \quad A^3 = \begin{bmatrix} 3 & 2 \\ 2 & 1 \end{bmatrix},$$

and A^k tends to a unique limit because it is primitive. The graph

is reducible. Its matrix A and powers of A are as follows:

$$A = \begin{bmatrix} 1 & 0 \\ 1 & 1 \end{bmatrix}, A^2 = \begin{bmatrix} 1 & 0 \\ 2 & 1 \end{bmatrix}, A^3 = \begin{bmatrix} 1 & 0 \\ 3 & 1 \end{bmatrix}, \cdots, A^k = \begin{bmatrix} 1 & 0 \\ k & 1 \end{bmatrix}$$

which does not cycle. But the matrix of the following graph is reducible and cyclic:

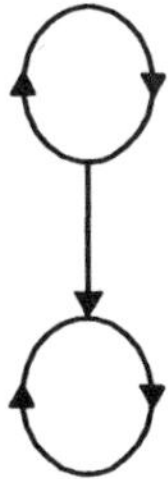

Remark: Occasionally, one can simplify much of the analysis of supermatrices by assuming that for some component there are influence priorities within the elements of that component, defined by an identity matrix, as we have just done by adding a loop at a vertex.

Irreducibility and Block Submatrices: The general normal form for an irreducible (in particular column stochastic) matrix is given by the following theorem.

Theorem: A square matrix A is either irreducible or can be reduced by a permutation of indices to a block diagonal matrix of irreducible matrices and other block matrices having the normal form

$$\begin{bmatrix} A_1 & 0 & 0 & A_{1,k+1} & \cdots & A_{1m} \\ 0 & A_2 & 0 & A_{2,k+1} & \cdots & A_{2m} \\ \vdots & \vdots & \vdots & \vdots & & \vdots \\ 0 & 0 & A_k & A_{k,k+1} & \cdots & A_{k+1,m} \\ \vdots & \vdots & \vdots & \vdots & \vdots & \vdots \\ 0 & 0 & 0 & 0 & \cdots & A_m \end{bmatrix}$$

At least one of the matrices with double subscripts in each column in which they appear is nonzero.

Among irreducible matrices W we need to distinguish two types: those that are primitive and thus $W^m > 0$ for some m (and therefore for all m sufficiently large), and those for which there is no such m. In the case of a column stochastic matrix W, these are, respectively, the acyclic and cyclic ones. Accordingly, an irreducible nonnegative matrix W is called *acyclic* if $W^m > 0$ for some m. Otherwise it is called *cyclic* with cycle $c \geq 2$ if there exists a permutation which puts it in the form:

$$W' = \begin{bmatrix} 0 & 0 & \cdots & 0 & W_c \\ W_1 & 0 & \cdots & 0 & 0 \\ 0 & W_2 & \cdots & 0 & 0 \\ \vdots & \vdots & \ddots & \vdots & \vdots \\ 0 & 0 & \cdots & W_{c-1} & 0 \end{bmatrix}$$

where the diagonal blocks are square, but $W_1, \ldots, W_c$ may not be square. Then the powers of W have the form

$$W^c = \begin{bmatrix} V_1 & & & 0 \\ & V_2 & & \\ & & \vdots & \\ 0 & & & V_c \end{bmatrix}$$

where the matrices $V_1, \ldots, V_c$ are all irreducible and acyclic and

$$V_1 = W_c W_{c-1} \cdots W_2 W_1; V_2 = W_1 W_c \cdots W_3 W_2; \cdots; V_c = W_{c-1} W_{c-2} \cdots W_1 W_c$$

STOCHASTIC MATRICES

$W \geq 0$ is stochastic if and only if $WE=E$ where E is the $n \times n$ matrix of 1's. Because of this it follows that if W and X are stochastic, then so is WX. W $\geq$ 0 is stochastic if and only if $e = (1, 1, ..., 1)$ is its principal eigenvector corresponding to the principal eigenvalue 1. The moduli of the eigenvalues of a stochastic matrix cannot exceed 1.

If W is an irreducible stochastic matrix, then the matrix $W^{\infty} = \lim_{k\to\infty} W^k$ exists if and only if W is primitive.

To summarize, if W be an irreducible stochastic matrix, then the number 1 is a simple eigenvalue of A. For any other eigenvalue λ of W, we have $|\lambda| \leq 1$. If W is also primitive, then $|\lambda| < 1$ for all other eigenvalues λ of W. If W is imprimitive with index (period) length c, then there are c eigenvalues with absolute value one.

STOCHASTICITY AND PERRON-FROBENIUS

Let W be an irreducible acyclic stochastic matrix. Then for all i, j,

$$\lim_{k\to\infty} W^k = we > 0, Ww = w, eW = e, e = (1,1,\cdots,1)$$

The row vector w is the unique solution of

$$Ww = w, \quad \sum w_i = 1$$

Moreover, the convergence is geometric[6]: there exist constants $\alpha > 0$ and $0 \leq \beta < 1$ such that

$$\left|W^k - we\right| \leq \alpha\, \beta^k, k = 1,2,\cdots$$

for all i, j. The constant β can be taken to be the largest modulus of the eigenvalues other than $\lambda_{\max} = 1$.

If W is irreducible but imprimitive (cyclic) with cycle length c, then the foregoing holds for each one of the irreducible acyclic matrices $V_1, ..., V_c$ on the diagonal of W^c. If W is reducible, then again the result applies to each irreducible block separately.

A-2. GRAPHS

There are at least two reasons why we need some knowledge of graphs for our analysis of priorities of influence. The first is obvious. Graphs are a geometric framework to structure a decision problem based on priorities. We need to identify and draw a diagram of the components, their elements, and the connections between them to represent their interactions. The second has to do with a characterization of irreducible matrices in terms of their associated graphs. A graph is a set of points V called *vertices* or *nodes* and a set of simple curves E called *edges* with a rule (of incidence) which associates each edge with vertices which are called its end points. The vertices are said to be incident with the edge. An *open* edge is incident with precisely two distinct vertices. A *closed* edge (called a loop) is incident with precisely one vertex and hence its end points coincide. No edges have points in common other than vertices [12, 16].

In Figure A-1 v_1 and v_2 are examples of vertices; e_1 is a loop whose end point is v_5; e_2 is an open edge whose end points are v_2 and v_3.

Two edges with a common vertex or two vertices that are the end points of an edge are said to be *adjacent.* A vertex is *isolated* if it is not incident with any edge. We denote a graph by $G = (V,E)$.

A *subgraph* of a graph G is a subset V_1 of the set of vertices V and a subset E_1 of the set of edges E with the same incidence between vertices and edges as in G.

A graph is called *simple* if it has neither loops nor parallel edges, i.e., multiple edges between pairs of vertices. Most of the time we shall be concerned with simple graphs, but since we have allowed for loops and parallel edges in our definition of graphs, we will usually make it clear when we are considering nonsimple graphs.

With each edge, one may associate a direction or orientation indicated by an arrow. The resulting graph is then called a *directed graph* and its edges are called arcs (see Figure A-2). A directed graph is denoted by $D = (V, A)$.

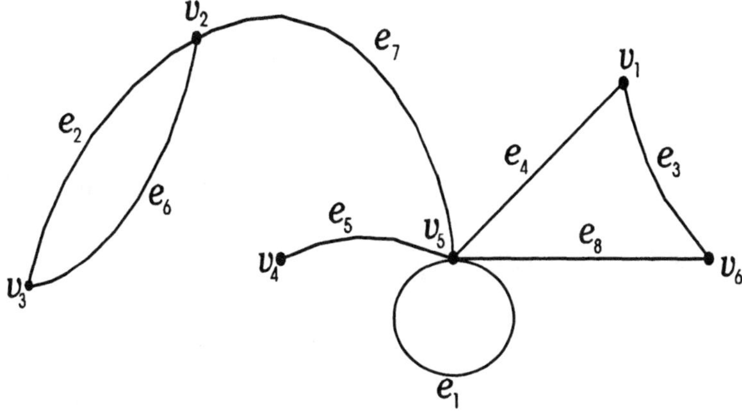

Figure A-1: A Graph with Vertices, Loops and Open Edges.

The number of edges incident with a vertex $v \in V$ is called the degree of the vertex and is denoted by $d(v)$. We denote by $d^-(v)$ the number of arcs directed toward v, and by $d^+(v)$ the number of arcs directed away from v. A loop incident with a vertex is counted twice in determining the degree. For an isolated vertex we have $d(v)=0$.

For a graph $G = (V,E)$ we denote the number of vertices and the number of edges by $|V|$ and $|E|$, respectively, and $|V|$ is called the order of the graph. The graph in Figure 3 has $|V|=7$ and $|E|=10$. A graph is called finite if both $|V|$ and $|E|$ are finite, and infinite if either is infinite. We shall be concerned exclusively with finite graphs. In the graph of Figure 3, the degree of v_1 is 5; v_7 is isolated.

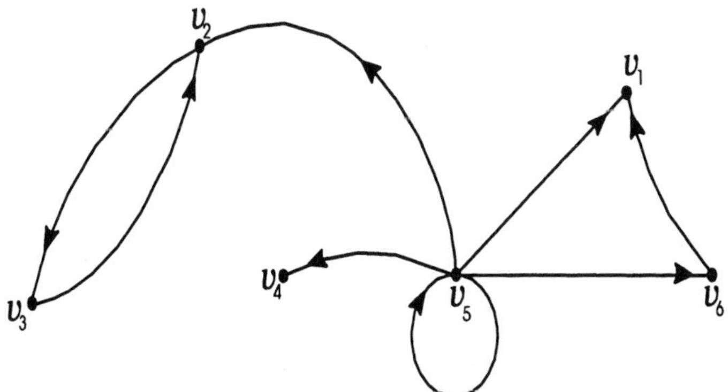

Figure A-2: A Directed Graph

A sequence of k edges $e_1, \ldots, e_k$ in a graph G is called a *walk* or *edge progression* if there exists an appropriate sequence of $k+1$ (not necessarily distinct) vertices $v_0, v_1, \ldots, v_n$ such that e_i is incident with v_i and v_j, $i,j = 1, \ldots, n$. The walk is *closed* if $v_0 = v_n$ and *open* otherwise. If $e_i \neq e_j$ for all i and j, $i \neq j$, the walk is called a *tour* or a *chain*. A closed chain is called a *circuit*. If all the vertices are distinct, a walk is called a *simple chain,* while if $v_1 = v_n$ and all other vertices are distinct, we have a *simple* circuit provided that $n \geq 3$. An example of a simple chain is given in Figure 3 by the edge sequence

$$\{e_3, e_2, e_1, e_8\} \equiv \{(v_4, v_3), (v_3, v_2), (v_2, v_1), (v_1, v_6)\}$$

Here we have replaced each edge in the sequence by the pair of vertices that are its end points as they succeed each other in the walk v_4, v_3, v_2, v_1, v_6.

Similar definitions may be given for directed graphs, giving attention to the direction on each arc. There we have *arc progressions*, *paths*, and *cycles*; *simple paths* and *simple cycles*.

A graph is called *connected* (strongly connected) in the undirected (directed) sense if there is a simple chain (path) between any pair of vertices. A graph of n+1 vertices is n-tuply connected if the removal of n-1 or fewer edges does not disconnect it. Two chains are said to be disjoint if they have no vertices in common, except perhaps for their end points.

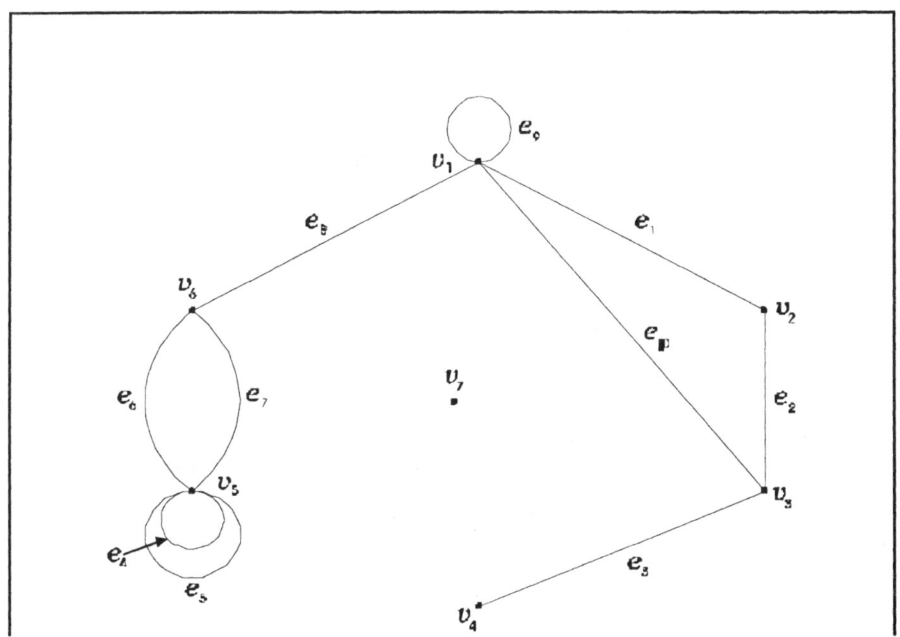

Figure A-3: A Directed Graph with Seven Vertices and Ten Edges

A component C of a graph G is a connected subgraph which is maximal (i.e., every vertex that is adjacent to a vertex in C is also in C, and all edges of G incident with vertices in C are also in C).

A *subtree* is a connected subgraph which has no circuits. A *spanning tree* is a (maximal) subtree which contains all the vertices of the graph. An edge of the graph that is not in the tree is called a *chord*. An edge of the graph that is in the tree is known as a *branch*. When a chord is added to a spanning tree, the result is a circuit called a *fundamental circuit*. Figure A-4 shows a spanning tree for a directed graph. The tree is *rooted* at v_0, from which all paths that are in the tree begin.

A special type of circuit in a graph, important for practical applications, is named after the famous Irish mathematician William Rowan Hamilton (1805-1865).

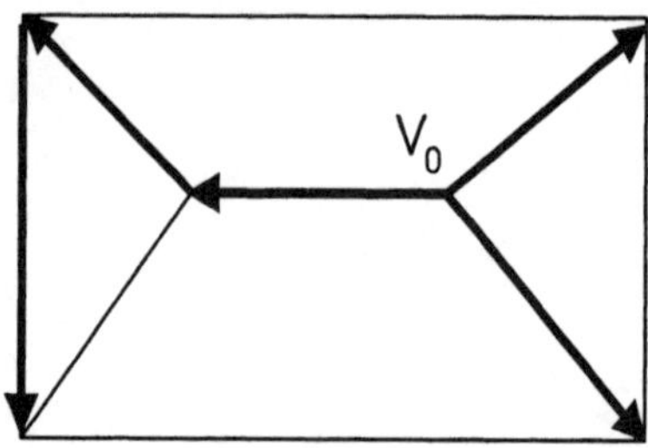

Figure A-4: A Spanning Tree

We call a circuit which passes through every vertex of the graph once and only once a *Hamiltonian circuit*. In contrast, the name of the Swiss mathematician Leonard Euler (1707-1783) is associated with a *Eulerian graph*, in which the edges form a chain, with each edge of the graph included in the chain once and only once. The chain may be open or it may form a circuit.

A simple graph $G = (V,E)$ having $|V| = n$ and such that every pair of vertices is joined by an edge is called a *complete graph on n vertices*. It is easily verified that a complete graph has $n(n-1)/2$ edges. Since any two complete graphs having the same number of vertices are isomorphic, we speak of the complete graph on n vertices.

A graph is called *bipartite* if its vertices can be partitioned into two disjoint sets such that the only edges in the graph are those which connect vertices from one set to those in the other (see Figure A-5).

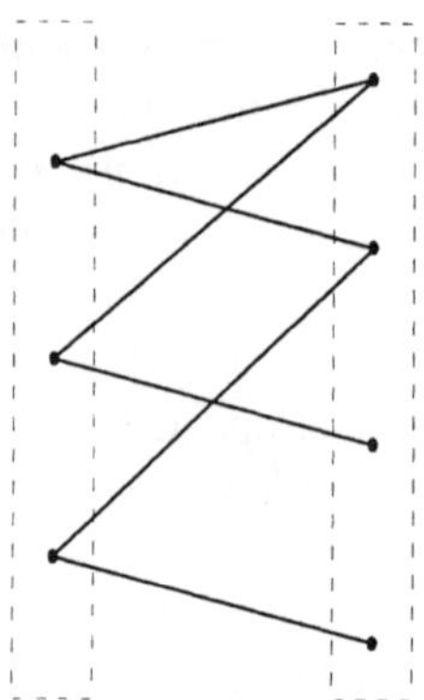

Figure A-5: Bipartite Graph

An important elementary concept associated with a graph G on n vertices is that of connectedness. Intrinsically, much of algorithmic graph theory is concerned with connectivity, its redundancy and even absence in the graph.

A graph is not connected (or disconnected) when the set of vertices V can be separated into two sets V_1 and V_2 with no edge joining a vertex in V_1 to a vertex in V_2; otherwise it is said to be connected. Although two vertices may not be directly connected by an edge, it may be possible to reach one of them from the other by a simple chain. If there is such a chain connecting every pair of vertices, then the graph is said to be connected. Sometimes it is preferable to use the first definition, but more frequently the equivalent second definition is used. In fact, the second definition is much richer, as it opens up the entire area of problems of *reachability* or *traceability* of a graph or of subgraphs of the graph. For example, we can begin to ask for more. Can we start at a vertex and travel or trace the edges of the graph sequentially without repetition? Can we do so and still terminate at the starting vertex? Can we, by starting at a vertex, trace a simple chain through all the vertices with or without returning to our initial vertex? Can we do so if we considered only subgraphs of n-1 vertices?

Another type of question is concerned with how much connectivity there is in a graph. There are two ways to look at this type of question: (1) through the edges of the graph, and (2) through its vertices. A graph may be disconnected by the removal of several edges taken together. A minimum collection of such edges is known as a *cut set*, and the smallest number of edges in a cut set is called the *degree of connectivity* of the graph. A tree is connected of degree one. Clearly a tree is the weakest type of connected graph. On the other hand, in a circuit the removal of an edge leaves a connected graph (in fact a tree) behind.

There are also two ways to look at how vertices disconnect a graph. The first is associated with the concept of the *degree* of a vertex. For example, if in a tree we have a vertex of degree two and we remove it together with its incident edges, the remaining graph is disconnected. On the other hand, if the graph is a simple circuit and hence every vertex has degree two, the removal of a vertex does not disconnect the graph. It seems reasonable that the higher the degrees of the vertices, the stronger the connectivity should be. But this type of statement is too general and needs to be made specific in the context of a particular problem.

A vertex of a graph is called a *point of articulation* or *cut-vertex* if its removal disconnects or separates the graph. The *multiplicity* of a cut-vertex is the number of components which result from its deletion. More than one vertex may be a point of articulation. For example, in Figure 3 v_1 and v_6 are points of articulation. However, v_5 is not. The collection of articulation points forms a set of articulation vertices which, in the context of communication networks, may be regarded as the vulnerability set of the graph. Of course, a graph may have no point of articulation (such a graph is said to be nonseparable), but the removal of k vertices together disconnects it. Such a set is known as an *articulation set of order k*.

A graph is k-connected, for $0 \leq k < n$, if the removal of k-1 vertices or fewer does not disconnect it. Any pair of vertices of such a graph can be connected by k disjoint chains (no two of which have vertices in common). A graph which has no articulation set of order k is called *k-irreducible*. Otherwise it is known as *k-reducible*.

So far we have been speaking of a general undirected graph. Connectivity questions are somewhat more complicated if a direction is assigned to the edges of the graph. Here a graph may be connected in the undirected sense, yet only *weakly connected* in the directed sense. Thus there may be a path from one vertex to another, but not conversely; i.e., it is not strongly connected. It is clear that cycles play an important role in strongly connected graphs.

The Adjacency and Path Matrices

The question often arises as to why raising the matrix of judgments or sometimes the supermatrix to a power determines for its entries the number of paths between the corresponding vertices, whose length is equal to that power. The vertex matrix is a first step for understanding this concept. We define a vertex (or adjacency) matrix for both directed and undirected graphs. The element in the (i,j) position of the matrix is equal to the number of edges incident with both vertex i and vertex j (or directed from vertex i to vertex j in the directed case). Thus for the directed graph of Figure 2 we have:

$$\vec{V} = \begin{array}{c} \\ v_1 \\ v_2 \\ v_3 \\ v_4 \\ v_5 \\ v_6 \end{array} \begin{array}{c} \begin{array}{cccccc} v_1 & v_2 & v_3 & v_4 & v_5 & v_6 \end{array} \\ \begin{bmatrix} 0 & 0 & 0 & 0 & 0 & 0 \\ 0 & 0 & 1 & 0 & 0 & 0 \\ 0 & 1 & 0 & 0 & 0 & 0 \\ 0 & 0 & 0 & 0 & 0 & 0 \\ 1 & 1 & 0 & 1 & 1 & 1 \\ 1 & 0 & 0 & 0 & 0 & 0 \end{bmatrix} \end{array}$$

In general, we have the following theorem regarding the vertex matrix $\vec{V}$ of a graph:

Theorem: The matrix $\vec{V}^n$ gives the number of arc progressions of length n between any two vertices of a directed graph.

Proof: If a_{ik} is the number of arcs joining v_i to v_k and a_{kj} is the number of arcs joining v_k to v_j, then $a_{ik}\, a_{kj}$ is the number of different paths each consisting of two arcs joining v_i to v_j and passing through v_k. If this is summed over all values of k, that is, over all the intermediate vertices, one obtains the number of paths of length 2 between v_i and v_j. If we now use a_{ij} to form $a_{ij}a_{jm}$, we have the number of different paths of length 3 between v_i and v_m passing through v_j, and so on. Thus if we assume the theorem is true for $\vec{V}^{n-1}$, then the coefficients of $\vec{V}^n = \vec{V}^{n-1}\,\vec{V}$ give the number of paths of length n between corresponding vertices. This completes the proof. A similar theorem holds for undirected graphs.

Sometimes when we refer to a graph with a certain property, we think of its adjacency matrix. For example, a directed graph is said to be primitive if it is strongly connected. This is reflected by the fact that $\vec{V}^m > 0$ for some integer $m > 0$, in which case $\vec{V}$ is primitive. A strongly connected graph $D = (V,A)$ with $n \geq 2$ vertices is primitive if and only if the greatest common divisor of the lengths of all simple cycles in D is equal to one. The concept of a vertex matrix may be generalized to that of a path matrix in which appropriate numbers are used as in a judgment matrix. Raising the matrix to powers gives the dominance of one element over another over a path whose length is equal to that power of the matrix.

References

[1] Andreichicov, A., and Andreichicova, O. "A Choice of a Perspective System for Vibration Isolation in Conditions of Varying Environment," pp. 13-24, ISAHP Proceedings 2001, Bern, Switzerland, 2001.

[2] Barzilai, J. "Consistency Measures for Pairwise Comparison Matrices," *Journal of Multi-Criteria Decision Analysis* 7, 1998b, pp.1232-132.

[3] Barzilai, J. "On the Decomposition of Value Functions," *Operations Research Letters* 22, 1998a, pp. 159-170.

[4] Barzilai, J., and Lootsma, F. A. "Power Relations and Group Aggregation in the Multiplicative AHP and SMART," *Journal of Multi-Criteria Decision Analysis* 6, 1997, pp. 155-165.

[5] Bauer, R. A., Collar, E., and Tang, V. *The Silverlake Project*, New York: Oxford University Press, 1992.

[6] Belton, V., and Gear, A. E. "On a Short-coming of Saaty's Method of Analytic Hierarchies," *Omega* 11 (3), 1983, pp.228-230.

[7] Belton, V., and Gear, A. E. "The Legitimacy of Rank Reversal - A Comment," *Omega* 13, 3, 1985, pp. 143-144.

[8] Berman, A., and Plemmons, R. J. *Nonnegative Matrices in the Mathematical Sciences*, New York: Academic Press, 1979.

[9] Beynon, M. J. "An Investigation of the Role of Scale Values in the DS/AHP Method of Multi-Criteria Decision Making, " *Journal of Multi-Criteria Decision Analysis* 11, 2002, pp. 327-343.

[10] Blair, A. R., Nachtmann, R., Olson, J., and Saaty, T. L. "Forecasting Foreign Exchange Rates: An Expert Judgment Approach," *Socio-Economic Planning Sciences* 21, 6, 1987, pp. 363-369.

[11] Blair, A. R., Nachtmann, R., Saaty, T. L., and Whitaker, R. "Forecasting the Resurgence of the US Economy in 2001: An Expert Judgment Approach," *Socio-Economic Planning Sciences*, 36, 2002, pp. 77-91.

[12] Busacker, R.G., and Saaty, T. L. *Finite Graphs and Networks*, New York: McGraw-Hill Book Company, 1965.

[13] Cinlar, E. *Introduction to Stochastic Process*, Englewood Cliffs: Prentice-Hall; 1974.

[14] Costa, C. A. B. e. and Vansnick, J. C. "A Fundamental Criticism to Saaty's Use of the Eigenvalue Procedure to Derive Priorities," The London School of Economics and Political Science, Working Paper: LSEOR 01.42, 2001.

[15] Creative Decisions Foundation, go to www.superdecisions.com to download the SuperDecisions Software to use for free for several months. For more information contact Creative Decisions Foundation, or email rozann@creativedecisions.net.

[16] Cullen, C.G. *An Introduction to Numerical Linear Algebra,* Boston: PWS publishing Co., 1994.

[17] Dantzig, T., *Number the Language of Science*, The Macmillan Company, 1954.

[18] Dehaene, S., *The Number Sense, How the Mind Creates Mathematics*, Oxford University Press, p. 73, 1997.

[19] Dyer, J. S. "Remarks on the Analytic Hierarchy Process," *Management Science* 36, 3, 1990, pp. 249-258.

[20] Faddeev, D.K. "On the Transportation of the Scalar Equation of a Matrix," Leningrad: *Trudy Inst. Inzh. Prom. Stroit*, 4, 1937, pp. 78-86.

[21] Finan, J. S., and Hurley, W.J. "The Analytic Hierarchy Process: Can Wash Criteria Be Ignored?" *Computers and Operations Research* 29, 8, 2002, pp. 1025-1030.

[22] Gantmacher, F.R., *Applications of the Theory of Matrices*, New York: Interscience Publishers, 1959.

[23] Harker, P. T. "Derivatives of the Perron root of a positive reciprocal matrix: with applications to the Analytic Hierarchy Process," *Appl. Math. Comput.*, Vol. 22, 1987, pp. 217-232.

[24] Holder, R. D. "Some Comments on the Analytic Hierarchy Process," *Journal of the Operational Research Society* 41, 11, 1990, pp. 1073-1076.

[25] Horn, R. A., and Johnson, C.R., *Matrix Analysis*, New York: Cambridge University Press, 1985.

[26] Hurley, W. J. "Letters to the Editor: Strategic Risk Assessment," *Canadian Military Journal, Vol. Summer*, 2002, pp. 3-4.

[27] Kamenetzky, R. D. "The Additive Value Function," *Decision Sciences* 13, 4, 1982, pp. 702-713.

[28] King, R. B., *Beyond the Quartic Equation*, Birkhaüser, 1994.

[29] Kuffler, S., and Nichols, J. G., *From Neuron toRain*. Sunderland, MA, USA: Sinauer Associates, 1976.

[30] Lancaster, P., and Tismenetsky, M., *The Theory of Matrices*, Orlando: Academic Press Harcourt Brace Jovanovich, 1985.

[31] Leskinen, P. "Measurement Scales and Scale Independence in the Analytic Hierarchy Process," *Journal of Multi-Criteria Decision Analysis* 9, 2000, pp. 163-174.

[32] Leverrier, "Sur les Variations Reculaire des Elements des Orbites pour les Sept Planetes Principales," *J. de Math.*, 5, 1840, pg. 230.

[33] Lootsma, F. A. "Scale Sensitivity in the Multiplicative AHP and SMART," *Journal of Multi-Criteria Decision Analysis,* 2, 1993, pp. 87-110.

[34] Luce, R. and Raiffa, H., *Games and Decisions*, John Wiley and Sons, 1957.

[35] Machina, M. J. "Choice under uncertainty: Problems solved and unsolved," *Economic Perspectives* Vol. 1, No. 1, 1987, pp. 121-154.

[36] McCord, M., and de Neufville, R. "Empirical Demonstration that Expected Utility Decision Analysis is Not Operational," Chapter in *Foundation of Utility and Risk Theory with Applications*, Stigun Wenstop (ed.), Boston: Reidel Publishing Company, 1983, pp. 181-200.

[37] Millet, I., and Wedley, W. C. "Modeling Risk and Uncertainty with the Analytic Hierarchy Process," *Journal of Multi-Criteria Decision Analysis* 11, 2002, pp. 97-107.

[38] Minc, H., *Nonnegative Matrices*, New York: John Wiley & Sons, 1988.

[39] Perez, J., Jimeno, J. L., and Mokotoff, E. "Another Potential Strong Shortcoming on AHP," Working Paper, Universidad de Alcala, Spain, 2004.

[40] Roberts, F. S. "Limitations on Conclusions Using Scales of Measurement," *RUTCOR Research Report* #48-91, Rutgers University, New Brunswick, NJ 08903-5062, 1991.

[41] Russell, B., *Introduction to Mathematical Philosophy*, London: George Allen and Unwin, LTD., 1948.

[42] Saaty, R. W. "Why Barzilai's Criticisms of the AHP are Incorrect," Proceedings of the International MCDM meeting at Whistler Canada. P, 2004

[43] Saaty, T. L. "A Scaling Method for Priorities in Hierarchical Structures," *Journal of Mathematical Psychology* 15, No. 3, 1977, pp. 234-281.

[44] Saaty, T. L. "Axiomatic Foundations of the Analytic Hierarchy Process," *Management Science* 21, 1986.

[45] Saaty, T. L. "Decision-Making – The Analytic Hierarchy and Network Processes (AHP/ANP)," JSSSE, January 2004.

[46] Saaty, T. L. "How to make a decision: the Analytic Hierarchy Process," *Interfaces*, Vol. 24, No. 6, 1994, pp. 19-43.

[47] Saaty, T. L. "Presidential Elections, the Superconducting Supercollider, and Organ Transplant Decisions," *Multiple Criteria Decision Making*, edited by A. Goicoechea, L. Duckstein, and S. Zionts, Springer-Verlag, p. 345, 1992.

[48] Saaty, T. L. "Rank generation, preservation, and reversal in the Analytic Hierarchy Decision Process," *Journal of the Decision Sciences Institute*, Vol. 18, No. 2, 1987.

[49] Saaty, T. L. "Seven Pillars of the Analytic Hierarchy Process," in *Proceedings of the 5th International Symposium on the AHP*, Kobe, Japan, August 12-14, 1999.

[50] Saaty, T. L. "That is Not the Analytic Hierarchy Process: What the AHP is and what it is Not," *Journal of Multi-Criteria Decision Analysis* 6, 1997, pp. 320-339.

[51] Saaty, T. L. "Time Dependent Decision- Making; Dynamic Priorities In The AHP/ANP; Generalizing From Points To Functions And From Real To Complex Variables," *Proceedings of the ISAHP 2003*, Bali, Indonesia, August 7-9, 2003.

[52] Saaty, T. L., *Decision Making with Dependence and Feedback: The Analytic Network Process*, Pittsburgh: RWS Publications, 4922 Ellsworth Avenue, Pittsburgh, PA 15213, 2001.

[53] Saaty, T. L., *Fundamental of Decision Making and Priority Theory*, Pittsburgh: RWS Publications, 2000.

[54] Saaty, T. L., *Fundamentals of Decision Making with the Analytic Hierarchy Process*, Pittsburgh: RWS Publications, 2000b.

[55] Saaty, T. L., *The Analytic Hierarchy Process*, McGraw Hill, New York, 1980. Reprinted by Pittsburgh: RWS Publications, 2000a.

[56] Saaty, T. L., *The Analytic Network Process: Decision Making with Dependence and Feedback*, Pittsburgh: RWS Publications, 1996, completely revised and published 2001, completely revised 2004.

[57] Saaty, T. L., *The Brain, Unraveling the Mystery of How it Works: The Neural Network Process*, Pittsburgh: RWS Publications, 2000.

[58] Saaty, T. L. "Time Dependent Decision-Making; Dynamic Priorities in the AHP/ANP, Generalizing from Points to Functions and From Real to Complex Variables," Proceedings of the 7th ISAHP Symposium on the AHP, Bali, Indonesia, August, 2003.

[59] Saaty, T. L., and Cho, Y. "The Decision by the US Congress on China's Trade Status: A Multicriteria Analysis," *Socio-Economic Planning Sciences*, 35, 2001, pp. 243-252.

[60] Saaty, T. L., and Gholamnezhad, H. "A Desired Energy Mix for the United States in the Year 2000: An Analytic Hierarchy Approach," *International Journal of Policy Analysis and Information Systems*, Vol. 6, No. 1, 1982.

[61] Saaty, T. L., and Kearns, K. P., *Analytical Planning; The Organization of Systems*, Oxford: Pergamon Press, 1985. Translated to Russian. Paperback edition, Pittsburgh: RWS Publications, 1991.

[62] Saaty, T. L., and Kearns, K., *Analytical Planning*, Pittsburgh: RWS Publications, 1991.

[63] Saaty, T. L., and Khouja, M. "A Measure of World Influence," *Journal of Peace Science*, Spring, 1976.

[64] Saaty, T. L., and Ozdemir, M. "Negative priorities in the Analytic Hierarchy Process," *Mathematical and Computer Modeling*, Vol. 37, 2003b, pp. 1063-1075.

[65] Saaty, T. L., and Ozdemir, M. "Why the magic number seven plus or minus two," *Mathematical and Computer Modeling*, Vol. 38, 2003a, pp. 233-244.

[66] Saaty, T. L., and Ozdemir, M. *The Encyclicon: a Dictionary of ANP Applications,* Pittsburgh: RWS Publications, 2005.

[67] Saaty, T. L., and Peniwati, K. "The Analytic Hierarchy Process and Linear Programming in Human Resource Allocation," *Proceedings of the Fourth ISAHP*, Simon Fraser University, Burnaby, B.C., Canada, July 12-15, 1996, pp. 492-504.

[68] Saaty, T. L., and Turner, D.S. "Prediction of the 1996 Super Bowl," proceedings of the Fourth International Symposium on The Analytic Hierarchy Process, Simon Fraser University, Burnaby, B.C., Canada, July 12-15, 1996.

[69] Saaty, T. L., and Vargas, L. G. "Comparison of eigenvalue, logarithmic least squares and least squares methods in estimating ratios," *Mathematical Modeling*, Vol. 5, No. 5, 1984b, pp. 309-324.

[70] Saaty, T. L., and Vargas, L. G. "Diagnosis with Dependent Symptoms: Bayes' Theorem and the Analytic Hierarchy Process," *Operations Research*, Vol. 46, No. 4, July-August, 1998.

[71] Saaty, T. L., and Vargas, L. G. "Estimating Technological Coefficients by the Analytic Hierarchy Process," *Socio-Economic Planning Sciences*, Vol. 13, 1979, pp. 333-336.

[72] Saaty, T. L., and Vargas, L. G. "Experiments on rank preservation and reversal in relative measurement," *Mathematical and Computer Modeling*, Vol.17, Nos. 4-5, 1993, pp. 13-18.

[73] Saaty, T. L., and Vargas, L. G. "Inconsistency and rank preservation," *Journal of Mathematical Psychology*, Vol. 28, No. 2, June 1984a.

[74] Saaty, T. L., and Vargas, L. G. "The Analytic Hierarchy Process: Can Wash Criteria be ignored?" *International Journal of Management and Decision Making*, pending, 2005.

[75] Saaty, T. L., and Vargas, L. G. "The Legitimacy of Rank Reversal," *Omega* 12, 5, 1984, pp. 513-516.

[76] Saaty, T. L., and Vargas, L. G. "The possibility of group choice: pairwise comparisons and merging functions," Submitted to *Operations Research* 2005.

[77] Saaty, T. L., and Vargas, L. G., Models, *Methods, Concepts and Applications of the Analytic Hierarchy Process*, Boston: Kluwer Academic Publishers, 2000.

[78] Saaty, T. L., and Vargas, L. G., *Prediction, Projection and Forecasting*, Boston: Kluwer Academic Publishers, 1991 (b).

[79] Saaty, T. L., and Vargas, L. G., *The Logic of Priorities*, Pittsburgh: RWS Publications, 1991(a).

[80] Saaty, T. L., Vargas, L. G., and Dellmann, K. "The allocation of intangible resources: the Analytic Hierarchy Process and Linear Programming," *Socio-Econ. Planning Sci.*, Vol. 37, 2003, pp 169-184.

[81] Saaty, T. L., Vargas, L. G., and Wendell, R. E. "Assessing Attribute Weights by Ratios," *OMEGA: The International Journal of Management Science*, Vol. 11, No. 1, 1983, pp. 9-13.

[82] Saaty, T. L., and Wong, M. "The Average Family Size in Rural India," *Journal of Mathematical Sociology*, Vol.9, 1983, pp. 181-209.

[83] Salo, A. A. and Hamalainen, R. P. "On the Measurement of Preferences in the Analytic Hierarchy Process," *Journal of Multi-Criteria Decision Analysis* 6, 6, 1997, pp. 309-319.

[84] Sarin, R.K. "Strength of Preference and Risky Choice," *Operations Research*, 30, 5, 1982, pp.982-997.

[85] Schenkerman, S. "Avoiding Rank Reversal in AHP Decision-Support Models," *European Journal of Operational Research* 74, 1994, pp. 407-419.

[86] Schenkerman, S. "Inducement of Nonexistent Order by the Analytic Hierarchy Process," *Decision Sciences*, 28, 2, 1997, pp. 475-482.

[87] Schoner, B., Wedley, W. C., and Choo, E. U. "A Unified Approach to AHP with Linking Pins," *European Journal of Operational Research*, 64, 1993, pp. 345-354.

[88] Stam, A., and Duarte Silva, A.P. "On multiplicative priority ranking methods for the AHP," *European Journal of Operational Research*, 145, 1, 2003, pp. 92-108.

[89] Stewart, T. J. "A Critical Survey on the Status of Multicriteria Decision Making Theory and Practice," *Omega*, 20, 5-6, 1992, pp. 569-586.

[90] Sturmfels, B. "Solving algebraic equations in terms of A-hypergeometric series," *Discrete Math*, 210, No. 1-3, 2000, pp. 71-181.

[91] Surowiecki, J., *The Wisdom of Crowds: Why the Many Are Smarter Than the Few and How Collective Wisdom Shapes Business, Economies, Societies and Nations*, Doubleday, Little, Brown, 2004, reviewed in The Economist, May 29, 2004.

[92] Triantaphyllou, E. "Two New Cases of Rank Reversals when the AHP and Some of its Additive Variants are Used that do not Occur with the Multiplicative AHP," *Journal of Multi-Criteria Decision Analysis*, 10, 2001, pp. 11-25.

[93] Watson, S. R., and Freeling, A. N. S. "Assessing Attribute Weights," *Omega*, 10, 6, 1982, pp. 582-583.

[94] Watson, S. R., and Freeling, A. N. S. "Comments on: Assessing Attribute Weights by Ratios," *Omega*, 11, 1, 1983, pg. 13.

[95] Wedley, W.C., Choo, E.U., and Schoner, B. "Magnitude adjustment for AHP benefit/cost ratios," *European Journal of Operational Research*, 133, 2, 2001, pp. 342-351.

[96] Wind, Y., and Saaty, T. L. "Marketing Applications of the Analytic Hierarchy Process," *Management Science*, 26, 7.

Index